MORE PRAISE FROM A...
FOR THE JOBBA...

"If you are looking for a job ... before you go to the newspapers and the help-wanted ads, listen to Bob Adams, publisher of *The Metropolitan New York JobBank*."
-Tom Brokaw, *NBC*

"Help on the job hunt ... Anyone who is job-hunting in the New York area can find a lot of useful ideas in a new paperback called *The Metropolitan New York JobBank* ..."
-Angela Taylor, *New York Times*

"For those graduates whose parents are pacing the floor, conspicuously placing circled want ads around the house and typing up resumes, [*The Carolina JobBank*] answers job-search questions."
-Greensboro News and Record

"A timely book for Chicago job hunters follows books from the same publisher that were well received in New York and Boston ... [*The Chicago JobBank* is] a fine tool for job hunters ..."
-Clarence Peterson, *Chicago Tribune*

"Because our listing is seen by people across the nation, it generates lots of resumes for us. We encourage unsolicited resumes. We'll always be listed [in *The Chicago JobBank*] as long as I'm in this career."
-Tom Fitzpatrick, Director of Human Resources
Merchandise Mart Properties, Inc.

"Job-hunting is never fun, but this book can ease the ordeal ... [*The Los Angeles JobBank*] will help allay fears, build confidence, and avoid wheel-spinning."
-Robert W. Ross, *Los Angeles Times*

"Job hunters can't afford to waste time. *The Minneapolis-St. Paul JobBank* contains information that used to require hours of research in the library."
-Carmella Zagone
Minneapolis-based Human Resources Administrator

"*The Florida JobBank* is an invaluable job-search reference tool. It provides the most up-to-date information and contact names available for companies in Florida. I should know -- it worked for me!"
-Rhonda Cody, Human Resources Consultant
Aetna Life and Casualty

"*The Boston JobBank* provides a handy map of employment possibilities in greater Boston. This book can help in the initial steps of a job search by locating major employers, describing their business activities, and for most firms, by naming the contact person and listing typical professional positions. For recent college graduates, as well as experienced professionals, *The Boston JobBank* is an excellent place to begin a job search."

-Juliet F. Brudney, Career Columnist
Boston Globe

"No longer can jobseekers feel secure about finding employment just through want ads. With the tough competition in the job market, particularly in the Boston area, they need much more help. For this reason, *The Boston JobBank* will have a wide and appreciative audience of new graduates, job changers, and people relocating to Boston. It provides a good place to start a search for entry-level professional positions."

-Journal of College Placement

"*The Phoenix JobBank* is a first-class publication. The information provided is useful and current."

-Lyndon Denton
Director of Human Resources and Materials Management
Apache Nitrogen Products, Inc.

"*The Seattle JobBank* is an essential resource for job hunters."

-Gil Lopez, Staffing Team Manager
Battelle Pacific Northwest Laboratories

"I read through the 'Basics of Job Winning' and 'Resumes' sections [in *The Dallas-Fort Worth JobBank*] and found them to be very informative, with some positive tips for the job searcher. I believe the strategies outlined will bring success to any determined candidate."

-Camilla Norder, Professional Recruiter
Presbyterian Hospital of Dallas

"Through *The Dallas-Fort Worth JobBank,* we've been able to attract high-quality candidates for several positions."

-Rob Bertino, Southern States Sales Manager
CompuServe

"Packed with helpful contacts, *The Houston JobBank* empowers its reader to launch an effective, strategic job search in the Houston metropolitan area."

-Andrew Ceperley, Director
College of Communication Career Services
The University of Texas at Austin

What makes the JobBank series the nation's premier line of employment guides?

With vital employment information on thousands of employers across the nation, the JobBank series is the most comprehensive and authoritative set of career directories available today.

Each book in the series provides information on **dozens of different industries** in a given city or area, with the primary employer listings providing contact information, telephone and fax numbers, e-mail addresses, Websites, a summary of the firm's business, internships, and in many cases descriptions of the firm's typical professional job categories.

All of the reference information in the JobBank series is as up-to-date and accurate as possible. Every year, the entire database is thoroughly researched and verified by mail and by telephone. Adams Media Corporation publishes **more local employment guides more often** than any other publisher of career directories.

The JobBank series offers **28 regional titles**, from Minneapolis to Houston, and from Boston to San Francisco as well as **two industry-specific titles**. All of the information is organized geographically, because most people look for jobs in specific areas of the country.

A condensed, but thorough, review of the entire job search process is presented in the chapter **The Basics of Job Winning**, a feature which has received many compliments from career counselors. In addition, each JobBank directory includes a section on **resumes and cover letters** the *New York Times* has acclaimed as "excellent."

The JobBank series gives job hunters the most comprehensive, timely, and accurate career information, organized and indexed to facilitate your job search. An entire career reference library, JobBank books are designed to help you find optimal employment in any market.

Top career publications from Adams Media Corporation

The JobBank Series:
each JobBank book is $16.95

The Atlanta JobBank, 14th Ed.
The Austin/San Antonio JobBank, 3rd Ed.
The Boston JobBank, 19th Ed.
The Carolina JobBank, 6th Ed.
The Chicago JobBank, 18th Ed.
The Colorado JobBank, 13th Ed.
The Connecticut JobBank, 2nd Ed.
The Dallas-Fort Worth JobBank, 13th Ed.
The Detroit JobBank, 9th Ed.
The Florida JobBank, 15th Ed.
The Houston JobBank, 11th Ed.
The Indiana JobBank, 3rd Ed.
The Las Vegas JobBank, 2nd Ed.
The Los Angeles JobBank, 17th Ed.
The Minneapolis-St. Paul JobBank, 11th Ed.
The Missouri JobBank, 3rd Ed.
The New Jersey JobBank, 1st Ed.
The Metropolitan New York JobBank, 18th Ed.
The Ohio JobBank, 10th Ed.
The Greater Philadelphia JobBank, 14th Ed.
The Phoenix JobBank, 8th Ed.
The Pittsburgh JobBank, 2nd Ed.
The Portland JobBank, 3rd Ed.
The San Francisco Bay Area JobBank, 16th Ed.
The Seattle JobBank, 12th Ed.
The Tennessee JobBank, 5th Ed.
The Virginia JobBank, 3rd Ed.
The Metropolitan Washington DC JobBank, 15th Ed.

The JobBank Guide to Computer & High-Tech Companies, 2nd Ed. ($17.95)
The JobBank Guide to Health Care Companies, 2nd Ed. ($17.95)

The National JobBank, 2003 (Covers the entire U.S.: $450.00 hc)

Other Career Titles:
The Adams Cover Letter Almanac ($12.95)
The Adams Internet Job Search Almanac, 6th Ed. ($12.95)
The Adams Executive Recruiters Almanac, 2nd Ed. ($17.95)
The Adams Job Interview Almanac ($12.95)
The Adams Jobs Almanac, 8th Ed. ($16.95)
The Adams Resume Almanac ($10.95)
Business Etiquette in Brief ($7.95)
Campus Free College Degrees, 8th Ed. ($16.95)
Career Tests ($12.95)
Closing Techniques, 2nd Ed. ($8.95)
Cold Calling Techniques, 4th Ed. ($8.95)
College Grad Job Hunter, 4th Ed. ($14.95)
The Complete Resume & Job Search Book for College Students, 2nd Ed. ($12.95)
Cover Letters That Knock 'em Dead, 5th Ed. ($12.95)
Every Woman's Essential Job Hunting & Resume Book ($11.95)
The Everything Cover Letter Book ($12.95)
The Everything Get-A-Job Book ($12.95)
The Everything Hot Careers Book ($12.95)
The Everything Job Interview Book ($12.95)
The Everything Online Business Book ($12.95)
The Everything Online Job Search Book ($12.95)
The Everything Resume Book ($12.95)
The Everything Selling Book ($12.95)
First Time Resume ($7.95)
How to Start and Operate a Successful Business ($9.95)
Knock 'em Dead, 2003 ($14.95)
Knock 'em Dead Business Presentations ($12.95)
Market Yourself and Your Career, 2nd Ed. ($12.95)
The New Professional Image ($12.95)
The 150 Most Profitable Home Businesses for Women ($9.95)
The Resume Handbook, 3rd Ed. ($7.95)
Resumes That Knock 'em Dead, 5th Ed. ($12.95)
The Road to CEO ($20.00 hc)
The 250 Job Interview Questions You'll Most Likely Be Asked ($9.95)
Your Executive Image ($10.95)

If you cannot find these titles at your favorite book outlet, you may order them directly from the publisher. **BY PHONE:** Call 800/872-5627 (in Massachusetts 508/427-7100). We accept Visa, Mastercard, and American Express. $4.95 will be added to your total for shipping and handling. **BY MAIL:** Write out the full titles of the books you'd like to order and send payment, including $4.95 for shipping and handling to: Adams Media Corporation, 57 Littlefield Street, Avon MA 02322. 30-day money back guarantee.
BY FAX: 800/872-5628.
Discounts available for standing orders.

14th Edition
THE Greater
Philadelphia
JobBank

Reference Editor:	Christie L. Barros
Assistant Reference Editor:	Lisa A. Geraghty
Production Manager:	Michelle Roy Kelly

Adams Media Corporation
AVON, MASSACHUSETTS

Published by Adams Media Corporation
57 Littlefield Street, Avon, MA 02322 U.S.A.
www.adamsmedia.com

ISBN: 1-58062-818-4
ISSN: 1072-575X
Manufactured in Canada.

Because addresses and telephone numbers of smaller companies change rapidly, we recommend you call each company and verify the information before mailing to the employers listed in this book. Mass mailings are not recommended.

While the publisher has made every reasonable effort to obtain and verify accurate information, occasional errors are possible due to the magnitude of the data. Should you discover an error, or if a company is missing, please write the editors at the above address so that we may update future editions.

"This publication is designed to provide accurate and authoritative information with regard to the subject matter covered. It is sold with the understanding that the publisher is not engaged in rendering legal, accounting, or other professional advice. If legal advice or other expert assistance is required, the services of a competent professional person should be sought."

--From a Declaration of Principles jointly adopted by a Committee of the American Bar Association and a Committee of Publishers and Associations

This book is available on standing order and at quantity discounts for bulk purchases. For information, call 800/872-5627 (in Massachusetts, 508/427-7100).

TABLE OF CONTENTS

- *Automotive Stampings*
- *Industrial Vehicles and Moving Equipment*
- *Motor Vehicles and Equipment*
- *Travel Trailers and Campers*

Banking/Savings and Loans/88

Biotechnology, Pharmaceuticals, and Scientific R&D/97

- *Clinical Labs*
- *Lab Equipment Manufacturers*
- *Pharmaceutical Manufacturers and Distributors*

Business Services and Non-Scientific Research/105

- *Adjustment and Collection Services*
- *Cleaning, Maintenance, and Pest Control Services*
- *Credit Reporting Services*
- *Detective, Guard, and Armored Car Services/Security Systems Services*
- *Miscellaneous Equipment Rental and Leasing*
- *Secretarial and Court Reporting Services*

Charities and Social Services/110

- *Job Training and Vocational Rehabilitation Services*

Chemicals/Rubber and Plastics/112

- *Adhesives, Detergents, Inks, Paints, Soaps, Varnishes*
- *Agricultural Chemicals and Fertilizers*
- *Carbon and Graphite Products*
- *Chemical Engineering Firms*
- *Industrial Gases*

Communications: Telecommunications and Broadcasting/121

- *Cable/Pay Television Services*
- *Communications Equipment*
- *Radio and Television Broadcasting Stations*
- *Telephone, Telegraph, and Other Message Communications*

Computer Hardware, Software, and Services/126

- *Computer Components and Hardware Manufacturers*
- *Consultants and Computer Training Companies*
- *Internet and Online Service Providers*
- *Networking and Systems Services*
- *Repair Services/Rental and Leasing*
- *Resellers, Wholesalers, and Distributors*
- *Software Developers/Programming Services*

Educational Services/145

- *Business/Secretarial/Data Processing Schools*
- *Colleges/Universities/Professional Schools*
- *Community Colleges/Technical Schools/Vocational Schools*
- *Elementary and Secondary Schools*
- *Preschool and Child Daycare Services*

Electronic/Industrial Electrical Equipment/152

- *Electronic Machines and Systems*
- *Semiconductor Manufacturers*

Environmental and Waste Management Services/162

- *Environmental Engineering Firms*
- *Sanitary Services*

Fabricated/Primary Metals and Products//164

- *Aluminum and Copper Foundries*
- *Die-Castings*
- *Iron and Steel Foundries/Steel Works, Blast Furnaces, and Rolling Mills*

Financial Services/170

- *Consumer Financing and Credit Agencies*
- *Investment Specialists*
- *Mortgage Bankers and Loan Brokers*

SECTION FOUR: INDEX

Index of Primary Employers by Industry/294

INTRODUCTION

HOW TO USE THIS BOOK

Right now, you hold in your hands one of the most effective job-hunting tools available anywhere. In *The Greater Philadelphia JobBank*, you will find valuable information to help you launch or continue a rewarding career. But before you open to the book's employer listings and start calling about current job openings, take a few minutes to learn how best to use the resources presented in *The Greater Philadelphia JobBank*.

The Greater Philadelphia JobBank will help you to stand out from other jobseekers. While many people looking for a new job rely solely on newspaper help-wanted ads, this book offers you a much more effective job-search method – direct contact. The direct contact method has been proven twice as effective as scanning the help-wanted ads. Instead of waiting for employers to come looking for you, you'll be far more effective going to them. While many of your competitors will use trial and error methods in trying to set up interviews, you'll learn not only how to get interviews, but what to expect once you've got them.

In the next few pages, we'll take you through each section of the book so you'll be prepared to get a jump-start on your competition.

Basics of Job Winning

Preparation. Strategy. Time management. These are three of the most important elements of a successful job search. *Basics of Job Winning* helps you address these and all the other elements needed to find the right job.

One of your first priorities should be to define your personal career objectives. What qualities make a job desirable to you? Creativity? High pay? Prestige? Use *Basics of Job Winning* to weigh these questions. Then use the rest of the chapter to design a strategy to find a job that matches your criteria.

In *Basics of Job Winning,* you'll learn which job-hunting techniques work, and which don't. We've reviewed the pros and cons of mass mailings, help-wanted ads, and direct contact. We'll show you how to develop and approach contacts in your field; how to research a prospective employer; and how to use that information to get an interview and the job.

Also included in *Basics of Job Winning*: interview dress code and etiquette, the "do's and don'ts" of interviewing, sample interview questions, and more. We also deal with some of the unique problems faced by those jobseekers who are currently employed, those who have lost a job, and college students conducting their first job search.

Resumes and Cover Letters

The approach you take to writing your resume and cover letter can often mean the difference between getting an interview and never being noticed. In this section, we discuss different formats, as well as what to put on (and what to leave off) your resume. We review the benefits and drawbacks of professional resume writers, and the importance of a follow-up letter. Also included in this section are sample resumes and cover letters you can use as models.

The Employer Listings

Employers are listed alphabetically by industry. When a company does business under a person's name, like "John Smith & Co.," the company is usually listed by the surname's spelling (in this case "S"). Exceptions occur when a company's name is widely recognized, like "JCPenney" or "Howard Johnson Motor Lodge." In those cases, the company's first name is the key ("J" and "H" respectively).

The Greater Philadelphia JobBank covers a very wide range of industries. Each company profile is assigned to one of the industry chapters listed below.

Accounting and Management Consulting	*Fabricated/Primary Metals and Products*
Advertising, Marketing, and Public Relations	*Financial Services*
Aerospace	*Food and Beverages/Agriculture*
Apparel, Fashion, and Textiles	*Government*
Architecture, Construction, and Engineering	*Health Care: Services, Equipment, and*
Arts, Entertainment, Sports, and Recreation	*Products*
Automotive	*Hotels and Restaurants*
Banking/Savings and Loans	*Insurance*
Biotechnology, Pharmaceuticals, and	*Legal Services*
Scientific R&D	*Manufacturing: Miscellaneous Consumer*
Business Services and Non-Scientific	*Manufacturing: Miscellaneous Industrial*
Research	*Mining/Gas/Petroleum/Energy Related*
Charities and Social Services	*Paper and Wood Products*
Chemicals/Rubber and Plastics	*Printing and Publishing*
Communications: Telecommunications and	*Real Estate*
Broadcasting	*Retail*
Computer Hardware, Software, and Services	*Stone, Clay, Glass, and Concrete Products*
Educational Services	*Transportation/Travel*
Electronic/Industrial Electrical Equipment	*Utilities: Electric/Gas/Water*
Environmental and Waste Management	*Miscellaneous Wholesaling*
Services	

Many of the company listings offer detailed company profiles. In addition to company names, addresses, and phone numbers, these listings also include contact names or hiring departments, and descriptions of each company's products and/or services. Many of these listings also feature a variety of additional information including:

Common positions - A list of job titles that the company commonly fills when it is hiring, organized in alphabetical order from Accountant to X-ray Technician. Note: Keep in mind that *The Greater Philadelphia JobBank* is a directory of major employers in the area, not a directory of openings currently available. Many of the companies listed will be hiring, others will not. However, since most professional job openings are filled without the placement of help-wanted ads, contacting the employers in this book directly is still a more effective method than browsing the Sunday papers.

Special programs - Does the company offer training programs, internships, or apprenticeships? These programs can be important to first time jobseekers and college students looking for practical work experience. Many employer profiles will include information on these programs.

Parent company - If an employer is a subsidiary of a larger company, the name of that parent company will often be listed here. Use this information to supplement your company research before contacting the employer.

Number of employees - The number of workers a company employs.

Company listings may also include information on other U.S. locations and any stock exchanges the firm may be listed on.

A note on all employer listings that appear in *The Greater Philadelphia JobBank*: This book is intended as a starting point. It is not intended to replace any effort that you, the jobseeker, should devote to your job hunt. Keep in mind that while a great deal of effort has been put into collecting and verifying the company profiles provided in this book, addresses and contact names change regularly. Inevitably, some contact names listed herein have changed even before you read this. We recommend you contact a company before mailing your resume to ensure nothing has changed.

Index

The Greater Philadelphia JobBank index is listed alphabetically by industry.

THE JOB SEARCH

THE BASICS OF JOB WINNING: A CONDENSED REVIEW

This chapter is divided into four sections. The first section explains the fundamentals that every jobseeker should know, especially first-time jobseekers. The next three sections deal with special situations faced by specific types of jobseekers: those who are currently employed, those who have lost a job, and college students.

THE BASICS:
Things Everyone Needs to Know

Career Planning

The first step to finding your ideal job is to clearly define your objectives. This is better known as career planning (or life planning if you wish to emphasize the importance of combining the two). Career planning has become a field of study in and of itself.

If you are thinking of choosing or switching careers, we particularly emphasize two things. First, choose a career where you will enjoy most of the day-to-day tasks. This sounds obvious, but most of us have at some point found the idea of a glamour industry or prestigious job title attractive without thinking of the key consideration: Would we enjoy performing the *everyday* tasks the position entails?

The second key consideration is that you are not merely choosing a career, but also a lifestyle. Career counselors indicate that one of the most common problems people encounter in jobseeking is that they fail to consider how well-suited they are for a particular position or career. For example, some people, attracted to management consulting by good salaries, early responsibility, and high-level corporate exposure, do not adapt well to the long hours, heavy travel demands, and constant pressure to produce. Be sure to ask yourself how you might adapt to the day-to-day duties and working environment that a specific position entails. Then ask yourself how you might adapt to the demands of that career or industry as a whole.

Choosing Your Strategy

Assuming that you've established your career objectives, the next step of the job search is to develop a strategy. If you don't take the time to develop a plan, you may find yourself going in circles after several weeks of randomly searching for opportunities that always seem just beyond your reach.

The most common jobseeking techniques are:

- following up on help-wanted advertisements (in the newspaper or online)
- using employment services
- relying on personal contacts
- contacting employers directly (the Direct Contact method)

Each of these approaches can lead to better jobs. However, the Direct Contact method boasts twice the success rate of the others. So unless you have specific reasons to employ other strategies, Direct Contact should form the foundation of your job search.

If you choose to use other methods as well, try to expend at least half your energy on Direct Contact. Millions of other jobseekers have already proven that Direct Contact has been twice as effective in obtaining employment, so why not follow in their footsteps?

Setting Your Schedule

Okay, so now that you've targeted a strategy it's time to work out the details of your job search. The most important detail is setting up a schedule. Of course, since job searches aren't something most people do regularly, it may be hard to estimate how long each step will take. Nonetheless, it is important to have a plan so that you can monitor your progress.

When outlining your job search schedule, have a realistic time frame in mind. If you will be job-searching full-time, your search could take at least two months or more. If you can only devote part-time effort, it will probably take at least four months.

You probably know a few people who seem to spend their whole lives searching for a better job in their spare time. Don't be one of them. If you are presently working and don't feel like devoting a lot of energy to jobseeking right now, then wait. Focus on enjoying your present position, performing your best on the job, and storing up energy for when you are really ready to begin your job search.

> **The first step in beginning your job search is to clearly define your objectives.**

Those of you who are currently unemployed should remember that *job-hunting is tough work, both physically and emotionally*. It is also intellectually demanding work that requires you to be at your best. So don't tire yourself out by working on your job campaign around the clock. At the same time, be sure to discipline yourself. The most logical way to manage your time while looking for a job is to keep your regular working hours.

If you are searching full-time and have decided to choose several different strategies, we recommend that you divide up each week, designating some time for each method. By trying several approaches at once, you can evaluate how promising each seems and alter your schedule accordingly. Keep in mind that the *majority of openings are filled without being advertised*. Remember also that positions advertised on the Internet are just as likely to already be filled as those found in the newspaper!

If you are searching part-time and decide to try several different contact methods, we recommend that you try them sequentially. You simply won't have enough time to put a meaningful amount of effort into more than one method at once. Estimate the length of your job search, and then allocate so many weeks or months for each contact method, beginning with Direct Contact. The purpose of setting this schedule is not to rush you to your goal but to help you periodically evaluate your progress.

The Direct Contact Method

Once you have scheduled your time, you are ready to begin your search in earnest. Beginning with the Direct Contact method, the first step is to develop a checklist for categorizing the types of firms for which you'd like to work. You might categorize firms by product line, size, customer type (such as industrial or consumer), growth prospects, or geographical location. Keep in mind, the shorter the list the easier it will be to locate a company that is right for you.

Next you will want to use this *JobBank* book to assemble your list of potential employers. Choose firms where *you* are most likely to be able to find a job. Try matching your skills with those that a specific job demands. Consider where your skills might be in demand, the degree of competition for employment, and the employment outlook at each company.

Separate your prospect list into three groups. The first 25 percent will be your primary target group, the next 25 percent will be your secondary group, and the remaining names will be your reserve group.

After you form your prospect list, begin working on your resume. Refer to the Resumes and Cover Letters section following this chapter for more information.

Once your resume is complete, begin researching your first batch of prospective employers. You will want to determine whether you would be happy working at the firms you are researching and to get a better idea of what their employment needs might be. You also need to obtain enough information to sound highly informed about the company during phone conversations and in mail correspondence. But don't go all out on your research yet! You probably won't be able to arrange interviews with some of these firms, so save your big research effort until you start to arrange interviews. Nevertheless, you should plan to spend several

The more you know about a company, the more likely you are to catch an interviewer's eye. (You'll also face fewer surprises once you get the job!)

hours researching each firm. Do your research in batches to save time and energy. Start with this book, and find out what you can about each of the firms in your primary target group. For answers to specific questions, contact any pertinent professional associations that may be able to help you learn more about an employer. Read industry publications looking for articles on the firm. (Addresses of associations and names of important publications are listed after each section of employer listings in this book.) Then look up the company on the Internet or try additional resources at your local library. Keep organized, and maintain a folder on each firm.

Information to look for includes: company size; president, CEO, or owner's name; when the company was established; what each division does; and benefits that are important to you. An abundance of company information can now be found electronically, through the World Wide Web or commercial online services. Researching companies online is a convenient means of obtaining information quickly and easily. If you have access to the Internet, you can search from your home at any time of day.

You may search a particular company's Website for current information that may be otherwise unavailable in print. In fact, many companies that maintain a site update their information daily. In addition, you may also search articles written about the company online. Today, most of the nation's largest newspapers, magazines, trade publications, and regional business periodicals have online versions of their publications. To find additional resources, use a search engine like Yahoo! or Alta Vista and type in the keyword "companies" or "employers."

If you discover something that really disturbs you about the firm (they are about to close their only local office), or if you discover that your chances of getting a job there are practically nil (they have just instituted a hiring freeze), then cross them off your prospect list. If possible, supplement your research efforts by contacting individuals who know the firm well. Ideally you should make an informal contact with someone at that particular firm, but often a direct competitor or a major customer will be able to supply you with just as much information. At the very least, try to obtain whatever printed information the company has available — not just annual reports, but product brochures, company profiles, or catalogs. This information is often available on the Internet.

Getting the Interview

Now it is time to make Direct Contact with the goal of arranging interviews. If you have read any books on job-searching, you may have noticed that most of these books tell you to avoid the human resources office like the plague. It is said that the human resources office never hires people; they screen candidates. Unfortunately, this is often the case. If you can identify the appropriate manager with the authority to hire you, you should try to contact that person directly.

The obvious means of initiating Direct Contact are:

- Mail (postal or electronic)
- Phone calls

Mail contact is a good choice if you have not been in the job market for a while. You can take your time to prepare a letter, say exactly what you want, and of course include your resume. Remember that employers receive many resumes every day. Don't be surprised if you do not get a response to your inquiry, *and don't spend weeks waiting for responses that may never come.* If you do send a letter, follow it up (or precede it) with a phone call. This will increase your impact, and because of the initial research you did, will underscore both your familiarity with and your interest in the firm. Bear in mind that your goal is to make your name a familiar one with prospective employers, so that when a position becomes available, your resume will be one of the first the hiring manager seeks out.

DEVELOPING YOUR CONTACTS: NETWORKING

Some career counselors feel that the best route to a better job is through somebody you already know or through somebody to whom you can be introduced. These counselors recommend that you build your contact base beyond your current acquaintances by asking each one to introduce you, or refer you, to additional people in your field of interest.

The theory goes like this: You might start with 15 personal contacts, each of whom introduces you to three additional people, for a total of 45 additional contacts. Then each of these people introduces you to three additional people, which adds 135 additional contacts. Theoretically, you will soon know every person in the industry.

Of course, developing your personal contacts does not work quite as smoothly as the theory suggests because some people will not be able to introduce you to anyone. The further you stray from your initial contact base, the weaker your references may be. So, if you do try developing your own contacts, try to begin with as many people that you know personally as you can. Dig into your personal phone book and your holiday greeting card list and locate old classmates from school. Be particularly sure to approach people who perform your personal business such as your lawyer, accountant, banker, doctor, stockbroker, and insurance agent. These people develop a very broad contact base due to the nature of their professions.

If you send a fax, always follow with a hard copy of your resume and cover letter in the mail. Often, through no fault of your own, a fax will come through illegibly and employers do not often have time to let candidates know.

Another alternative is to make a "cover call." Your cover call should be just like your cover letter: concise. Your first statement should interest the employer in you. Then try to subtly mention your familiarity with the firm. Don't be overbearing; keep your introduction to three sentences or less. Be pleasant, self-confident, and relaxed. This will greatly increase the chances of the person at the other end of the line developing the conversation. But don't press. If you are asked to follow up with "something in the mail," this signals the conversation's natural end. Don't try to prolong the conversation once it has ended, and don't ask what they want to receive in the mail. Always send your resume and a highly personalized follow-up letter, reminding the addressee of the phone conversation. *Always* include a cover letter if you are asked to send a resume, and treat your resume and cover letter as a total package. Gear your letter toward the specific position you are applying for and prove why you would be a "good match" for the position.

> **Always include a cover letter if you are asked to send a resume.**

Unless you are in telephone sales, making smooth and relaxed cover calls will probably not come easily. Practice them on your own, and then with your friends or relatives.

DON'T BOTHER WITH MASS MAILINGS OR BARRAGES OF PHONE CALLS

Direct Contact does not mean burying every firm within a hundred miles with mail and phone calls. Mass mailings rarely work in the job hunt. This also applies to those letters that are personalized -- but dehumanized -- on an automatic typewriter or computer. Don't waste your time or money on such a project; you will fool no one but yourself.

The worst part of sending out mass mailings, or making unplanned phone calls to companies you have not researched, is that you are likely to be remembered as someone with little genuine interest in the firm, who lacks sincerity -- somebody that nobody wants to hire.

If you obtain an interview as a result of a telephone conversation, be sure to send a thank-you note reiterating the points you made during the conversation. You will appear more professional and increase your impact. However, unless specifically requested, don't mail your resume once an interview has been arranged. Take it with you to the interview instead.

You should never show up to seek a professional position without an appointment. Even if you are somehow lucky enough to obtain an interview, you will appear so unprofessional that you will not be seriously considered.

HELP WANTED ADVERTISEMENTS

Only a small fraction of professional job openings are advertised. Yet the majority of jobseekers -- and quite a few people not in the job market -- spend a lot of time studying the help wanted ads. As a result, the competition for advertised openings is often very severe.

A moderate-sized employer told us about their experience advertising in the help wanted section of a major Sunday newspaper:

It was a disaster. We had over 500 responses from this relatively small ad in just one week. We have only two phone lines in this office and one was totally knocked out. We'll never advertise for professional help again.

If you insist on following up on help wanted ads, then research a firm before you reply to an ad. Preliminary research might help to separate you from all of the other professionals responding to that ad, many of whom will have only a passing interest in the opportunity. It will also give you insight about a particular firm, to help you determine if it is potentially a good match. That said, your chances of obtaining a job through the want ads are still much smaller than they are with the Direct Contact method.

Preparing for the Interview

As each interview is arranged, begin your in-depth research. You should arrive at an interview knowing the company upside-down and inside-out. You need to know the company's products, types of customers, subsidiaries, parent company, principal locations, rank in the industry, sales and profit trends, type of ownership, size, current plans, and much more. By this time you have probably narrowed your job search to one industry. Even if you haven't, you should still be familiar with common industry terms, the trends in the firm's industry, the firm's principal competitors and their relative performance, and the direction in which the industry leaders are headed.

Dig into every resource you can! Surf the Internet. Read the company literature, the trade press, the business press, and if the company is public, call your stockbroker (if you have one) and ask for additional information. If possible, speak to someone at the firm before the interview, or if not, speak to someone at a competing firm. The more time you spend, the better. Even if you feel extremely pressed for time, you should set aside several hours for pre-interview research.

> **You should arrive at an interview knowing the company upside-down and inside-out.**

If you have been out of the job market for some time, don't be surprised if you find yourself tense during your first few interviews. It will probably happen every time you re-enter the market, not just when you seek your first job after getting out of school.

Tension is natural during an interview, but knowing you have done a thorough research job should put you more at ease. Make a list of questions that you think might be asked in each interview. Think out your answers carefully and practice them with a friend. Tape record your responses to the problem questions. (*See also in this chapter: Informational Interviews.*) If you feel particularly unsure of your interviewing skills, arrange your first interviews at firms you are not as interested in. (But remember it is common courtesy to seem enthusiastic about the possibility of working for any firm at which you interview.) Practice again on your own after these first few interviews. Go over the difficult questions that you were asked.

Take some time to really think about how you will convey your work history. Present "bad experiences" as "learning experiences." Instead of saying "I hated my position as a salesperson because I had to bother people on the phone," say "I realized that cold-calling was not my strong suit. Though I love working with people, I decided my talents would be best used in a more face-to-face atmosphere." Always find some sort of lesson from previous jobs, as they all have one.

Interview Attire

How important is the proper dress for a job interview? Buying a complete wardrobe, donning new shoes, and having your hair styled every morning are not enough to guarantee you a career position as an investment banker. But on the other hand, if you can't find a clean, conservative suit or won't take the time to wash your hair, then you are just wasting your time by interviewing at all.

Personal grooming is as important as finding appropriate clothes for a job interview. Careful grooming indicates both a sense of thoroughness and self-confidence. This is not the time to make a statement – take out the extra earrings and avoid any garish hair colors not found in nature. Women should not wear excessive makeup, and both men and women should refrain from wearing any perfume or cologne (it only takes a small spritz to leave an allergic interviewer with a fit of sneezing and a bad impression of your meeting). Men should be freshly shaven, even if the interview is late in the day, and men with long hair should have it pulled back and neat.

Men applying for any professional position should wear a suit, preferably in a conservative color such as navy or charcoal gray. It is easy to get away with wearing the same dark suit to consecutive interviews at the same company; just be sure to wear a different shirt and tie for each interview.

Women should also wear a business suit. Professionalism still dictates a suit with a skirt, rather than slacks, as proper interview garb for women. This is usually true even at companies where pants are acceptable attire for female employees. As much as you may disagree with this guideline, the more prudent time to fight this standard is after you land the job.

The final selection of candidates for a job opening won't be determined by dress, of course. However, inappropriate dress can quickly eliminate a first-round candidate. So while you shouldn't spend a fortune on a new wardrobe, you should be sure that your clothes are adequate. The key is to dress at least as formally or slightly more formally and more conservatively than the position would suggest.

What to Bring

Be complete. Everyone needs a watch, a pen, and a notepad. Finally, a briefcase or a leather-bound folder (containing extra, *unfolded*, copies of your resume) will help complete the look of professionalism.

Sometimes the interviewer will be running behind schedule. Don't be upset, be sympathetic. There is often pressure to interview a lot of candidates and to quickly fill a demanding position. So be sure to come to your interview with good reading material to keep yourself occupied and relaxed.

The Interview

The very beginning of the interview is the most important part because it determines the tone for the rest of it. Those first few moments are especially crucial. Do you smile when you meet? Do you establish enough eye contact, but not too much? Do you walk into the office with a self-assured and confident stride? Do you shake hands firmly? Do you make small talk easily without being garrulous? It is

---

BE PREPARED:
Some Common Interview Questions

Tell me about yourself.

Why did you leave your last job?

What excites you in your current job?

Where would you like to be in five years?

How much overtime are you willing to work?

What would your previous/present employer tell me about you?

Tell me about a difficult situation that you
faced at your previous/present job.

What are your greatest strengths?

What are your weaknesses?

Describe a work situation where you took initiative
and went beyond your normal responsibilities.

Why should we hire you?

---

human nature to judge people by that first impression, so make sure it is a good one. But most of all, try to be yourself.

Often the interviewer will begin, after the small talk, by telling you about the company, the division, the department, or perhaps, the position. Because of your detailed research, the information about the company should be repetitive for you, and the interviewer would probably like nothing better than to avoid this regurgitation of the company biography. So if you can do so tactfully, indicate to the interviewer that you are very familiar with the firm. If he or she seems intent on providing you with background information, despite your hints, then acquiesce.

But be sure to remain attentive. If you can manage to generate a brief discussion of the company or the industry at this point, without being forceful, great. It will help to further build rapport, underscore your interest, and increase your impact.

> **The interviewer's job is to find a reason to turn you down; your job is to not provide that reason.**
>
> -John L. LaFevre, author,
> *How You Really Get Hired*
>
> Reprinted from the 1989/90 *CPC Annual*, with permission of the National Association of Colleges and Employers (formerly College Placement Council, Inc.), copyright holder.

Soon (if it didn't begin that way) the interviewer will begin the questions, many of which you will have already practiced. This period of the interview usually falls into one of two categories (or somewhere in between): either a structured interview, where the interviewer has a prescribed set of questions to ask; or an unstructured interview, where the interviewer will ask only leading questions to get you to talk about yourself, your experiences, and your goals. Try to sense as quickly as possible in which direction the interviewer wishes to proceed. This will make the interviewer feel more relaxed and in control of the situation.

Remember to keep attuned to the interviewer and make the length of your answers appropriate to the situation. If you are really unsure as to how detailed a response the interviewer is seeking, then ask.

As the interview progresses, the interviewer will probably mention some of the most important responsibilities of the position. If applicable, draw parallels between your experience and the demands of the position as detailed by the interviewer. Describe your past experience in the same manner that you do on your resume: emphasizing results and achievements and not merely describing activities. But don't exaggerate. Be on the level about your abilities.

The first interview is often the toughest, where many candidates are screened out. If you are interviewing for a very competitive position, you will have to make an impression that will last. Focus on a few of your greatest strengths that are relevant to the position. Develop these points carefully, state them again in different words, and then try to summarize them briefly at the end of the interview.

Often the interviewer will pause toward the end and ask if you have any questions. Particularly in a structured interview, this might be the one chance to really show your knowledge of and interest in the firm. Have a list prepared of specific questions that are of real interest to you. Let your questions subtly show your research and your knowledge of the firm's activities. It is wise to have an extensive list of questions, as several of them may be answered during the interview.

Do not turn your opportunity to ask questions into an interrogation. Avoid reading directly from your list of questions, and ask questions that you are fairly certain the interviewer can answer (remember how you feel when you cannot answer a question during an interview).

Even if you are unable to determine the salary range beforehand, do not ask about it during the first interview. You can always ask later. Above all, don't ask about fringe benefits until you have been offered a position. (Then be sure to get all the details.)

Try not to be negative about anything during the interview, particularly any past employer or any previous job. Be cheerful. Everyone likes to work with someone who seems to be happy. Even if you detest your current/former job or manager, do not make disparaging comments. The interviewer may construe this as a sign of a potential attitude problem and not consider you a strong candidate.

Don't let a tough question throw you off base. If you don't know the answer to a question, simply say so – do not apologize. Just smile. Nobody can answer every question – particularly some of the questions that are asked in job interviews.

Before your first interview, you may be able to determine how many rounds of interviews there usually are for positions at your level. (Of course it may differ quite a bit even within the different levels of one firm.) Usually you can count on attending at least two or three interviews, although some firms are known to give a minimum of six interviews for all professional positions. While you should be more relaxed as you return for subsequent interviews, the pressure will be on. The more prepared you are, the better.

Depending on what information you are able to obtain, you might want to vary your strategy quite a bit from interview to interview. For instance, if the first interview is a screening interview, then be sure a few of your strengths really stand out. On the other hand, if later interviews are primarily with people who are in a position to veto your hiring, but not to push it forward, then you should primarily focus on building rapport as opposed to reiterating and developing your key strengths.

If it looks as though your skills and background do not match the position the interviewer was hoping to fill, ask him or her if there is another division or subsidiary that perhaps could profit from your talents.

After the Interview

Write a follow-up letter immediately after the interview, while it is still fresh in the interviewer's mind (see the sample follow-up letter format found in the Resumes and Cover Letters chapter). Not only is this a thank-you, but it also gives you the chance to provide the interviewer with any details you may have forgotten (as long as they can be tactfully added in). If you haven't heard back from the interviewer within a week of sending your thank-you letter, call to stress your continued interest in the firm and the position. If you lost any points during the interview for any reason, this letter can help you regain footing. Be polite and make sure to stress your continued interest and competency to fill the position. Just don't forget to proofread it thoroughly. If you are unsure of the spelling of the interviewer's name, call the receptionist and ask.

THE BALANCING ACT:
Looking for a New Job While Currently Employed

For those of you who are still employed, job-searching will be particularly tiring because it must be done in addition to your normal work responsibilities. So don't overwork yourself to the point where you show up to interviews looking exhausted or start to slip behind at your current job. On the other hand, don't be tempted to quit your present job! The long hours are worth it. Searching for a job while you have one puts you in a position of strength.

Making Contact

If you must be at your office during the business day, then you have additional problems to deal with. How can you work interviews into the business day? And if you work in an open office, how can you even call to set up interviews? Obviously, you should keep up the effort and the appearances on your present job. So maximize your use of the lunch hour, early mornings, and late afternoons for calling. If you keep trying, you'll be surprised how often you will be able to reach the executive you are trying to contact during your out-of-office hours. You can catch people as early as 8 a.m. and as late as 6 p.m. on frequent occasions.

Scheduling Interviews

Your inability to interview at any time other than lunch just might work to your advantage. If you can, try to set up as many interviews as possible for your lunch hour. This will go a long way to creating a relaxed atmosphere. But be sure the interviews don't stray too far from the agenda on hand.

Lunchtime interviews are much easier to obtain if you have substantial career experience. People with less experience will often find no alternative to taking time off for interviews. If you have to take time off, you have to take time off. But try to do this as little as possible. Try to take the whole day off in order to avoid being blatantly obvious about your job search, and try to schedule two to three interviews for the same day. (It is very difficult to maintain an optimum level of energy at more than three interviews in one day.) Explain to the interviewer why you might have to juggle your interview schedule; he/she should honor the respect you're showing your current employer by minimizing your days off and will probably appreciate the fact that another prospective employer is interested in you.

> **Try calling as early as 8 a.m. and as late as 6 p.m. You'll be surprised how often you will be able to reach the executive you want during these times of the day.**

References

What do you tell an interviewer who asks for references from your current employer? Just say that while you are happy to have your former employers contacted, you are trying to keep your job search confidential and would rather that your current employer not be contacted until you have been given a firm offer.

IF YOU'RE FIRED OR LAID OFF:
Picking Yourself Up and Dusting Yourself Off

If you've been fired or laid off, you are not the first and will not be the last to go through this traumatic experience. In today's changing economy, thousands of professionals lose their jobs every year. Even if you were terminated with just cause, do not lose heart. Remember, being fired is not a reflection on you as a person. It is usually a reflection of your company's staffing needs and its perception of your recent job performance and attitude. And if you were not performing up to par or enjoying your work, then you will probably be better off at another company anyway.

> **Be prepared for the question "Why were you fired?" during job interviews.**

A thorough job search could take months, so be sure to negotiate a reasonable severance package, if possible, and determine to what benefits, such as health insurance, you are still legally entitled. Also, register for unemployment compensation immediately. Don't be surprised to find other professionals collecting unemployment compensation – it is for everyone who has lost their job.

Don't start your job search with a flurry of unplanned activity. Start by choosing a strategy and working out a plan. Now is not the time for major changes in your life. If possible, remain in the same career and in the same geographical location, at least until you have been working again for a while. On the other hand, if the only industry for which you are trained is leaving, or is severely depressed in your area, then you should give prompt consideration to moving or switching careers.

Avoid mentioning you were fired when arranging interviews, but be prepared for the question "Why were you fired?" during an interview. If you were laid off as a result of downsizing, briefly explain, being sure to reinforce that your job loss was not due to performance. If you were in fact fired, be honest, but try to detail the reason as favorably as possible and portray what you have learned from your mistakes. If you are confident one of your past managers will give you a good reference, tell the interviewer to contact that person. Do not to speak negatively of your past employer and try not to sound particularly worried about your status of being temporarily unemployed.

Finally, don't spend too much time reflecting on why you were let go or how you might have avoided it. Think positively, look to the future, and be sure to follow a careful plan during your job search.

THE COLLEGE STUDENT:
Conducting Your First Job Search

While you will be able to apply many of the basics covered earlier in this chapter to your job search, there are some situations unique to the college student's job search.

THE GPA QUESTION

You are interviewing for the job of your dreams. Everything is going well: You've established a good rapport, the interviewer seems impressed with your qualifications, and you're almost positive the job is yours. Then you're asked about your GPA, which is pitifully low. Do you tell the truth and watch your dream job fly out the window?

Never lie about your GPA (they may request your transcript, and no company will hire a liar). You can, however, explain if there is a reason you don't feel your grades reflect your abilities, and mention any other impressive statistics. For example, if you have a high GPA in your major, or in the last few semesters (as opposed to your cumulative college career), you can use that fact to your advantage.

Perhaps the biggest problem college students face is lack of experience. Many schools have internship programs designed to give students exposure to the field of their choice, as well as the opportunity to make valuable contacts. Check out your school's career services department to see what internships are available. If your school does not have a formal internship program, or if there are no available internships that appeal to you, try contacting local businesses and offering your services. Often, businesses will be more than willing to have an extra pair of hands (especially if those hands are unpaid!) for a day or two each week. Or try contacting school alumni to see if you can "shadow" them for a few days, and see what their daily duties are like.

Informational Interviews

Although many jobseekers do not do this, it can be extremely helpful to arrange an informational interview with a college alumnus or someone else who works in your desired industry. You interview them about their job, their company, and their industry with questions you have prepared in advance. This can be done over the phone but is usually done in person. This will provide you with a contact in the industry who may give you more valuable information -- or perhaps even a job opportunity -- in the future. Always follow up with a thank you letter that includes your contact information.

The goal is to try to begin building experience and establishing contacts as early as possible in your college career.

What do you do if, for whatever reason, you weren't able to get experience directly related to your desired career? First, look at your previous jobs and see if there's anything you can highlight. Did you supervise or train other employees? Did you reorganize the accounting system, or boost productivity in some way? Accomplishments like these demonstrate leadership, responsibility, and innovation -- qualities that most companies look for in employees. And don't forget volunteer activities and school clubs, which can also showcase these traits.

On-Campus Recruiting

Companies will often send recruiters to interview on-site at various colleges. This gives students a chance to interview with companies that may not have interviewed them otherwise. This is particularly true if a company schedules "open" interviews, in which the only screening process is who is first in line at the sign-ups. Of course, since many more applicants gain interviews in this format, this also means that many more people are rejected. The on-campus interview is generally a screening interview, to see if it is worth the company's time to invite you in for a second interview. So do everything possible to make yourself stand out from the crowd.

The first step, of course, is to check out any and all information your school's career center has on the company. If the information seems out of date, check out the company on the Internet or call the company's headquarters and ask for any printed information.

Many companies will host an informational meeting for interviewees, often the evening before interviews are scheduled to take place. DO NOT MISS THIS MEETING. The recruiter will almost certainly ask if you attended. Make an effort to stay after the meeting and talk with the company's representatives. Not only does this give you an opportunity to find out more information about both the company and the position, it also makes you stand out in the recruiter's mind. If there's a particular company that you had your heart set on, but you weren't able to get an interview with them, attend the information session anyway. You may be able to persuade the recruiter to squeeze you into the schedule. (Or you may discover that the company really isn't the right fit for you after all.)

Try to check out the interview site beforehand. Some colleges may conduct "mock" interviews that take place in one of the standard interview rooms. Or you may be able to convince a career counselor (or even a custodian) to let you sneak a peek during off-hours. Either way, having an idea of the room's setup will help you to mentally prepare.

Arrive at least 15 minutes early to the interview. The recruiter may be ahead of schedule, and might meet you early. But don't be surprised if previous interviews have run over, resulting in your 30-minute slot being reduced to 20 minutes (or less). Don't complain or appear anxious; just use the time you do have as efficiently as possible to showcase the reasons *you* are the ideal candidate. Staying calm and composed in these situations will work to your advantage.

LAST WORDS

A parting word of advice. Again and again during your job search you will face rejection. You will be rejected when you apply for interviews. You will be rejected after interviews. For every job offer you finally receive, you probably will have been rejected many times. Don't let rejections slow you down. Keep reminding yourself that the sooner you go out, start your job search, and get those rejections flowing in, the closer you will be to obtaining the job you want.

RESUMES AND COVER LETTERS

When filling a position, an employer will often have 100-plus applicants, but time to interview only a handful of the most promising ones. As a result, he or she will reject most applicants after only briefly skimming their resumes.

Unless you have phoned and talked to the employer – which you should do whenever you can -- you will be chosen or rejected for an interview entirely on the basis of your resume and cover letter. *Your cover letter must catch the employer's attention, and your resume must hold it.* (But remember – a resume is no substitute for a job search campaign. *You* must seek a job. Your resume is only one tool, albeit a critical one.)

RESUME FORMAT:
Mechanics of a First Impression

The Basics

Employers dislike long resumes, so unless you have an unusually strong background with many years of experience and a diversity of outstanding achievements, keep your resume length to one page. If you must squeeze in more information than would otherwise fit, try using a smaller typeface or changing the margins. Watch also for "widows" at the end of paragraphs. You can often free up some space if you can shorten the information enough to get rid of those single words taking up an entire line. Another tactic that works with some word processing programs is to decrease the font size of your paragraph returns and changing the spacing between lines.

Print your resume on standard 8 1/2" x 11" paper. Since recruiters often get resumes in batches of hundreds, a smaller-sized resume may be lost in the pile. Oversized resumes are likely to get crumpled at the edges, and won't fit easily in their files.

First impressions matter, so make sure the recruiter's first impression of your resume is a good one. Never hand-write your resume (or cover letter)! Print your resume on quality paper that has weight and texture, in a conservative color such as white, ivory, or pale gray. Good resume paper is easy to find at many stores that sell stationery or office products. It is even available at some drug stores. Use *matching* paper and envelopes for both your resume and cover letter. One hiring manager at a major magazine throws out all resumes that arrive on paper that differs in color from the envelope!

Do not buy paper with images of clouds and rainbows in the background or anything that looks like casual stationery that you would send to your favorite aunt. Do not spray perfume or cologne on your resume. Do not include your picture with your resume unless you have a specific and appropriate reason to do so.

Another tip: Do a test print of your resume (and cover letter), to make sure the watermark is on the same side as the text so that you can read it. Also make sure it is right-side up. As trivial as this may sound, some recruiters check for this! One recruiter at a law firm in New Hampshire sheepishly admitted this is the first thing he checks. *"I open each envelope and check the watermarks on the resume and cover letter. Those candidates that have it wrong go into a different pile."*

Getting it on Paper

Modern photocomposition typesetting gives you the clearest, sharpest image, a wide variety of type styles, and effects such as italics, bold-facing, and book-like justified margins. It is also too expensive for many jobseekers. The quality of today's laser printers means that a computer-generated resume can look just as impressive as one that has been professionally typeset.

A computer with a word processing or desktop publishing program is the most common way to generate your resume. This allows you the flexibility to make changes almost instantly and to store different drafts on disk. Word processing and desktop publishing programs also offer many different fonts to choose from, each taking up different amounts of space. (It is generally best to stay between 9-point and 12-point font size.) Many other options are also available, such as bold-facing or italicizing for emphasis and the ability to change and manipulate spacing. It is generally recommended to leave the right-hand margin unjustified as this keeps the spacing between the text even and therefore easier to read. It is not wrong to justify both margins of text, but if possible try it both ways before you decide.

For a resume on paper, the end result will be largely determined by the quality of the printer you use. Laser printers will generally provide the best quality. Do not use a dot matrix printer.

Many companies now use scanning equipment to screen the resumes they receive, and certain paper, fonts, and other features are more compatible with this technology. White paper is preferable, as well as a standard font such as Courier or Helvetica. You should use at least a 10-point font, and avoid bolding, italics, underlining, borders, boxes, or graphics.

Household typewriters and office typewriters with nylon or other cloth ribbons are *not* good enough for typing your resume. If you don't have access to a quality word processing program, hire a professional with the resources to prepare your resume for you. Keep in mind that businesses such as Kinko's (open 24 hours) provide access to computers with quality printers.

Don't make your copies on an office photocopier. Only the human resources office may see the resume you mail. Everyone else may see only a copy of it, and copies of copies quickly become unreadable. Furthermore, sending photocopies of your resume or cover letter is completely unprofessional. Either print out each copy individually, or take your resume to a professional copy shop, which will generally offer professionally-maintained, extra-high-quality photocopiers and charge fairly reasonable prices. You want your resume to represent you with the look of polished quality.

Proof with Care

Whether you typed it or paid to have it produced professionally, mistakes on resumes are not only embarrassing, but will usually remove you from consideration (particularly if something obvious such as your name is misspelled). No matter how much you paid someone else to type, write, or typeset your resume, *you* lose if there is a mistake. So proofread it as carefully as possible. Get a friend to help you. Read your draft aloud as your friend checks the proof copy. Then have your friend read aloud while you check. Next, read it letter by letter to check spelling and punctuation.

If you are having it typed or typeset by a resume service or a printer, and you don't have time to proof it, pay for it and take it home. Proof it there and bring it back later to get it corrected and printed.

If you wrote your resume with a word processing program, use the built-in spell checker to double-check for spelling errors. Keep in mind that a spell checker will not find errors such as "to" for "two" or "wok" for "work." Many spell check programs do not recognize missing or misused punctuation, nor are they set to check the spelling of capitalized words. It's important that you still proofread your resume to check for grammatical mistakes and other problems, even after it has been spellchecked. If you find mistakes, do not make edits in pen or pencil or use white-out to fix them on the final copy!

Electronic Resumes

As companies rely increasingly on emerging technologies to find qualified candidates for job openings, you may opt to create an electronic resume in order to remain competitive in today's job market. Why is this important? Companies today sometimes request that resumes be submitted by e-mail, and many hiring managers regularly check online resume databases for candidates to fill unadvertised job openings. Other companies enlist the services of electronic employment database services, which charge jobseekers a nominal fee to have their resumes posted to the database to be viewed by potential employers. Still other companies use their own automated applicant tracking systems, in which case your resume is fed through a scanner that sends the image to a computer that "reads" your resume, looking for keywords, and files it accordingly in its database.

Whether you're posting your resume online, e-mailing it directly to an employer, sending it to an electronic employment database, or sending it to a company you suspect uses an automated applicant tracking system, you must create some form of electronic resume to take advantage of the technology. Don't panic! An electronic resume is simply a modified version of your conventional resume. An electronic resume is one that is sparsely formatted, but filled with keywords and important facts.

In order to post your resume to the Internet -- either to an online resume database or through direct e-mail to an employer -- you will need to change the way your resume is formatted. Instead of a Word, WordPerfect, or other word processing document, save your resume as a plain text, DOS, or ASCII file. These three terms are basically interchangeable, and describe text at its simplest, most basic level, without the formatting such as boldface or italics that most jobseekers use to make their resumes look more interesting. If you use e-mail, you'll notice that all of your messages are written and received in this format. First, you should remove all formatting from your resume including boldface, italics, underlining, bullets, differing font sizes, and graphics. Then, convert and save your resume as a plain text file. Most word processing programs have a "save as" feature that allows you to save files in different formats. Here, you should choose "text only" or "plain text."

Another option is to create a resume in HTML (hypertext markup language), the text formatting language used to publish information on the World Wide Web. However, the real usefulness of HTML resumes is still being explored. Most of the major online databases do not accept HTML resumes, and the vast majority of companies only accept plain text resumes through their e-mail.

Finally, if you simply wish to send your resume to an electronic employment database or a company that uses an automated applicant tracking system, there is no need to convert your resume to a plain text file. The only change you need to make is to organize the information in your resume by keywords. Employers are likely to do keyword searches for information, such as degree held or knowledge of particular types of software. Therefore, using the right keywords or key phrases in your resume is critical to its ultimate success. Keywords are usually nouns or short phrases that the computer searches for which refer to experience, training, skills, and abilities. For example, let's say an employer searches an employment database for a sales representative with the following criteria:

BS/BA
exceeded quota
cold calls
high energy
willing to travel

Even if you have the right qualifications, neglecting to use these keywords would result in the computer passing over your resume. Although there is no way to know for sure which keywords employers are most likely to search for, you can make educated guesses by checking the help-wanted ads or online job postings for your type of job. You should also arrange keywords in a keyword summary, a paragraph listing your qualifications that immediately follows your name and address (see sample letter in this chapter). In addition, choose a nondecorative font with clear, distinct characters, such as Helvetica or Times. It is more difficult for a scanner to accurately pick up the more unusual fonts. Boldface and all capital letters are best used only for major section headings, such as "Experience" and "Education." It is also best to avoid using italics or underlining, since this can cause the letters to bleed into one another.

For more specific information on creating and sending electronic resumes, see *The Adams Internet Job Search Almanac.*

Types of Resumes

The most common resume formats are the functional resume, the chronological resume, and the combination resume. (Examples can be found at the end of this chapter.) A functional resume focuses on skills and de-emphasizes job titles, employers, etc. A functional resume is best if you have been out of the work force for a long time or are changing careers. It is also good if you want to highlight specific skills and strengths, especially if all of your work experience has been at one company. This format can also be a good choice if you are just out of school or have no experience in your desired field.

Choose a chronological format if you are currently working or were working recently, and if your most recent experiences relate to your desired field. Use reverse chronological order and include dates. To a recruiter your last job and your latest schooling are the most important, so put the last first and list the rest going back in time.

A combination resume is perhaps the most common. This resume simply combines elements of the functional and chronological resume formats. This is used by many jobseekers with a solid track record who find elements of both types useful.

Organization

Your name, phone number, e-mail address (if you have one), and a complete mailing address should be at the top of your resume. Try to make your name stand out by using a slightly larger font size or all capital letters. Be sure to spell out everything. Never abbreviate St. for Street or Rd. for Road. If you are a college student, you should also put your home address and phone number at the top.

Change your message on your answering machine if necessary – RUSH blaring in the background or your sorority sisters screaming may not come across well to all recruiters. If you think you may be moving within six months then include a second address and phone number of a trusted friend or relative who can reach you no matter where you are.

Remember that employers will keep your resume on file and may contact you months later if a position opens that fits your qualifications. All too often, candidates are unreachable because they have moved and had not previously provided enough contact options on their resume.

Next, list your experience, then your education. If you are a recent graduate, list your education first, unless your experience is more important than your education. (For example, if you have just graduated from a teaching school, have some business experience, and are applying for a job in business, you would list your business experience first.)

Keep everything easy to find. Put the dates of your employment and education on the left of the page. Put the names of the companies you worked for and the schools you attended a few spaces to the right of the dates. Put the city and state, or the city and country, where you studied or worked to the right of the page.

The important thing is simply to break up the text in some logical way that makes your resume visually attractive and easy to scan, so experiment to see which layout works best for your resume. However you set it up, *stay consistent.* Inconsistencies in fonts, spacing, or tenses will make your resume look sloppy. Also, be sure to use tabs to keep your information vertically lined up, rather than the less precise space bar.

RESUME CONTENT:
Say it with Style
Sell Yourself

You are selling your skills and accomplishments in your resume, so it is important to inventory yourself and know yourself. If you have achieved something, say so. Put it in the best possible light, but avoid subjective statements, such as "I am a hard worker" or "I get along well with my coworkers." Just stick to the facts.

While you shouldn't hold back or be modest, don't exaggerate your achievements to the point of misrepresentation. <u>Be honest</u>. Many companies will immediately drop an applicant from consideration (or fire a current employee) upon discovering inaccurate or untrue information on a resume or other application material.

Write down the important (and pertinent) things you have done, but do it in as few words as possible. Your resume will be scanned, not read, and short, concise phrases are much more effective than long-winded sentences. Avoid the use of "I" when emphasizing your accomplishments. Instead, use brief phrases beginning with action verbs.

While some technical terms will be unavoidable, you should try to avoid excessive "technicalese." Keep in mind that the first person to see your resume may be a human resources person who won't necessarily know all the jargon – and how can they be impressed by something they don't understand?

Keep it Brief

Also, try to hold your paragraphs to six lines or less. If you have more than six lines of information about one job or school, put it in two or more paragraphs. A short resume will be examined more carefully. Remember: Your resume usually has between eight and 45 seconds to catch an employer's eye. So make every second count.

Job Objective

A functional resume may require a job objective to give it focus. One or two sentences describing the job you are seeking can clarify in what capacity your skills will be best put to use. Be sure that your stated objective is in line with the position you're applying for.

Examples:

> An entry-level editorial assistant position in the publishing industry.
> A senior management position with a telecommunications firm.

Don't include a job objective on a chronological resume unless your previous work experiences are <u>completely</u> unrelated to the position for which you're applying. The presence of an overly specific job objective might eliminate you from consideration for other positions that a recruiter feels are a better match for your qualifications. But even if you don't put an objective on paper, having a career goal in mind as you write can help give your resume a solid sense of direction.

USE ACTION VERBS

How you write your resume is just as important as *what* you write. In describing previous work experiences, the strongest resumes use short phrases beginning with action verbs. Below are a few you may want to use. (This list is not all-inclusive.)

achieved	developed	integrated	purchased
administered	devised	interpreted	reduced
advised	directed	interviewed	regulated
arranged	distributed	launched	represented
assisted	established	managed	resolved
attained	evaluated	marketed	restored
budgeted	examined	mediated	restructured
built	executed	monitored	revised
calculated	expanded	negotiated	scheduled
collaborated	expedited	obtained	selected
collected	facilitated	operated	served
compiled	formulated	ordered	sold
completed	founded	organized	solved
computed	generated	participated	streamlined
conducted	headed	performed	studied
consolidated	identified	planned	supervised
constructed	implemented	prepared	supplied
consulted	improved	presented	supported
controlled	increased	processed	tested
coordinated	initiated	produced	trained
created	installed	proposed	updated
determined	instructed	published	wrote

Some jobseekers may choose to include both "Relevant Experience" and "Additional Experience" sections. This can be useful, as it allows the jobseeker to place more emphasis on certain experiences and to de-emphasize others.

Emphasize continued experience in a particular job area or continued interest in a particular industry. De-emphasize irrelevant positions. It is okay to include one opening line providing a general description of each company you've worked at. Delete positions that you held for less than four months (unless you are a very recent college grad or still in school). Stress your <u>results</u> and your achievements, elaborating on how you contributed in your previous jobs. Did you increase sales, reduce costs, improve a product, implement a new program? Were you promoted? Use specific numbers (i.e., quantities, percentages, dollar amounts) whenever possible.

Education

Keep it brief if you have more than two years of career experience. Elaborate more if you have less experience. If you are a recent college graduate, you may choose to include any high school activities that are directly relevant to your career. If you've been out of school for a while you don't need to list your education prior to college.

Mention degrees received and any honors or special awards. Note individual courses or projects you participated in that might be relevant for employers. For example, if you are an English major applying for a position as a business writer, be sure to mention any business or economics courses. Previous experience such as Editor-in-Chief of the school newspaper would be relevant as well.

If you are uploading your resume to an online job hunting site such as CareerCity.com, action verbs are still important, but the key words or key nouns that a computer would search for become more important. For example, if you're seeking an accounting position, key nouns that a computer would search for such as "Lotus 1-2-3" or "CPA" or "payroll" become very important.

Highlight Impressive Skills

Be sure to mention any computer skills you may have. You may wish to include a section entitled "Additional Skills" or "Computer Skills," in which you list any software programs you know. An additional skills section is also an ideal place to mention fluency in a foreign language.

Personal Data

This section is optional, but if you choose to include it, keep it brief. A one-word mention of hobbies such as fishing, chess, baseball, cooking, etc., can give the person who will interview you a good way to open up the conversation.

Team sports experience is looked at favorably. It doesn't hurt to include activities that are somewhat unusual (fencing, Akido, '70s music) or that somehow relate to the position or the company to which you're applying. For instance, it would be worth noting if you are a member of a professional organization in your industry of interest. Never include information about your age, alias, date of birth, health, physical characteristics, marital status, religious affiliation, or political/moral beliefs.

References

The most that is needed is the sentence "References available upon request" at the bottom of your resume. If you choose to leave it out, that's fine. This line is not really necessary. It is understood that references will most likely be asked for and provided by you later on in the interviewing process. Do not actually send references with your resume and cover letter unless specifically requested.

HIRING A RESUME WRITER:
Is it the Right Choice for You?

If you write reasonably well, it is to your advantage to write your own resume. Writing your resume forces you to review your experiences and figure out how to explain your accomplishments in clear, brief phrases. This will help you when you explain your work to interviewers. It is also easier to tailor your resume to each position you're applying for when you have put it together yourself.

If you write your resume, everything will be in your own words; it will sound like you. It will say what you want it to say. If you are a good writer, know yourself well, and have a good idea of which parts of your background employers are looking for, you should be able to write your own resume better than someone else. If you decide to write your resume yourself, have as many people as possible review and proofread it. Welcome objective opinions and other perspectives.

When to Get Help

If you have difficulty writing in "resume style" (which is quite unlike normal written language), if you are unsure which parts of your background to emphasize, or if you think your resume would make your case better if it did not follow one of the standard forms outlined either here or in a book on resumes, then you should consider having it professionally written.

Even some professional resume writers we know have had their resumes written with the help of fellow professionals. They sought the help of someone who could be objective about their background, as well as provide an experienced sounding board to help focus their thoughts.

If You Hire a Pro

The best way to choose a writer is by reputation: the recommendation of a friend, a personnel director, your school placement officer, or someone else knowledgeable in the field.

Important questions:
· "How long have you been writing resumes?"
· "If I'm not satisfied with what you write, will you go over it with me and change it?"
· "Do you charge by the hour or a flat rate?"

There is no sure relation between price and quality, except that you are unlikely to get a good writer for less than $50 for an uncomplicated resume and you shouldn't have to pay more than $300 unless your experience is very extensive or complicated. There will be additional charges for printing. Assume nothing no matter how much you pay. It is your career at stake if there are mistakes on your resume!

Few resume services will give you a firm price over the phone, simply because some resumes are too complicated and take too long to do for a predetermined price. Some services will quote you a price that applies to almost all of their customers. Once you decide to use a specific writer, you should insist on a firm price quote *before* engaging their services. Also, find out how expensive minor changes will be.

COVER LETTERS:
Quick, Clear, and Concise

Always mail a cover letter with your resume. In a cover letter you can show an interest in the company that you can't show in a resume. You can also point out one or two of your skills or accomplishments the company can put to good use.

Make it Personal

The more personal you can get, the better, so long as you keep it professional. If someone known to the person you are writing has recommended that you contact the company, get permission to include his/her name in the letter. If you can get the name of a person to send the letter to, address it directly to that person (after first calling the company to verify the spelling of the person's name, correct title, and mailing address). Be sure to put the person's name and title on both the letter and the envelope. This will ensure that your letter will get through to the proper person, even if a new person now occupies this position. It will not always be possible to get the name of a person. Always strive to get at least a title.

Be sure to mention something about why you have an interest in the company - - *so many candidates apply for jobs with no apparent knowledge of what the company does!* This conveys the message that they just want any job.

Type cover letters in full. Don't try the cheap and easy ways, like using a computer mail merge program or photocopying the body of your letter and typing in the inside address and salutation. You will give the impression that you are mailing to a host of companies and have no particular interest in any one.

Print your cover letter on the same color and same high-quality paper as your resume.

Cover letter basic format

<u>Paragraph 1:</u> State what the position is that you are seeking. It is not always necessary to state how you found out about the position -- often you will apply without knowing that a position is open.

<u>Paragraph 2:</u> Include what you know about the company and why you are interested in working there. Mention any prior contact with the company or someone known to the hiring person if relevant. Briefly state your qualifications and what you can offer. (Do not talk about what you cannot do).

<u>Paragraph 3:</u> Close with your phone number and where/when you can be reached. Make a request for an interview. State when you will follow up by phone (or mail or e-mail if the ad requests no phone calls). Do not wait long -- generally five working days. If you say you're going to follow up, then actually do it! This phone call can get your resume noticed when it might otherwise sit in a stack of 225 other resumes.

Cover letter do's and don'ts

- *Do* keep your cover letter brief and to the point.
- *Do* be sure it is error-free.
- *Do* accentuate what you can offer the company, not what you hope to gain.
- *Do* be sure your phone number and address is on your cover letter just in case it gets separated from your resume (this happens!).
- *Do* check the watermark by holding the paper up to a light – be sure it is facing forward so it is readable – on the same side as the text, and right-side up.
- *Do* sign your cover letter (or type your name if you are sending it electronically). Blue or black ink are both fine. Do not use red ink.
- *Don't* just repeat information verbatim from your resume.
- *Don't* overuse the personal pronoun "I."
- *Don't* send a generic cover letter – show your personal knowledge of and interest in that particular company.

THANK YOU LETTERS:
Another Way to Stand Out

As mentioned earlier, *always* send a thank you letter after an interview (see the sample later in this section). So few candidates do this and it is yet another way for you to stand out. Be sure to mention something specific from the interview and restate your interest in the company and the position.

It is generally acceptable to handwrite your thank you letter on a generic thank you card (but *never* a postcard). Make sure handwritten notes are neat and legible. However, if you are in doubt, typing your letter is always the safe bet. If you met with several people it is fine to send them each an individual thank you letter. Call the company if you need to check on the correct spelling of their names.

Remember to:
- Keep it short.
- Proofread it carefully.
- Send it *promptly.*

FUNCTIONAL RESUME

C.J. RAVENCLAW
129 Pennsylvania Avenue
Washington DC 20500
202/555-6652
e-mail: ravenclaw@dcpress.net

Objective
A position as a graphic designer commensurate with my acquired skills and expertise.

Summary
Extensive experience in plate making, separations, color matching, background definition, printing, mechanicals, color corrections, and personnel supervision. A highly motivated manager and effective communicator. Proven ability to:

- **Create Commercial Graphics**
- **Produce Embossed Drawings**
- **Color Separate**

- **Control Quality**
- **Resolve Printing Problems**
- **Analyze Customer Satisfaction**

Qualifications
Printing:
Knowledgeable in black and white as well as color printing. Excellent judgment in determining acceptability of color reproduction through comparison with original. Proficient at producing four- or five-color corrections on all media, as well as restyling previously reproduced four-color artwork.

Customer Relations:
Routinely work closely with customers to ensure specifications are met. Capable of striking a balance between technical printing capabilities and need for customer satisfaction through entire production process.

Specialties:
Practiced at creating silk screen overlays for a multitude of processes including velo bind, GBC bind, and perfect bind. Creative design and timely preparation of posters, flyers, and personalized stationery.

Personnel Supervision:
Skillful at fostering atmosphere that encourages highly talented artists to balance high-level creativity with maximum production. Consistently beat production deadlines. Instruct new employees, apprentices, and students in both artistry and technical operations.

Experience
Graphic Arts Professor, Ohio State University, Columbus OH (1992-1996).
Manager, Design Graphics, Washington DC (1997-present).

Education
Massachusetts Conservatory of Art, Ph.D. 1990
University of Massachusetts, B.A. 1988

CHRONOLOGICAL RESUME

HARRY SEABORN
557 Shoreline Drive
Seattle, WA 98404
(206) 555-6584
e-mail: hseaborn@centco.com

EXPERIENCE

THE CENTER COMPANY   Seattle, WA
Systems Programmer   1996-present
- Develop and maintain customer accounting and order tracking database using a Visual Basic front end and SQL server.
- Plan and implement migration of company wide transition from mainframe-based dumb terminals to a true client server environment using Windows NT Workstation and Server.
- Oversee general local and wide area network administration including the development of a variety of intranet modules to improve internal company communication and planning across divisions.

INFO TECH, INC.   Seattle, WA
Technical Manager   1994-1996
- Designed and managed the implementation of a network providing the legal community with a direct line to Supreme Court cases across the Internet using SQL Server and a variety of Internet tools.
- Developed a system to make the entire library catalog available on line using PERL scripts and SQL.
- Used Visual Basic and Microsoft Access to create a registration system for university registrar.

EDUCATION

SALEM STATE UNIVERSITY   Salem, OR
    M.S. in Computer Science.   1993
    B.S. in Computer Science.   1991

COMPUTER SKILLS

- Programming Languages: Visual Basic, Java, C++, SQL, PERL
- Software: SQL Server, Internet Information Server, Oracle
- Operating Systems: Windows NT, UNIX, Linux

FUNCTIONAL RESUME

Donna Hermione Moss
703 Wizard's Way
Chicago, IL 60601
(312) 555-8841
e-mail: donna@cowfire.com

OBJECTIVE:
To contribute over five years of experience in promotion, communications, and administration to an entry-level position in advertising.

SUMMARY OF QUALIFICATIONS:
- Performed advertising duties for small business.
- Experience in business writing and communications skills.
- General knowledge of office management.
- Demonstrated ability to work well with others, in both supervisory and support staff roles.
- Type 75 words per minute.

SELECTED ACHIEVEMENTS AND RESULTS:
Promotion:
Composing, editing, and proofreading correspondence and public relations materials for own catering service. Large-scale mailings.

Communication:
Instruction; curriculum and lesson planning; student evaluation; parent-teacher conferences; development of educational materials. Training and supervising clerks.

Computer Skills:
Proficient in MS Word, Lotus 1-2-3, Excel, and Filemaker Pro.

Administration:
Record-keeping and file maintenance. Data processing and computer operations, accounts receivable, accounts payable, inventory control, and customer relations. Scheduling, office management, and telephone reception.

PROFESSIONAL HISTORY:
Teacher; Self-Employed (owner of catering service); Floor Manager; Administrative Assistant; Accounting Clerk.

EDUCATION:
Beloit College, Beloit, WI, BA in Education, 1991

CHRONOLOGICAL RESUME

PERCY ZIEGLER
16 Josiah Court
Marlborough CT 06447
203/555-9641 (h)
203/555-8176, x14 (w)

EDUCATION

Keene State College, Keene NH
Bachelor of Arts in Elementary Education, 1998
- Graduated *magna cum laude*
- English minor
- Kappa Delta Pi member, inducted 1996

EXPERIENCE
September 1998-
Present

Elmer T. Thienes Elementary School, Marlborough CT
Part-time Kindergarten Teacher
- Instruct kindergartners in reading, spelling, language arts, and music.
- Participate in the selection of textbooks and learning aids.
- Organize and supervise class field trips and coordinate in-class presentations.

Summers
1995-1997

Keene YMCA, Youth Division, Keene NH
Child-care Counselor
- Oversaw summer program for low-income youth.
- Budgeted and coordinated special events and field trips, working with Program Director to initiate variations in the program.
- Served as Youth Advocate in cooperation with social worker to address the social needs and problems of participants.

Spring 1997

Wheelock Elementary School, Keene NH
Student Teacher
- Taught third-grade class in all elementary subjects.
- Designed and implemented a two-week unit on Native Americans.
- Assisted in revision of third-grade curriculum.

Fall 1996

Child Development Center, Keene NH
Daycare Worker
- Supervised preschool children on the playground and during art activities.
- Created a "Wishbone Corner," where children could quietly look at books or take a voluntary "time-out."

ADDITIONAL INTERESTS

Martial arts, Pokemon, politics, reading, skiing, writing.

ELECTRONIC RESUME

GRIFFIN DORE
69 Dursley Drive
Cambridge, MA 02138
(617) 555-5555

KEYWORD SUMMARY

Senior financial manager with over ten years experience in Accounting and Systems Management, Budgeting, Forecasting, Cost Containment, Financial Reporting, and International Accounting. MBA in Management. Proficient in Lotus, Excel, Solomon, and Windows.

EXPERIENCE

COLWELL CORPORATION, Wellesley, MA
Director of Accounting and Budgets, 1990 to present
   Direct staff of twenty in General Ledger, Accounts Payable, Accounts Receivable, and International Accounting.
   Facilitate month-end closing process with parent company and auditors.
   Implemented team-oriented cross-training program within accounting group, resulting in timely month-end closings and increased productivity of key accounting staff.
   Developed and implemented a strategy for Sales and Use Tax Compliance in all fifty states.
   Prepare monthly financial statements and analyses.

FRANKLIN AND DELANEY COMPANY, Melrose, MA
Senior Accountant, 1987-1990
   Managed Accounts Payable, General Ledger, transaction processing, and financial reporting. Supervised staff of five.

Staff Accountant, 1985-1987
   Managed Accounts Payable, including vouchering, cash disbursements, and bank reconciliation.
   Wrote and issued policies.
   Maintained supporting schedules used during year-end audits.
   Trained new employees.

EDUCATION

MBA in Management, Northeastern University, Boston, MA, 1989
BS in Accounting, Boston College, Boston, MA, 1985

ASSOCIATIONS

National Association of Accountants

GENERAL MODEL
FOR A COVER LETTER

Your mailing address
Date

Contact's name
Contact's title
Company
Company's mailing address

Dear Mr./Ms. _____ :

Immediately explain why your background makes you the best candidate for the position that you are applying for. Describe what prompted you to write (want ad, article you read about the company, networking contact, etc.). Keep the first paragraph short and hard-hitting.

Detail what you could contribute to this company. Show how your qualifications will benefit this firm. Describe your interest in the corporation. Subtly emphasizing your knowledge about this firm and your familiarity with the industry will set you apart from other candidates. Remember to keep this letter short; few recruiters will read a cover letter longer than half a page.

If possible, your closing paragraph should request specific action on the part of the reader. Include your phone number and the hours when you can be reached. Mention that if you do not hear from the reader by a specific date, you will follow up with a phone call. Lastly, thank the reader for their time, consideration, etc.

Sincerely,

(signature)

Your full name (typed)

Enclosure (use this if there are other materials, such as your resume, that are included in the same envelope)

SAMPLE COVER LETTER

16 Josiah Court
Marlborough CT 06447
January 16, 2000

Ms. Leona Malfoy
Assistant Principal
Laningham Elementary School
43 Mayflower Drive
Keene NH 03431

Dear Ms. Malfoy:

Toby Potter recently informed me of a possible opening for a third grade teacher at Laningham Elementary School. With my experience instructing third-graders, both in schools and in summer programs, I feel I would be an ideal candidate for the position. Please accept this letter and the enclosed resume as my application.

Laningham's educational philosophy that every child can learn and succeed interests me, since it mirrors my own. My current position at Elmer T. Thienes Elementary has reinforced this philosophy, heightening my awareness of the different styles and paces of learning and increasing my sensitivity toward special needs children. Furthermore, as a direct result of my student teaching experience at Wheelock Elementary School, I am comfortable, confident, and knowledgeable working with third-graders.

I look forward to discussing the position and my qualifications for it in more detail. I can be reached at 203/555-9641 evenings or 203/555-8176, x14 weekdays. If I do not hear from you before Tuesday of next week, I will call to see if we can schedule a time to meet. Thank you for your time and consideration.

Sincerely,

Percy Ziegler

Percy Ziegler

Enclosure

GENERAL MODEL FOR A
THANK YOU/FOLLOW-UP LETTER

Your mailing address
Date

Contact's name
Contact's title
Company
Company's mailing address

Dear Mr./Ms._____:

Remind the interviewer of the reason (i.e., a specific opening, an informational interview, etc.) you were interviewed, as well as the date. Thank him/her for the interview, and try to personalize your thanks by mentioning some specific aspect of the interview.

Confirm your interest in the organization (and in the opening, if you were interviewing for a particular position). Use specifics to re-emphasize that you have researched the firm in detail and have considered how you would fit into the company and the position. This is a good time to say anything you wish you had said in the initial meeting. Be sure to keep this letter brief; a half page is plenty.

If appropriate, close with a suggestion for further action, such as a desire to have an additional interview, if possible. Mention your phone number and the hours you can be reached. Alternatively, you may prefer to mention that you will follow up with a phone call in several days. Once again, thank the person for meeting with you, and state that you would be happy to provide any additional information about your qualifications.

Sincerely,

(signature)

Your full name (typed)

PRIMARY EMPLOYERS

ACCOUNTING AND MANAGEMENT CONSULTING

You can expect to find the following types of companies in this chapter:

Consulting and Research Firms • Industrial Accounting Firms • Management Services • Public Accounting Firms • Tax Preparation Companies

ARTHUR ANDERSEN
1601 Market Street, Philadelphia PA 19103-2944. 267/675-6000. **Contact:** Human Resources. **World Wide Web address:** http://www.andersen.com. **Description:** One of the largest certified public accounting firms in the world. Arthur Andersen's four key practice areas include Audit and Business Advisory, Tax and Business Advisory, Business Consulting, and Economic and Financial Consulting. **NOTE:** This firm does not accept unsolicited resumes. Please check the Website for available positions. **Corporate headquarters location:** Chicago IL. **Other U.S. locations:** Nationwide. **International locations:** Worldwide. **Parent company:** Arthur Andersen Worldwide Organization, one of the leading providers of professional services in the world. With over 380 worldwide locations, the global practice of its member firms is conducted through two business units: Arthur Andersen and Andersen Consulting, which provides global management and technology consulting. **Number of employees worldwide:** 91,000.

BOWMAN & COMPANY LLP
601 White Horse Road, Voorhees NJ 08043. 856/435-6200. **Fax:** 856/435-0440. **Contact:** John Daniels, Human Resources Department. **E-mail address:** jdaniels@bowmanllp.com. **World Wide Web address:** http://www.bowmanllp.com. **Description:** A certified public accounting firm. Founded in 1939. **NOTE:** Entry-level positions are offered. **Common positions include:** Accountant/Auditor. **Special programs:** Internships; Co-ops. **Corporate headquarters location:** This location. **Listed on:** Privately held. **Annual sales/revenues:** $5 - $10 million. **Number of employees at this location:** 90.

ERNST & YOUNG LLP
2 Commerce Square, 2001 Market Street, Suite 4000, Philadelphia PA 19103-7096. 215/448-5000. **Contact:** Thomas G. Elicker, Director of Human Resources. **World Wide Web address:** http://www.ey.com. **Description:** A certified public

accounting firm that also provides management consulting services. Services include data processing, financial modeling, financial feasibility studies, production planning and inventory management, management sciences, health care planning, human resources, cost accounting, and budgeting systems. **Common positions include:** Accountant/Auditor. **Corporate headquarters location:** New York NY.

HAY GROUP INC.
The Wanamaker Building, 100 Penn Square East, Philadelphia PA 19107. 215/861-2000. **Contact:** Personnel. **World Wide Web address:** http://www.haygroup.com. **Description:** An international human resources and management consulting firm that provides a variety of services including total compensation planning, strategic management, business culture, employee surveys, and outplacement. **Common positions include:** Accountant/Auditor; Actuary; Computer Programmer; Customer Service Representative; Human Resources Manager; Marketing Specialist; Systems Analyst. **Corporate headquarters location:** This location.

KPMG
1600 Market Street, 12th Floor, Philadelphia PA 19103. 215/299-3100. **Contact:** Human Resources. **World Wide Web address:** http://www.kpmg.com. **Description:** KPMG delivers a wide range of value-added assurance, tax, and consulting services. **Corporate headquarters location:** Montvale NJ. **Other U.S. locations:** Nationwide. **International locations:** Worldwide. **Parent company:** KPMG International is a leader among professional services firms engaged in capturing, managing, assessing, and delivering information to create knowledge that will help its clients maximize shareholder value. **Listed on:** NASDAQ. **Stock exchange symbol:** KCIN. **Number of employees worldwide:** 85,000.

ARTHUR D. LITTLE, INC.
Noble Plaza, Suite 210, 801 Old York Road, Jenkintown PA 19046-1611. 215/576-8700. **Contact:** Human Resources. **E-mail address:** careers.mc@adlittle.com. **World Wide Web address:** http://www.arthurdlittle.com. **Description:** An employee-owned, international management and technology consulting firm. The company offers services in three areas: management consulting; technology and product development; and environmental, health, and safety consulting. Services include cost reduction, total quality management consulting, market assessments, logistics management, telecommunications management, auditing,

safety programs, software development, and toxicology. Clients operate in a variety of industries including aerospace, automotive, telecommunications, electronics, and consumer products. Founded in 1886. **NOTE:** Mail resumes to: Human Resources, Acorn Park, Cambridge MA 02140-2390. 617/498-5000. **International locations:** Asia; Europe; Latin America; Middle East.

PRICEWATERHOUSECOOPERS

2 Commerce Square, Suite 1700, 2001 Market Street, Philadelphia PA 19103. 215/575-5000. **Contact:** Human Resources Department. **World Wide Web address:** http://www.pricewaterhousecoopers.com. **Description:** One of the largest certified public accounting firms in the world. PricewaterhouseCoopers provides public accounting, business advisory, management consulting, and taxation services. **Corporate headquarters location:** New York NY. **Other U.S. locations:** Nationwide.

RIGHT MANAGEMENT CONSULTANTS

1818 Market Street, 33rd Floor, Philadelphia PA 19103. 215/988-1588. **Toll-free phone:** 800/237-4448. **Contact:** Human Resources Department. **World Wide Web address:** http://www.right.com. **Description:** Provides management and human resources consulting services. Founded in 1980. **Corporate headquarters location:** This location. **Listed on:** NASDAQ. **Stock exchange symbol:** RMCI.

SYNYGY, INC.

555 North Lane, Suite 6000, Conshohocken PA 19428. 610/664-7433. **Fax:** 610/664-7343. **Contact:** Stephanie Salamon, Recruiter. **E-mail address:** salamon@synygy.com. **World Wide Web address:** http://www.synygy.com. **Description:** A management consulting and information technology company. Founded in 1991. **NOTE:** Entry-level positions are offered. **Company slogan:** Turning information into action. **Common positions include:** Computer Programmer; Consultant; Sales Representative. **Special programs:** Summer Jobs. **Office hours:** Monday - Friday, 9:00 a.m. - 6:00 p.m. **Corporate headquarters location:** This location. **Listed on:** Privately held. **CEO:** Mark Stiffler. **Annual sales/revenues:** $5 - $10 million. **Number of employees at this location:** 50.

ADVERTISING, MARKETING, AND PUBLIC RELATIONS

You can expect to find the following types of companies in this chapter:

Advertising Agencies • Direct Mail Marketers •
Market Research Firms • Public Relations Firms

CC3 COMMUNICATIONS CONCEPTS
1044 Pulinski Road, Ivyland PA 18974. 215/672-6900. **Fax:** 215/957-4366. **Contact:** Rita Chrismer, Human Resources. **World Wide Web address:** http://www.cc3.com. **Description:** A direct mail marketing company. Founded in 1972.

DAVIS ADVERTISING INC.
1700 Market Street, Suite 2626, Philadelphia PA 19103. 215/282-2500. **Contact:** Human Resources Manager. **World Wide Web address:** http://www.davisadv.com. **Description:** An advertising company specializing in recruitment advertising.

R. H. DONNELLEY
Bert Collins Drive, 11 Keystone Industrial Park, Dunmore PA 18512. 570/348-6900. **Contact:** Personnel. **World Wide Web address:** http://www.rhdonnelley.com. **Description:** Engaged in selling advertising space in the Yellow Pages. Founded in 1886. **Corporate headquarters location:** Chicago IL. **Other U.S. locations:** Los Angeles CA; Miami FL; Chicago IL; New York NY. **Parent company:** Dun & Bradstreet Corporation. **Listed on:** New York Stock Exchange. **Stock exchange symbol:** RHD.

EARLE PALMER BROWN
400 Shurs Lane, Philadelphia PA 19128. 215/487-2200. **Contact:** Human Resources. **World Wide Web address:** http://www.epb.com. **Description:** An agency offering advertising, public relations, marketing research, direct marketing, and sales promotion services. Founded in 1952. **NOTE:** For employment opportunities contact the New York City office: 685 Third Avenue, New York NY 10017. 212-986-4122. **Common positions include:** Account Manager; Account Representative; Administrative Assistant; Art Director; Buyer; Copywriter; Media Specialist; Production Manager; Transportation/Traffic Specialist. **Special programs:** Internships. **Corporate headquarters location:** New York NY. **Other U.S.**

locations: Stamford CT; Washington DC. **Number of employees nationwide:** 750.

HARTE-HANKS, INC.
2050 Cabot Boulevard West, Langhorne PA 19047. 215/750-6600. **Contact:** Brian Jacobs, Human Resources Director. **World Wide Web address:** http://www7.harte-hanks.com. **Description:** Provides direct marketing services for various companies and publishes a weekly shopping guide.

HARTE-HANKS RESPONSE MANAGEMENT
One Mall Drive, 7th Floor, Cherry Hill NJ 08002. 856/482-8400. **Fax:** 856/482-7920. **Contact:** Personnel Manager. **World Wide Web address:** http://www.harte-hanks.com. **Description:** A telemarketing company. **Corporate headquarters location:** San Antonio TX. **Parent company:** Harte-Hanks, Inc. provides direct mail marketing services and publishes a weekly shopping guide.

ICT GROUP, INC.
100 Brandywine Boulevard, Newtown PA 18940. 267/685-5000. **Toll-free phone:** 800/799-6880. **Contact:** Human Resources Department. **World Wide Web address:** http://www.ictgroup.com. **Description:** A direct marketing agency engaged in telemarketing, customer service, and market research. The company serves the energy, financial services, health care, insurance, media, and telecommunications industries. Founded in 1983. **Common positions include:** Branch Manager; Computer Programmer; Operations/Production Manager. **Corporate headquarters location:** This location. **Listed on:** NASDAQ. **Stock exchange symbol:** ICTG. **Number of employees at this location:** 270. **Number of employees nationwide:** 2,140.

INTER-MEDIA MARKETING SOLUTIONS
204 Carter Drive, West Chester PA 19382. 610/696-4646. **Contact:** Human Resources. **World Wide Web address:** http://www.intermediamarketing.com. **Description:** A direct marketing and research firm. Founded in 1983.

AL PAUL LEFTON COMPANY, INC.
100 Independence Mall West, Philadelphia PA 19106. 215/923-9600. **Fax:** 215/351-4297. **Contact:** Human Resources. **World Wide Web address:** http://www.lefton.com. **Description:** A full-service advertising and public relations firm. Founded in 1928. **Corporate headquarters location:** This location.

LEVLANE ADVERTISING/PR/INTERACTIVE

One Belmont Avenue, Bala-Cynwyd PA 19004. 610/667-7313. **Fax:** 610/667-3176. **Contact:** Human Resources. **World Wide Web address:** http://www.levlane.com. **Description:** An advertising agency and public relations firm. Founded in 1984. **NOTE:** Entry-level positions are offered. **Common positions include:** Advertising Executive; Computer Support Technician; Controller; Copywriter; Graphic Designer; Help-Desk Technician; Media Planner; Multimedia Designer; Network/Systems Administrator; Public Relations Specialist; Technical Writer/Editor; Video Production Coordinator; Web Advertising Specialist; Website Developer. **Special programs:** Internships; Apprenticeships. **Office hours:** Monday - Friday, 9:00 a.m. - 5:30 p.m. **Corporate headquarters location:** This location. **Other U.S. locations:** Tampa FL. **Listed on:** Privately held. **Annual sales/revenues:** $21 - $50 million. **Number of employees at this location:** 40.

NATIONAL FULFILLMENT SERVICES

100 Pine Avenue, Building 4, Holmes PA 19043. 610/532-4700. **Contact:** Human Resources. **World Wide Web address:** http://www.nfsrv.com. **Description:** Provides direct marketing services. **Common positions include:** Customer Service Representative. **Corporate headquarters location:** This location. **Operations at this facility include:** Administration; Sales; Service. **Listed on:** Privately held. **Number of employees at this location:** 110.

TIERNEY & PARTNERS

200 South Broad Street, Philadelphia PA 19102. 215/732-4100. **Contact:** Bernadette Nolan, Personnel. **World Wide Web address:** http://www.tierneypartners.com. **Description:** A full-service advertising and public relations firm. **Common positions include:** Accountant/Auditor; Advertising Clerk; Computer Programmer; Human Resources Manager; Public Relations Specialist; Systems Analyst; Technical Writer/Editor. **Special programs:** Internships. **Corporate headquarters location:** This location. **Other U.S. locations:** Los Angeles CA; San Francisco CA; New York NY. **Parent company:** Foote, Cone & Belding, Inc.

VERTIS

181 Rittenhouse Circle, Bristol PA 19007. 215/785-0101. **Contact:** Human Resources. **Description:** Develops a variety of direct marketing services including inline printing and finishing, promotional printing, and personalization technologies.

AEROSPACE

You can expect to find the following types of companies in this chapter:

Aerospace Products and Services • Aircraft Equipment and Parts

HEXCEL CORPORATION

P.O. Box 179, Pottsville PA 17901. 570/429-1741. **Contact:** Human Resources Department. **World Wide Web address:** http://www.hexcel.com. **Description:** This location manufactures structural honeycomb products for the aerospace industry. Overall, Hexcel Corporation is a manufacturing firm engaged in two primary business segments. The structural materials segment includes aerospace products, nonaerospace honeycomb resins, resin-impregnated industrial fabrics, and nonimpregnated fabrics. The specialty chemicals segment includes bulk pharmaceuticals, custom and special purpose chemicals, specialty resins, and industrial maintenance chemicals. **Listed on:** New York Stock Exchange. **Stock exchange symbol:** HXL.

KING FIFTH WHEEL COMPANY

P.O. Box 68, 701 Crestwood Drive, Mountain Top PA 18707. 570/474-6371. **Fax:** 570/474-9901. **Contact:** Human Resources Manager. **World Wide Web address:** http://www.kfw.microserve.net. **Description:** Manufactures flash welded rings and machined components for aerospace engines. **Other area locations:** Wilkes-Barre PA. **Other U.S. locations:** Agawam MA; Asheville NC; Laconia NH. **International locations:** Birmingham, England; Ontario, Canada.

LANCASTER AERO REFINISHERS

311 Airport Drive, Smoketown PA 17576. 877/574-5422. **Contact:** Human Resources. **World Wide Web address:** http://www.lancasteraero.com. **Description:** Engaged in the repair and service of aircraft parts and engines.

NARCO AVIONICS

270 Commerce Drive, Suite 200, Fort Washington PA 19034. 215/643-2905. **Toll-free phone:** 800/234-7551. **Fax:** 215/643-0197. **Contact:** Kevin Davis, Controller. **World Wide Web address:** http://www.narco-avionics.com. **Description:**

Produces a wide range of instruments and systems for general aviation uses.

SMITHS INDUSTRIES
101 Lindenwood Drive, Suite 125, Malvern PA 19355. 610/578-9600. **Contact:** Vice President of Human Resources. **World Wide Web address:** http://www.smiths-group.com. **Description:** Engaged in a variety of businesses through three business groups: Smiths Industries Aerospace Group manufactures instrumentation and systems for civil and military aircraft; Smiths Industries Medical Systems Group (SIMS) manufactures surgical, dental, veterinary, and home health care supplies; Smiths Industries Industrial Group operates in four divisions. Flex-Tek produces flexible ducting and conduits. Vent-Axia produces ventilation fans. Engineering produces specialized engineering products. Hypertac Interconnect manufactures electrical connectors. **NOTE:** Entry-level positions are offered. **Common positions include:** Accountant; Budget Analyst; Computer Programmer; Electrical/Electronics Engineer; Financial Analyst; Human Resources Manager; Marketing Manager; Marketing Specialist; Sales Engineer; Sales Representative; Software Engineer; Systems Analyst; Technical Writer/Editor. **Corporate headquarters location:** London, England. **Other U.S. locations:** Irvine CA; Sunnyvale CA; Clearwater FL; Fort Myers FL; Hudson MA; Rockland MA; Grand Rapids MI; St. Paul MN; Keene NH; Florham Park NJ; Abbeville SC; Cookeville TN. **Parent company:** Smiths Industries plc. **Annual sales/revenues:** More than $100 million. **Number of employees nationwide:** 6,000. **Number of employees worldwide:** 13,000.

SMITHS INDUSTRIES AEROSPACE
255 Great Valley Parkway, Malvern PA 19355. 610/296-5000. **Fax:** 610/296-0912. **Contact:** Human Resources Department. **World Wide Web address:** http://www.smithsind-aerospace.com. **Description:** Develops and manufactures instrumentation and systems for civil and military aircraft. Founded in 1920. **Common positions include:** Accountant; Administrative Assistant; Computer Support Technician; Computer Technician; Controller; Customer Service Representative; Database Administrator; Database Manager; Editorial Assistant; Finance Director; Financial Analyst; General Manager; Graphic Artist; Human Resources Manager; Industrial Production Manager; Internet Services Manager; Managing Editor; Marketing Manager; Marketing Specialist; MIS Specialist; Operations Manager; Production Manager; Purchasing Agent/Manager; Quality Control Supervisor; Vice

President. **Special programs:** Internships; Co-ops. **Internship information:** Internships are available in Engineering/Manufacturing, Engineering, and Marketing. **Corporate headquarters location:** London, England. **Other U.S. locations:** Nationwide. **International locations:** France; Germany; South America. **Parent company:** Smiths Industries. **Listed on:** European Bourse. **CEO:** Keith Butler-Wheelhouse. **Number of employees at this location:** 165. **Number of employees nationwide:** 2,500. **Number of employees worldwide:** 15,000.

APPAREL, FASHION, AND TEXTILES

You can expect to find the following types of companies in this chapter:

Broadwoven Fabric Mills • Knitting Mills • Curtains and Draperies • Footwear • Nonwoven Fabrics • Textile Goods and Finishing • Yarn and Thread Mills

ALFRED ANGELO, INC.
116 Welsh Road, Horsham PA 19044. 215/659-5300. **Contact:** Human Resources. **E-mail address:** info@alfredangelo.com. **World Wide Web address:** http://www.alfredangelo.com. **Description:** Designs, manufactures, and wholesales bridal gowns, special occasion dresses, and a wide range of related accessories. **Common positions include:** Accountant/Auditor; Computer Programmer; Credit Manager; Customer Service Rep.; Department Manager; Designer; Financial Analyst; Manufacturer's/Wholesaler's Sales Representative.; Marketing Specialist; Operations/Production Manager; Purchasing Agent/Manager; Systems Analyst; Warehouse/Distribution Worker. **Corporate headquarters location:** This location. **Operations at this facility include:** Administration; Design; Manufacturing; Sales; Service.

BOLLMAN HAT COMPANY
P.O. Box 517, Adamstown PA 19501. 717/484-4361. **Physical address:** 110 East Main Street, Adamstown PA 19501. **Contact:** Angie Bushong, Human Resources Manager. **World Wide Web address:** http://www.bollmanhats.com. **Description:** A manufacturer of wool, fur, cloth, and straw hats. Bollman Hat Company also cleans and processes wool. **Common positions include:** Accountant/Auditor; Administrator; Blue-Collar Worker Supervisor; Buyer; Chemical Engineer; Chemist; Department Manager; Electrical/Electronics Engineer; General Manager; Human Resources Manager; Industrial Designer; Industrial Engineer; Management Trainee; Mechanical Engineer; Operations/Production Manager. **Corporate headquarters location:** This location. **Operations at this facility include:** Administration; Manufacturing; Research and Development; Sales.

CITY SHIRT COMPANY
242 Industrial Park Road, Frackville PA 17931. 570/874-4251. **Contact:** Human Resources. **Description:** City Shirt Company is a manufacturer and retailer of uniform shirts and slacks.

CONGOLEUM CORPORATION

4401 Ridge Road, Marcus Hook PA 19061. 610/485-8890. **Contact:** Human Resources. **World Wide Web address:** http://www.congoleum.com. **Description:** This location manufactures sheet vinyl and floor tile. Overall, Congoleum Corporation is a diversified manufacturer and distributor operating in the areas of home furnishings, shipbuilding, and automotive and industrial distribution. **Common positions include:** Chemical Engineer; Chemist; Industrial Production Manager; Mechanical Engineer; Operations/Production Manager. **Special programs:** Internships. **Corporate headquarters location:** Mercerville NJ. **Other U.S. locations:** Cedarhurst MD; Mercerville NJ; Trenton NJ. **Operations at this facility include:** Administration; Manufacturing; Research and Development. **Listed on:** American Stock Exchange. **Stock exchange symbol:** CGM. **Number of employees at this location:** 1,400.

CRAFTEX MILLS, INC.

450 Sentry Parkway East, Blue Bell PA 19422. 610/941-1212. **Contact:** Human Resources. **World Wide Web address:** http://www.craftex.com. **Description:** Produces upholstery fabrics for furniture manufacturers. **Corporate headquarters location:** This location.

DALLCO INDUSTRIES INC.

1155 Elm Street, York PA 17403-2727. 717/854-7875. **Fax:** 717/845-5283. **Contact:** Human Resources. **Description:** Manufactures sleepwear and loungewear for women and children. **Common positions include:** Accountant/Auditor; Administrative Manager; Blue-Collar Worker Supervisor; Cost Estimator; Customer Service Rep.; Designer; Electrician; General Manager; Human Resources Manager; Industrial Production Manager; Management Analyst/Consultant; Management Trainee; Operations/Production Manager; Quality Control Supervisor; Transportation/Traffic Specialist. **Corporate headquarters location:** This location. **Number of employees at this location:** 300.

DELTA WUNDIES

1501 West Third Street, Williamsport PA 17701-7814. 570/326-2451. **Contact:** Human Resources Department. **Description:** Manufactures and wholesales women's and children's underwear and children's sleepwear.

DOUBLE-H BOOT COMPANY

30 North Third Street, Womelsdorf PA 19567. 610/589-4586. **Contact:** Human Resources. **World Wide Web address:** http://www.doublehboots.com. **Description:** Manufactures boots including the Harley-Davidson line, western, steel toe, biker, and pull-on work boots. Founded in 1955.

GOOD LAD APPAREL

431 East Tioga Street, Philadelphia PA 19134. 215/739-0200. **Contact:** Personnel Department. **Description:** A manufacturer of outerwear and children's clothing.

HUTSPAH SHIRTS

185 West Wyoming Avenue, Philadelphia PA 19140-1691. 215/329-7700. **Fax:** 215/329-4650. **Contact:** Ken Williams, Personnel Director. **Description:** An apparel manufacturer specializing in shirts and nightwear. **Common positions include:** Accountant/Auditor; Clerical Supervisor; Computer Operator; Credit Manager; Order Clerk; Receptionist; Secretary; Stock Clerk. **Corporate headquarters location:** This location. **Operations at this facility include:** Administration.

JONES APPAREL GROUP, INC.

180 Rittenhouse Circle, Bristol PA 19007. 215/785-4000. **Fax:** 215/826-8902. **Contact:** Aida Decolli, Human Resources Director. **World Wide Web address:** http://www.jny.com. **Description:** Designs, manufactures, and markets a broad range of women's sportswear, suits, and dresses. Jones Apparel Group markets its products under the brand names Jones New York, Jones*Wear, Saville, Rena Rowan for Saville, Evan-Picone, Ellen Kaye, and under the licensed name Christian Dior. The company also has licenses for the Jones New York brand name and for the Evan-Picone brand name with selected manufacturers of related apparel and accessories such as women's rainwear, coats, footwear, intimate apparel, hosiery, handbags, belts, men's tailored clothing, and eyewear. **Common positions include:** Accountant/Auditor; Adjuster; Blue-Collar Worker Supervisor; Budget Analyst; Buyer; Clerical Supervisor; Computer Programmer; Credit Manager; Customer Service Representative; Designer; Electrician; Financial Analyst; General Manager; Human Resources Manager; Operations/Production Manager; Systems Analyst. **Corporate headquarters location:** This location. **Other U.S. locations:** Los Angeles CA; Atlanta GA; Chicago IL; New York NY; Lawrenceburg TN; Dallas TX; Seattle WA. **International locations:** Ciudad Juarez, Mexico; Kowloon, Hong Kong; Toronto, Canada. **Operations at this facility include:**

Administration; Research and Development; Service. **Listed on:** New York Stock Exchange. **Stock exchange symbol:** JNY. **Number of employees at this location:** 1,000. **Number of employees nationwide:** 2,000.

KLEINERT'S INC.
120 West Germantown Pike, Suite 100, Plymouth Meeting PA 19462. 610/828-7261. **Fax:** 610/828-4589. **Contact:** Denise Hale, Vice President of Human Resources. **Description:** Manufactures children's sportswear and sleepwear. The company is also engaged in knitting polyester, cotton/polyester blends, and acrylic fabrics for a variety of uses. Founded in 1869. **Corporate headquarters location:** This location. **Other U.S. locations:** Elba AL; Wilmington DE; Gastonia NC; New York NY. **International locations:** San Pedro Sula, Honduras. **Operations at this facility include:** Administration. **President/CEO:** Jack Brier. **Number of employees at this location:** 10. **Number of employees worldwide:** 1,000.

KRAEMER TEXTILES, INC.
P.O. Box 72, Nazareth PA 18064. 610/759-4030. **Contact:** Employment. **Description:** Manufactures spun yarns for the apparel, home furnishings, and crafts markets. **Corporate headquarters location:** This location.

MANNINGTON MILLS INC.
P.O. Box 30, Salem NJ 08079-0030. 856/935-3000. **Physical address:** 75 Mannington Mills Road, Salem NJ 08079. **Contact:** Tinique Peery, Manager of Human Resources. **World Wide Web address:** http://www.mannington.com. **Description:** Manufactures and wholesales various floor coverings including vinyl, wood, and carpet.

PINCUS BROTHERS, INC.
Independence Mall East, Fifth and Race Street, Philadelphia PA 19106. 215/922-4900. **Contact:** Personnel. **Description:** Manufactures men's suits and coats.

SETON COMPANY
1000 Madison Avenue, Norristown PA 19403. 610/666-9600. **Contact:** Human Resources Manager. **E-mail address:** hr@setonco.com. **World Wide Web address:** http://www.setonleather.com. **Description:** This location manufactures leather car seats. Overall, Seton's operations are conducted primarily through two business segments: Leather is involved in tanning, finishing, and distributing of whole-hide cattle leathers for the automotive and furniture upholstery

industries; cattle hide side leathers for the footwear, handbag, and other markets; and cattle hide products for collagen, rawhide pet items, and other applications; and Chemicals and Coated Products is engaged in the manufacture and distribution of epoxy and urethane chemicals, specialty leather finishes, industrial and medical tapes, foams, films, and laminates.

SURE FIT INC.
939 Marcon Boulevard, Allentown PA 18109. 610/264-7300. **Contact:** Kenneth J. Guerin, Director of Human Resources. **World Wide Web address:** http://www.surefit.com. **Description:** Manufactures decorative home textiles including furniture covers and throw pillows. **Common positions include:** Accountant/Auditor; Blue-Collar Worker Supervisor; Computer Programmer; Customer Service Representative; Industrial Engineer; Systems Analyst. **Corporate headquarters location:** New York NY. **Operations at this facility include:** Administration; Manufacturing.

TAMA MANUFACTURING COMPANY INC.
100A Cascade Drive, Allentown PA 18103. 610/231-3100. **Contact:** Human Resources. **Description:** A contract manufacturer of women's clothing. **NOTE:** Interested jobseekers should apply in person to the Human Resources office between the hours of 8:00 a.m. and 4:30 p.m.

VALLEY FORGE FLAG COMPANY, INC.
1700 Conrad Weiser Parkway, Womelsdorf PA 19567. 610/589-5888. **Fax:** 610/589-1145. **Contact:** Cindy O'Roark, Personnel. **Description:** Manufactures banners and flags. **Common positions include:** Blue-Collar Worker Supervisor; Computer Operator; Customer Service Representative; Manufacturer's/Wholesaler's Sales Rep.; Receptionist; Retail Sales Worker. **Corporate headquarters location:** Great Neck NY. **Operations at this facility include:** Manufacturing; Sales. **Number of employees at this location:** 310.

WOOLRICH, INC.
2 Mill Street, Woolrich PA 17779. 570/769-6464. **Contact:** Roger Sheets, Director of Human Resources. **World Wide Web address:** http://www.woolrich.com. **Description:** Manufactures a wide variety of outerwear and sweaters for men and women. **Corporate headquarters location:** This location.

ARCHITECTURE, CONSTRUCTION, AND ENGINEERING

You can expect to find the following types of companies in this chapter:

Architectural and Engineering Services • Civil and Mechanical Engineering Firms • Construction Products, Manufacturers, and Wholesalers • General Contractors/ Specialized Trade Contractors

ACME MANUFACTURING COMPANY
7601 State Road, Philadelphia PA 19136. 215/338-2850. **Contact:** General Manager. **World Wide Web address:** http://www.acmemfg.com. **Description:** Manufactures sheet metal products including heating and air conditioning equipment. **Corporate headquarters location:** Auburn Hills MI.

ALLEN-SHERMAN-HOFF
P.O. Box 3006, 185 Great Valley Parkway, Malvern PA 19355-1321. 610/647-9900. **Contact:** Human Resources. **World Wide Web address:** http://www.a-s-h.com. **Description:** Engaged in the design engineering of material handling systems for power plants and industrial applications.

BERGER BROTHERS
805 Pennsylvania Boulevard, Feasterville PA 19053. 215/355-1200. **Fax:** 215/355-0913. **Contact:** Personnel. **World Wide Web address:** http://www.bergerbros.com. **Description:** Manufactures roofing and drainage systems. Founded in 1874.

BUCKLEY & COMPANY, INC.
3401 Moore Street, Philadelphia PA 19145. 215/334-7500. **Contact:** Joseph Martosella, Vice President. **Description:** A heavy construction firm specializing in highways, bridges, tunnels, and other large-scale construction projects.

CANNON SLINE
213 Jones Boulevard, Suite 106, Pottstown PA 19464. 610/495-1444. **Contact:** Human Resources. **World Wide Web address:** http://www.cannonsline.com. **Description:** Provides painting, coating, and related services to industrial and commercial clients.

CARLISLE SYNTEC INCORPORATED

P.O. Box 7000, 1285 Ritner Highway, Carlisle PA 17013. 717/245-7000. **Fax:** 717/245-7285. **Contact:** Personnel. **World Wide Web address:** http://www.carlislesyntec.com. **Description:** Manufactures elastomeric roofing membrane and related building products for the commercial roofing market. **Common positions include:** Accountant/Auditor; Chemical Engineer; Chemist; Construction and Building Inspector; Credit Manager; Industrial Engineer; Mechanical Engineer; Operations/Production Manager. **Corporate headquarters location:** Syracuse NY. **Parent company:** Carlisle Companies Inc. **Operations at this facility include:** Divisional Headquarters; Manufacturing; Research and Development; Sales. **Listed on:** New York Stock Exchange. **Stock exchange symbol:** CSL. **Number of employees at this location:** 400. **Number of employees nationwide:** 1,040.

CERTAINTEED CORPORATION

P.O. Box 860, 750 East Swedesford Road, Valley Forge PA 19482. 610/341-7000. **Fax:** 610/341-7784. **Contact:** Ms. Kathyrn Ferrante, Human Resources Director. **E-mail address:** ctrecruitment@saint-gobain.com. **World Wide Web address:** http://www.certainteed.com. **Description:** Certainteed Corporation manufactures and distributes building materials, fiberglass products, and piping products. Principal products are used in residential, commercial, and industrial construction; repair and remodeling; fiberglass reinforcement applications; water and sewer systems; and other underground utility systems. Other products include roofing, acoustical insulation, fiberglass thermal insulation, air handling products, glass fiber, vinyl siding, and PVC piping. **Common positions include:** Accountant/Auditor; Financial Analyst; Human Resources Manager; Technical Writer/Editor. **Corporate headquarters location:** This location. **Other U.S. locations:** Nationwide. **Parent company:** Compagnie de Saint-Gobain. The U.S. and Canadian operations of four of the company's worldwide branches are Abrasives, Construction Materials, Industrial Ceramics, and Insulation and Reinforcements. The Saint-Gobain companies based in North America are organized under the umbrella of the Saint-Gobain Corporation, which includes the Certainteed Corporation, Norton Company, and all of their subsidiaries. **Operations at this facility include:** Administration. **Number of employees at this location:** 450. **Number of employees nationwide:** 8,000.

CONESTOGA WOOD SPECIALTIES, INC.

P.O. Box 158, East Earl PA 17519. 717/445-6701. **Physical address:** 245 Reading Road, East Earl PA 17519. **Fax:** 717/445-3428. **Contact:** Elizabeth Ford, Personnel Supervisor. **Description:** Manufactures and supplies wood products including panel doors, components, and moldings to the construction industry. **Common positions include:** Accountant/Auditor; Blue-Collar Worker Supervisor; Computer Programmer; Customer Service Representative; Department Manager; Draftsperson; Electrical/Electronics Engineer; Financial Analyst; General Manager; Human Resources Manager; Industrial Engineer; Industrial Production Manager; Marketing Specialist; Mechanical Engineer; Operations/Production Manager; Public Relations Specialist; Purchasing Agent/Manager; Quality Control Supervisor; Sales Executive; Systems Analyst; Transportation/Traffic Specialist. **Special programs:** Internships. **Corporate headquarters location:** This location. **Other U.S. locations:** Jacksonville AR; Darlington MD; Kenlet NC; Kramer PA. **Operations at this facility include:** Administration; Divisional Headquarters; Manufacturing; Sales; Service. **Listed on:** Privately held. **Number of employees at this location:** 675. **Number of employees nationwide:** 1,500.

EXPONENT, INC.

2300 Chestnut Street, Suite 150, Philadelphia PA 19103. 215/751-1661. **Contact:** Human Resources. **E-mail address:** hr@exponent.com. **World Wide Web address:** http://www.exponent.com. **Description:** A technical consulting firm dedicated to the investigation, analysis, and prevention of accidents and failures of an engineering or scientific nature. The company provides a multidisciplinary approach to analyze how failures occur. The company specializes in accident reconstruction, biomechanics, construction/structural engineering, aviation and marine investigations, environmental assessment, materials and product testing, warning and labeling issues, accident statistical data analysis, and risk prevention/mitigation. Founded in 1967. **NOTE:** All hiring is conducted through corporate headquarters. Please send resumes to Exponent, Inc., Human Resources, 149 Commonwealth Drive, Menlo Park CA 94025. 888/656-EXPO. **Corporate headquarters location:** Menlo Park CA. **Parent company:** Exponent, Inc. **Listed on:** NASDAQ. **Stock exchange symbol:** EXPO.

FM GLOBAL

101 Lindenwood Drive, Suite 200, Malvern PA 19355. 610/296-3100. **Contact:** Human Resources. **World Wide Web address:** http://www.fmglobal.com. **Description:** A loss control services organization. The primary objective of FM Global is to help owner company policyholders to protect their properties and occupancies from damage due to fire, wind, flood, and explosion; boiler, pressure vessel, and machinery accidents; and many other insured hazards. **Corporate headquarters location:** Johnston RI. **Other U.S. locations:** Nationwide. **International locations:** Worldwide.

FISCHBACH AND MOORE ELECTRIC, INC.

761 Fifth Avenue, King of Prussia PA 19406. 610/992-9442. **Fax:** 908/508-2624. **Contact:** Human Resources Department. **E-mail address:** cgraham@fmeinc.com. **World Wide Web address:** http://www.fischbachandmoore.com. **Description:** An electrical contracting firm. The company specializes in infrastructure electrical construction for traffic and transit management systems. Founded in 1924. **NOTE:** For employment opportunities contact: Ms. Cyndie Graham, Human Resources Manager, 675 Central Avenue, New Providence NJ 07974. 908/508-2612. **Common positions include:** Account Manager; Accountant; Administrative Assistant; Applications Engineer; Assistant Manager; Branch Manager; Construction Contractor; Cost Estimator; Design Engineer; Draftsperson; Electrical/Electronics Engineer; Electrician; Project Manager; Secretary; Transportation/Traffic Specialist. **Special programs:** Internships. **Internship information:** Internships are offered in field installation work. **Office hours:** Monday - Friday, 8:00 a.m. - 5:00 p.m. **Corporate headquarters location:** New Providence NJ. **Other U.S. locations:** Nationwide. **Parent company:** Exelon Infrastructure Services. **Operations at this facility include:** Regional Headquarters. **Listed on:** Privately held. **President:** James Kimsey. **Annual sales/revenues:** $21 - $50 million.

FLUOR DANIEL, INC.

15000 Commerce Parkway, Suite C, Mount Laurel NJ 08054. 856/552-6800. **Fax:** 856/552-6837. **Contact:** Human Resources Department. **E-mail address:** careers@fluor.com. **World Wide Web address:** http://www.fluordaniel.com. **Description:** A full-service engineering and construction company serving the power, industrial, hydrocarbon, and process industries, as well as the federal government. **Common positions include:** Chemical Engineer; Civil Engineer; Designer; Draftsperson; Electrical/Electronics Engineer;

Environmental Engineer; Mechanical Engineer; Structural Engineer. **Other U.S. locations:** Nationwide. **Parent company:** Fluor Corporation (Irvine CA) engages in engineering and construction, as well as the extraction of various natural resources. **Number of employees worldwide:** 20,000.

FRANCIS, CAUFFMAN, FOLEY, AND HOFFMAN

2120 Arch Street, Philadelphia PA 19103. 215/568-8250. **Fax:** 215/568-2639. **Contact:** Tom Gavin, Human Resources. **Description:** A full-service architectural firm serving the communications, health care, pharmaceutical, and corporate markets. Founded in 1954. **Other U.S. locations:** Syracuse NY.

GLASGOW, INC.

Willow Grove Avenue and Limekiln Pike, P.O. Box 1089, Glenside PA 19038-1089. 215/884-8800. **Fax:** 215/884-8302. **Contact:** Human Resources Department. **World Wide Web address:** http://www.glasgowinc.com. **Description:** A heavy construction and highway contracting firm. **Common positions include:** Civil Engineer; Construction Contractor; Cost Estimator. **Corporate headquarters location:** This location. **Operations at this facility include:** Administration. **Listed on:** Privately held. **President:** Bruce Rambo.

HERMAN GOLDNER COMPANY

7777 Brewster Avenue, Philadelphia PA 19153. 215/365-5400. **Contact:** Human Resources Department. **World Wide Web address:** http://www.goldner.com. **Description:** A mechanical construction company. The company also supplies pipes, valves, fittings, and building control systems to the construction industry.

HARSCO CORPORATION

P.O. Box 8888, Camp Hill PA 17001-8888. 717/763-7064. **Physical address:** 350 Poplar Church Road, Camp Hill PA 17001. **Fax:** 717/612-5619. **Contact:** Jerry Vinci, Director of Human Resources. **World Wide Web address:** http://www.harsco.com. **Description:** Harsco Corporation is a diversified industrial manufacturing and service company that conducts business through 10 divisions and has 16 classes of products and services. Operations fall into three groups: Metal Reclamation and Mill Services includes scrap management, slab management systems, iron making, materials handling, equipment rental, recycling technology, aggregate marketing, and nonferrous metallurgical industry services; Infrastructure and Construction includes railway maintenance equipment, industrial grating products, and scaffolding, shoring, and concrete forming equipment; and Process Industry Products includes industrial pipe fittings, process equipment, and gas control and containment equipment. **Common positions include:** Accountant/Auditor; Attorney; Buyer; Computer Programmer; Draftsperson; Editor; Environmental Engineer; Financial Analyst; Human Resources Manager; Industrial Production Manager; Mechanical Engineer; Public Relations Specialist; Purchasing Agent/Manager; Quality Control Supervisor; Structural Engineer; Systems Analyst. **Special programs:** Internships. **Corporate headquarters location:** This location. **Other U.S. locations:** Nationwide. **Listed on:** New York Stock Exchange. **Stock exchange symbol:** HSC. **Number of employees at this location:** 90. **Number of employees worldwide:** 13,000.

HENKELS & McCOY, INC.

985 Jolly Road, Blue Bell PA 19422-0900. 215/283-7688. **Contact:** Vincent Benedict, Human Resources Director. **World Wide Web address:** http://www.henkelsandmccoy.com. **Description:** An engineering and construction firm that specializes in designing, building, and maintaining infrastructure. Founded in 1923. **Common positions include:** Accountant/Auditor; Administrator; Architect; Buyer; Civil Engineer; Computer Programmer; Credit Manager; Department Manager; Draftsperson; Editor; Electrical/Electronics Engineer; Financial Analyst; General Manager; Human Resources Manager; Management Trainee; Marketing Specialist; Mechanical Engineer; Purchasing Agent/Manager; Reporter; Sales Executive; Technical Writer/Editor. **Corporate headquarters location:** This location. **Other U.S. locations:** Nationwide. **Listed on:** Privately held. **Number of employees nationwide:** 5,000.

HIGH INDUSTRIES, INC.

P.O. Box 10008, 1853 William Penn Way, Lancaster PA 17605-0008. 717/293-4486. **Contact:** Vincent Mizeras, Director of Human Resources. **World Wide Web address:** http://www.high.net. **Description:** Operates through several areas of business including design and construction, food services, hotel management, prestress/precast concrete products, real estate development and management, and steel fabrication. **Common positions include:** Accountant/Auditor; Architect; Civil Engineer; Computer Programmer; Customer Service Representative; Draftsperson; Hotel Manager; Human Resources Manager; Services Sales Representative; Systems Analyst. **Corporate headquarters location:** This location.

Operations at this facility include: Administration; Manufacturing.

HILL INTERNATIONAL
303 Lippincott Center, Marlton NJ 08053. 856/810-6200. **Contact:** Michelle Jablonski, Manager of Human Resources. **World Wide Web address:** http://www.hillintl.com. **Description:** Provides construction management and consulting services.

HONEYWELL INC.
P.O. Box 934, York PA 17405. 717/771-8100. **Contact:** Human Resources Department. **World Wide Web address:** http://www.honeywell.com. **Description:** This location manufactures industrial and programmable controls for a wide range of manufacturers. Overall, Honeywell is engaged in the research, development, manufacture, and sale of advanced technology products and services in the fields of chemicals, electronics, automation, and controls. The company's major businesses are home and building automation and control, performance polymers and chemicals, industrial automation and control, space and aviation systems, and defense and marine systems. **Listed on:** New York Stock Exchange. **Stock exchange symbol:** HON.

IRWIN & LEIGHTON, INC.
1030 Continental Avenue, King of Prussia PA 19406. 610/989-0100. **Fax:** 610/989-0200. **Contact:** Personnel. **World Wide Web address:** http://www.irwinleighton.com. **Description:** A full-service construction services firm. Founded in 1909. **Corporate headquarters location:** This location.

KAWNEER COMPANY, INC.
500 East 12th Street, Bloomsburg PA 17815. 570/784-8000. **Contact:** Human Resources Department. **World Wide Web address:** http://www.kawneer.com. **Description:** This location manufactures aluminum doors and windows. Overall, Kawneer Company manufactures and markets fabricated products including nonresidential architectural building products such as storefronts, building entrances, facings, window framing, and curtain wall systems. **Common positions include:** Accountant/Auditor; Buyer; Civil Engineer; Cost Estimator; Credit Manager; Draftsperson; Human Resources Manager; Industrial Production Manager; Management Trainee; Mechanical Engineer; Software Engineer. **Other U.S. locations:** Springdale AR; Visalia CA; Jonesboro GA; Franklin IN. **Parent company:** ALCOA. **Operations at this facility**

include: Manufacturing. **Listed on:** New York Stock Exchange. **Stock exchange symbol:** AA. **Number of employees at this location:** 485. **Number of employees worldwide:** 14,000.

KEATING BUILDING CORPORATION
One Bala Avenue, Bala-Cynwyd PA 19004. 610/668-4100. **Fax:** 610/660-4060. **Contact:** Career Coordinator. **E-mail address:** opportunities@keatingnet.com. **World Wide Web address:** http://www.keatingweb.com. **Description:** A general construction firm that specializes in development, emissions, construction, and housing programs. **NOTE:** Entry-level positions are offered. **Common positions include:** Civil Engineer; Construction Contractor; Cost Estimator; Structural Engineer; Typist/Word Processor. **Special programs:** Internships. **Corporate headquarters location:** This location. **Other U.S. locations:** CT; FL; NJ; OH. **Operations at this facility include:** Administration. **Listed on:** Privately held. **Annual sales/revenues:** More than $100 million. **Number of employees at this location:** 100. **Number of employees nationwide:** 175.

KLING LINDQUIST
2301 Chestnut Street, Philadelphia PA 19103. 215/569-2900. **Fax:** 215/569-5963. **Contact:** Sydney Koerner, Human Resources Director. **E-mail address:** employment@tklp.com. **World Wide Web address:** http://www.klinglindquist.com. **Description:** Provides architectural, engineering, and interior design services. Founded in 1946. **NOTE:** Entry-level positions are offered. **Common positions include:** Accountant; Administrative Assistant; Administrative Manager; Architect; Chief Financial Officer; Civil Engineer; Computer Animator; Computer Engineer; Computer Operator; Computer Programmer; Computer Support Technician; Computer Technician; Computer-Aided Designer; Database Administrator; Database Manager; Design Engineer; Desktop Publishing Specialist; Draftsperson; Electrical/Electronics Engineer; Human Resources Manager; Instrument Engineer; Interior Designer; Librarian; Marketing Manager; Mechanical Engineer; MIS Specialist; Network/Systems Administrator; Operations Manager; Project Manager; Public Relations Specialist; Purchasing Agent/Manager; Secretary; Software Engineer; Structural Engineer; Technical Writer/Editor; Typist/Word Processor. **Special programs:** Internships; Training; Co-ops; Summer Jobs. **Office hours:** Monday - Friday, 8:30 a.m. - 5:30 p.m. **Corporate headquarters location:** This location. **Other U.S. locations:** Washington DC; Fort Meade MD. **Listed on:** Privately held. **CEO:** Mel Sotnick.

Annual sales/revenues: $21 - $50 million. **Number of employees at this location:** 350. **Number of employees nationwide:** 400.

LIPINSKI LANDSCAPING

P.O. Box 1340, Marlton NJ 08053. 856/797-8000. **Physical address:** 100 Sharp Road, Marlton NJ 08053. **Fax:** 856/983-0500. **Contact:** Terri Stelweck, Human Resources Manager. **E-mail address:** humanresource@lipinskiland.com. **World Wide Web address:** http://www.lipinskiland.com. **Description:** Provides landscaping services to commercial and residential clients. This location also hires seasonally. **NOTE:** Entry-level positions are offered. **Common positions include:** Accountant; Administrative Assistant; Architect; Blue-Collar Worker Supervisor; Construction Contractor; Design Engineer; Draftsperson; Engineer; Horticulturist; Landscape Architect; Management Trainee; Operations Manager; Production Manager; Project Manager; Sales Manager; Sales Representative; Seasonal Worker; Secretary; Transportation/Traffic Specialist. **Special programs:** Internships; Apprenticeships; Summer Jobs. **Corporate headquarters location:** This location. **Other U.S. locations:** Princeton NJ. **Annual sales/revenues:** $21 - $50 million. **Number of employees at this location:** 320.

M&T COMPANY

3368 West Ridge Pike, Pottstown PA 19464. 610/495-9320. **Contact:** Personnel Department. **World Wide Web address:** http://www.cdicorp.com. **Description:** Provides a wide range of technical services including engineering, designing, drafting, and graphic arts services.

MI HOME PRODUCTS INC.

650 West Market Street, Gratz PA 17030. 717/365-3300. **Contact:** Human Resources. **World Wide Web address:** http://www.mihomeproducts.com. **Description:** Manufactures metal doors and frames.

JAMES D. MORRISSEY, INC.

9119 Frankford Avenue, Philadelphia PA 19114. 215/333-8000. **Contact:** Bruce Angst, Human Resources. **E-mail address:** jobs@jdm-inc.com. **World Wide Web address:** http://www.jdm-inc.com. **Description:** A heavy construction firm that specializes in large-scale projects such as highways and commercial buildings. **Common positions include:** Civil Engineer; Computer Programmer; Draftsperson; Management

Trainee; Mining Engineer; Purchasing Agent/Manager; Systems Analyst. **Corporate headquarters location:** This location.

OVERHEAD DOOR CORPORATION
23 Industrial Park Road, Lewistown PA 17044-0110. 717/248-0131. **Contact:** Carrie Williams, Director of Human Resources. **World Wide Web address:** http://www.overheaddoor.com. **Description:** Designs, manufactures, and installs upward-lifting doors including commercial and industrial systems and residential garage doors and openers. Founded in 1923. **Corporate headquarters location:** Dallas TX.

PACE RESOURCES INC.
P.O. Box 15040, York PA 17405-7040. **Physical address:** 445 West Philadelphia, York PA 17404. 717/852-1300. **Contact:** Frank Weaver, Human Resources Director. **Description:** A holding company for architectural and engineering firms, as well as a testing laboratory, a computer service center, and a printing company. Founded in 1970.

PARSONS POWER GROUP INC.
2675 Morgantown Road, Reading PA 19607. 610/855-2560. **Fax:** 610/855-2186. **Contact:** Denise Scibek, Human Resources Manager. **World Wide Web address:** http://www.parsons.com. **Description:** Provides a wide range of engineering and consulting services including electrical, mechanical, structural, and nuclear engineering; construction management; procurement; and consulting services. The company's major services are the design, engineering, and supervision of the construction of electrical power generating stations, and electrical transmission and distribution systems, as well as the upgrading and retrofitting of existing power plants. Parsons Power Group also renders services to industrial clients and various government agencies. **Common positions include:** Civil Engineer; Design Engineer; Draftsperson; Electrical/Electronics Engineer; Mechanical Engineer. **Parent company:** The Parsons Corporation.

STV INCORPORATED
205 West Welsh Drive, Douglassville PA 19518. 610/385-8213. **Fax:** 610/385-8515. **Contact:** Patrick Austin, Human Resources Director. **World Wide Web address:** http://www.stvinc.com. **Description:** Provides engineering and architectural consulting and design services for a variety of projects, as well as construction inspection services for numerous industries, institutions, and sectors. The company operates four business segments including civil engineering,

which provides services for the construction of highways, bridges, airports, and marine ports; defense systems engineering, which serves the U.S. Department of Defense in the development of equipment and special hardware; industrial process engineering, which consists of services for the development of manufacturing equipment and process systems; and transportation engineering, which involves consulting, design, and construction supervision services for transportation facilities. Founded in 1945. **Common positions include:** Account Manager; Accountant; Administrative Assistant; Administrative Manager; Architect; Chemical Engineer; Chief Financial Officer; Civil Engineer; Computer Operator; Computer Programmer; Design Engineer; Draftsperson; Electrical/Electronics Engineer; Environmental Engineer; Graphic Artist; Human Resources Manager; Industrial Engineer; Librarian; Purchasing Agent/Manager; Secretary; Technical Writer/Editor; Typist/Word Processor; Vice President. **Special programs:** Co-ops; Summer Jobs. **Corporate headquarters location:** This location. **Other U.S. locations:** Nationwide. **Parent company:** STV Group Inc. **Operations at this facility include:** Regional Headquarters. **Listed on:** NASDAQ. **Stock exchange symbol:** STVI. **Annual sales/revenues:** $51 - $100 million. **Number of employees at this location:** 275. **Number of employees nationwide:** 1,000.

R.M. SHOEMAKER COMPANY

One Tower Bridge, 100 Front Street, Suite 1300, P.O. Box 888, West Conshohocken PA 19428. 610/941-5500. **Fax:** 610/941-4203. **Contact:** Human Resources Department. **E-mail address:** hr@rmsco.com. **World Wide Web address:** http://www.rmshoemaker.com. **Description:** An industrial and commercial construction company.

TOLL BROTHERS, INC.

3103 Philmont Avenue, Huntingdon Valley PA 19006. 215/938-8000. **Fax:** 215/938-8291. **Contact:** Personnel. **World Wide Web address:** http://www.tollbrothers.com. **Description:** Designs and builds luxury homes. Founded in 1967. **Common positions include:** Accountant; Administrative Assistant; Applications Engineer; Architect; Attorney; Computer Support Technician; Computer Technician; Construction Contractor; Draftsperson; Financial Analyst; Graphic Artist; Graphic Designer; Insurance Agent/Broker; Management Trainee; MIS Specialist; Network/Systems Administrator; Sales Manager; Sales Representative; Secretary; Systems Analyst; Systems Manager; Typist/Word Processor; Underwriter/Assistant Underwriter. **Corporate headquarters location:** This location.

Other U.S. locations: Nationwide. **Subsidiaries include:** Coleman Homes; Geoffrey Edmonds & Associates. **Listed on:** New York Stock Exchange. **Stock exchange symbol:** TOL. **Annual sales/revenues:** More than $100 million. **Number of employees at this location:** 200. **Number of employees nationwide:** 2,000.

WASHINGTON GROUP INTERNATIONAL, INC.
301 Chelsea Parkway, Boothwyn PA 19061. 610/497-8000. **Fax:** 610/497-8005. **Contact:** Human Resources. **World Wide Web address:** http://www.wgint.com. **Description:** A diversified corporation engaged in the design, engineering, and construction of industrial plants; architectural and community services; heavy machinery design and construction; industrial facilities; and mining and metallurgy. **Operations at this facility include:** Environmental, Quality and Biopharm Programs Laboratory.

WILLIARD INC.
375 Highland Avenue, Jenkintown PA 19046. 215/885-5000. **Contact:** Human Resources. **World Wide Web address:** http://www.williard.com. **Description:** A mechanical/electrical contracting firm specializing in HVAC, electrical, plumbing, and water treatment construction and services. **Corporate headquarters location:** This location.

YORK INTERNATIONAL CORPORATION
P.O. Box 1592, York PA 17405-1592. 717/771-7890. **Physical address:** 631 South Richland Avenue, York PA 17403. **Contact:** Amanda King, Corporate Employment Recruiter. **World Wide Web address:** http://www.york.com. **Description:** Manufactures and markets a full line of residential, commercial, and industrial air conditioning and refrigeration equipment and systems, heating systems, and food refrigeration systems. **Common positions include:** Accountant/Auditor; Electrical/Electronics Engineer; Mechanical Engineer; MIS Specialist; Software Engineer. **Special programs:** Internships. **Corporate headquarters location:** This location. **International locations:** Worldwide. **Subsidiaries include:** York Engineered Systems; York Refrigeration; York Unitary Products. **Operations at this facility include:** Administration; Manufacturing; Research and Development; Sales; Service. **Listed on:** New York Stock Exchange. **Stock exchange symbol:** YRK. **Annual sales/revenues:** More than $100 million. **Number of employees worldwide:** 25,000.

YORKTOWNE, INC.
P.O. Box 231, Red Lion PA 17356. 717/244-4011. **Physical address:** 100 Redcoe Avenue, Red Lion PA 17356. **Contact:** James Burtnett, Vice President/Human Resources. **World Wide Web address:** http://www.yorktowneinc.com. **Description:** Manufactures and markets kitchen cabinets and bathroom vanities for the residential construction industry. **Parent company:** Wickes Corporation (San Diego CA).

ARTS, ENTERTAINMENT, SPORTS, AND RECREATION

You can expect to find the following types of companies in this chapter:

Botanical and Zoological Gardens • Entertainment Groups • Motion Picture and Video Tape Production and Distribution • Museums and Art Galleries • Physical Fitness Facilities • Professional Sports Clubs • Public Golf Courses • Racing and Track Operations • Sporting and Recreational Camps • Theatrical Producers

CMEINFO.COM

1008 Astoria Boulevard, Suite A, Cherry Hill NJ 08033. 856/874-0010. **Contact:** Human Resources. **World Wide Web address:** http://www.cmeinfo.com. **Description:** Produces educational videotapes, audiotapes, and CD-ROMs for professionals in the medical field.

COMCAST-SPECTACOR, LP

3601 South Broad Street, Philadelphia PA 19148. 215/336-3600. **Recorded jobline:** 215/952-4180. **Contact:** Human Resources Manager. **World Wide Web address:** http://www.comcast-spectacor.com. **Description:** A sports/entertainment firm managing the Philadelphia Flyers, 76ers, Wings, Kixx, and Phantoms; Comcast SportsNet; the First Union Spectrum; and the First Union Center. The First Union Spectrum and Center are host to Flyers and Phantoms hockey, 76ers basketball, Kixx soccer and over 500 other sporting, musical, and entertainment events each year. Comcast SportsNet is a 24-hour sports network dedicated to the Philadelphia-area sports world. **Common positions include:** Accountant/Auditor; Administrative Assistant; Administrator; Blue-Collar Worker Supervisor; Customer Service Representative; General Manager; Human Resources Manager; Marketing Specialist; MIS Specialist; Network/Systems Administrator; Operations/Production Manager; Public Relations Specialist; Radio/TV Announcer/Broadcaster; Sales Executive; Sales Representative; Services Sales Representative; Technical Writer/Editor. **Special programs:** Internships. **Internship information:** A variety of internship opportunities are available to college students during the fall, spring, and summer terms. **Corporate headquarters location:** This location. **Parent company:** Comcast Corporation. **Operations at this facility include:** Administration; Sales; Service. **Listed**

on: New York Stock Exchange. **Stock exchange symbol:** CCZ. **Number of employees at this location:** 800.

ELMWOOD PARK ZOO
1661 Harding Boulevard, Norristown PA 19401. 610/277-3825. **Contact:** Personnel. **World Wide Web address:** http://www.elmwoodparkzoo.com. **Description:** A zoo featuring over 150 wild animals of North America.

THE FRANKLIN INSTITUTE SCIENCE MUSEUM
222 North 20th Street, Philadelphia PA 19103. 215/448-1200. **Contact:** Human Resources. **World Wide Web address:** http://sln.fi.edu. **Description:** A nonprofit scientific and educational corporation. The Franklin Institute Science Museum consists of The Science Center, The Mandel Futures Center, The Fels Planetarium, and The Tuttleman Omniverse Theater, with a wide range of interactive and educational exhibits in many different scientific areas. Founded in 1824. **Common positions include:** Blue-Collar Worker Supervisor; Customer Service Representative; Designer; Graphic Artist; Sales Executive; Teacher/Professor.

LONGWOOD GARDENS INC.
Route 1, P.O. Box 501, Kennett Square PA 19348-0501. 610/388-1000. **Contact:** Administrative Services. **E-mail address:** jobs@longwoodgardens.org. **World Wide Web address:** http://www.longwoodgardens.org. **Description:** A horticultural display garden. Longwood Gardens also offers a restaurant and meeting facilities.

PENN NATIONAL RACE COURSE
P.O. Box 32, Grantville PA 17028. 717/469-2211. **Contact:** Human Resources Department. **World Wide Web address:** http://www.pnrc.com. **Description:** A thoroughbred racetrack. **Parent company:** Penn National Gaming, Inc.

PHILADELPHIA MUSEUM OF ART
P.O. Box 7646, Philadelphia PA 19101-7646. 215/763-8100. **Fax:** 215/684-7977. **Contact:** Human Resources. **E-mail address:** jobs@philamuseum.org. **World Wide Web address:** http://www.philamuseum.org. **Description:** An art museum housing a collection of European and American paintings and decorative arts, as well as Indian and East Asian art. Founded in 1876. **NOTE:** The museum also has many volunteer opportunities. **Special programs:** Internships. **Number of employees at this location:** 350.

PHILADELPHIA PARK RACETRACK
3001 Street Road, Bensalem PA 19020. 215/639-9000. **Contact:** Human Resources Department. **World Wide Web address:** http://www.philadelphiapark.com. **Description:** A thoroughbred racetrack. The company also operates several off-track betting facilities located throughout the greater Philadelphia area.

PHILADELPHIA ZOO
3400 West Girard Avenue, Philadelphia PA 19104. 215/243-1100. **Fax:** 215/243-5219. **Contact:** Human Resources. **E-mail address:** hr@phillyzoo.org. **World Wide Web address:** http://www.phillyzoo.org. **Description:** One of America's first zoos featuring over 2,000 animals and the Peco Primate Reserve exhibit. Founded in 1874.

SONY MUSIC
400 North Woodbury Road, Pitman NJ 08071. 856/589-8000. **Contact:** Human Resources. **World Wide Web address:** http://www.sony.com. **Description:** This location manufactures CDs and DVDs. Overall, Sony Music is a major recording company.

WEA MANUFACTURING INC.
1400 East Lackawanna Avenue, Olyphant PA 18448. 570/383-2471. **Contact:** Human Resources. **Description:** Produces and retails prerecorded music in the form of compact discs, records, cassettes, and CD-ROMs. **Parent company:** AOL Time Warner.

AUTOMOTIVE

You can expect to find the following types of companies in this chapter:

Automotive Repair Shops • Automotive Stampings • Industrial Vehicles and Moving Equipment • Motor Vehicles and Equipment • Travel Trailers and Campers

ALTEC INDUSTRIES, INC.
250 Laird Street, Plains PA 18705. 570/822-3104. **Fax:** 570/822-7437. **Contact:** Human Resources. **World Wide Web address:** http://www.altec.com. **Description:** Manufactures utility trucks and equipment. **Common positions include:** Accountant/Auditor; Blue-Collar Worker Supervisor; Manufacturer's/Wholesaler's Sales Rep.; Mechanical Engineer; Purchasing Agent/Manager. **Corporate headquarters location:** Birmingham AL. **Other U.S. locations:** Nationwide. **Operations at this facility include:** Administration; Manufacturing; Sales; Service. **Listed on:** Privately held. **Number of employees at this location:** 170. **Number of employees nationwide:** 1,400.

THE BUDD COMPANY
2450 West Hunting Park Avenue, Philadelphia PA 19129-1397. 215/221-7100. **Contact:** Human Resources Department. **World Wide Web address:** http://www.buddcompany.com. **Description:** This location is a manufacturing plant that produces auto body components. Overall, The Budd Company is a diversified transportation manufacturing firm with three primary operating segments: the Automotive Products Group manufactures products such as auto body parts, frames, wheels, and brakes; the Industrial Products Group manufactures railway cars, truck trailers, iron castings, plastic auto parts, and specialized fibers and nylon for industrial products; and the International Group has facilities in West Germany, France, Argentina, and Mexico. **Corporate headquarters location:** Troy MI.

CARDONE INDUSTRIES
5501 Whitaker Avenue, Philadelphia PA 19124-1799. 215/912-3000. **Contact:** Human Resources. **World Wide Web address:** http://www.cardoneonline.com. **Description:** Engaged in automotive reconditioning and rebuilding.

DANA CORPORATION

125 South Keim Street, Pottstown PA 19464. 610/323-4200. **Contact:** Linda Matz, Personnel Manager. **World Wide Web address:** http://www.dana.com. **Description:** This location builds driveshafts. Overall, Dana Corporation is a global leader in the engineering, manufacturing, and marketing of products and systems for the worldwide vehicular, industrial, and mobile off-highway original equipment markets and is a major supplier to the related aftermarkets. Dana Corporation is also a provider of lease financing services in selected markets. The company's products include drivetrain components such as axles, driveshafts, clutches, and transmissions; engine parts such as gaskets, piston rings, seals, pistons, and filters; chassis products such as vehicular frames and cradles and heavy-duty side rails; fluid power components such as pumps, motors, and control valves; and industrial products such as electrical and mechanical brakes and clutches, drives, and motion control devices. Dana's vehicular components and parts are used on automobiles, pickup trucks, vans, minivans, sport utility vehicles, medium and heavy trucks, and off-highway vehicles. The company's industrial products include mobile off-highway and stationary equipment. Founded in 1905. **Corporate headquarters location:** Toledo OH. **Listed on:** New York Stock Exchange. **Stock exchange symbol:** DCN. **Number of employees worldwide:** 55,000.

DANA CORPORATION
PARISH DIVISION

Robeson and Weiser Street, Reading PA 19601. 610/371-7000. **Contact:** Dan Hartung, Human Resources Manager. **World Wide Web address:** http://www.dana.com. **Description:** This location stamps, forms, and bends metal parts used in the assembly of vehicular frames for OEM customers. Overall, Dana Corporation is a global leader in the engineering, manufacturing, and marketing of products and systems for the worldwide vehicular, industrial, and mobile off-highway original equipment markets and is a major supplier to the related aftermarkets. Dana Corporation is also a provider of lease financing services in selected markets. The company's products include drivetrain components such as axles, driveshafts, clutches, and transmissions; engine parts such as gaskets, piston rings, seals, pistons, and filters; chassis products such as vehicular frames and cradles and heavy-duty side rails; fluid power components such as pumps, motors, and control valves; and industrial products such as electrical and mechanical brakes and clutches, drives, and motion control devices. Dana's vehicular components and parts are used on automobiles, pickup trucks, vans, minivans, sport utility vehicles, medium and heavy trucks, and off-highway vehicles. The company's industrial products include mobile off-highway and stationary equipment. Founded in 1905. **Common positions include:** Accountant/Auditor; Blue-Collar Worker Supervisor; Buyer; Computer Programmer; Department Manager; Draftsperson; Electrical/Electronics Engineer; Human Resources Manager; Industrial Engineer; Mechanical Engineer; Operations/Production Manager; Quality Control Supervisor; Systems Analyst; Transportation/Traffic Specialist. **Corporate headquarters location:** Toledo OH. **Listed on:** New York Stock Exchange. **Stock exchange symbol:** DCN. **Number of employees worldwide:** 55,000.

EAST PENN MANUFACTURING COMPANY INC.
P.O. Box 147, Deka Road, Lyon Station PA 19536. 610/682-6361. **Contact:** Human Resources Department. **World Wide Web address:** http://www.eastpenndeka.com. **Description:** Produces automotive and industrial batteries. Founded in 1946. **Common positions include:** Accountant/Auditor; Administrator; Advertising Clerk; Blue-Collar Worker Supervisor; Buyer; Chemical Engineer; Chemist; Computer Programmer; Draftsperson; Electrical/Electronics Engineer; Industrial Designer; Industrial Engineer; Marketing Specialist; Mechanical Engineer; Operations/Production Manager; Purchasing Agent/Manager; Quality Control Supervisor; Sales Executive; Transportation/Traffic Specialist. **Corporate headquarters location:** This location. **Operations at this facility include:** Administration; Manufacturing; Research and Development; Sales; Service.

FEDERAL-MOGUL CORPORATION
400 East Second Street, Boyertown PA 19512. 610/367-2604. **Contact:** Mishelle Wheeler, Director of Human Resources. **World Wide Web address:** http://www.federal-mogul.com. **Description:** This location manufactures sealed beam headlamps. Overall, Federal-Mogul designs, develops, manufactures, and markets automotive products that are sold to OEMs and auto parts distributors, as well as retailers of replacement parts and equipment. **Listed on:** New York Stock Exchange. **Stock exchange symbol:** FMO. **Annual sales/revenues:** More than $100 million.

HARLEY-DAVIDSON MOTOR COMPANY, INC.
1425 Eden Road, York PA 17402. 717/848-1177. **Contact:** Human Resources. **World Wide Web address:** http://www.harley-davidson.com. **Description:** Designs,

manufactures, and distributes a world-recognized line of motorcycles. **Common positions include:** Accountant/Auditor; Administrator; Buyer; Chemist; Computer Programmer; Electrical/Electronics Engineer; Financial Analyst; General Manager; Human Resources Manager; Industrial Engineer; Mechanical Engineer; Metallurgical Engineer; Operations/Production Manager; Production Manager; Purchasing Agent/Manager; Statistician; Systems Analyst; Transportation/Traffic Specialist. **Corporate headquarters location:** Milwaukee WI.

JOHNSON MATTHEY INC.
456 Devon Park Drive, Wayne PA 19087. 610/341-8300. **Fax:** 610/341-8259. **Contact:** Human Resources. **World Wide Web address:** http://www.matthey.com. **Description:** Manufactures automotive catalytic systems. **NOTE:** Entry-level positions and second and third shifts are offered. **Common positions include:** Chemical Engineer; Chemist; Manufacturing Engineer; Mechanical Engineer. **Special programs:** Summer Jobs.

LEAR CORPORATION
50 Spring Road, P.O. Box 40, Carlisle PA 17013. 717/249-1866. **Contact:** Rich Zeff, Vice President of Human Resources. **World Wide Web address:** http://www.lear.com. **Description:** A leading designer and manufacturer of automotive interior systems and components including floor systems, acoustic systems, soft-surface interior and luggage compartment trim components, and dash insulators for the global automotive market. **Corporate headquarters location:** Southfield MI. **Other U.S. locations:** Nationwide. **International locations:** Worldwide. **Number of employees at this location:** 3,250.

MACK TRUCKS INC.
P.O. Box M, Allentown PA 18105-5000. 610/709-3011. **Contact:** Bonnie Miller, Employment Manager. **World Wide Web address:** http://www.macktrucks.com. **Description:** Manufactures and sells heavy-duty trucks, truck tractors, and truck replacement parts. The company also provides repair and maintenance services for these products. Mack Trucks is one of the largest producers of oversized trucks in the United States. **Common positions include:** Accountant/Auditor; Attorney; Blue-Collar Worker Supervisor; Branch Manager; Buyer; Computer Programmer; Department Manager; Draftsperson; Electrical/Electronics Engineer; Human Resources Manager; Industrial Engineer; Manufacturer's/Wholesaler's Sales Rep.; Mechanical Engineer; Operations/Production Manager; Purchasing Agent/Manager; Quality Control Supervisor;

Systems Analyst. **Corporate headquarters location:** This location. **Operations at this facility include:** Administration. **Number of employees at this location:** 5,400.

NEAPCO, INC.
740 Queen Street, Pottstown PA 19464. 610/323-6000. **Contact:** Mary A. Csapo, Human Resources Manager. **World Wide Web address:** http://www.neapco.com. **Description:** Manufactures power driveline components, u-joints, and front-wheel drive products. NEAPCO operates in the OEM and aftermarket areas with customers in the automotive, heavy-duty, and agricultural lines. **Common positions include:** Customer Service Representative; Manufacturer's/Wholesaler's Sales Rep.; Mechanical Engineer. **Corporate headquarters location:** This location. **Other U.S. locations:** CA; MO; NE. **Parent company:** UIS, Inc. (New York NY). **Operations at this facility include:** Manufacturing; Research and Development; Sales.

OSRAM SYLVANIA, INC.
1128 Roosevelt Avenue, York PA 17404. 717/848-8080. **Fax:** 717/852-0875. **Contact:** Deb Barshinger, Human Resources. **E-mail address:** deb.barshinger@sylvania.com. **World Wide Web address:** http://www.sylvania.com. **Description:** This location manufactures automotive connectors, deep-drawn metal stampings, lighting components, metal base and stampings, wire drawing and lead wires, formed metal components for the lighting industry, custom metal stampings, and connector products. Overall, the company operates in four divisions: Coated Coil Operation produces tungsten filaments coated with high-performance insulator aluminum oxide for use in television electron guns; Special Refractory Products manufactures products made from refractory metals that are used as furnace hardware; The Ceramics Department produces various types of steatite ceramic electrical insulators used in bases of light bulbs; The Quartz Department produces and finishes quartz crucibles for use by the semiconductor industry. Founded in 1953. **NOTE:** Second and third shifts are offered. **Common positions include:** Accountant; Administrative Assistant; Controller; Design Engineer; Draftsperson; Electrical/Electronics Engineer; Electrician; Environmental Engineer; General Manager; Human Resources Manager; Mechanical Engineer; MIS Specialist; Operations Manager; Production Manager; Purchasing Agent/Manager; Quality Assurance Engineer; Quality Control Supervisor. **Special programs:** Apprenticeships; Co-ops. **Office hours:** Monday - Friday, 7:30 a.m. - 4:30 p.m. **Corporate headquarters**

location: Danvers MA. **Parent company:** OSRAM. **Listed on:** Privately held. **Annual sales/revenues:** $51 - $100 million. **Number of employees at this location:** 310. **Number of employees nationwide:** 16,000.

PPG INDUSTRIES, INC.
400 Park Drive, Carlisle PA 17013. 717/486-3366. **Contact:** Human Resources Department. **World Wide Web address:** http://www.ppg.com. **Description:** This location manufactures flat glass. Overall, PPG Industries is a diversified global manufacturer supplying products for manufacturing, building, automotive, processing, and numerous other world industries. The company makes decorative and protective coatings, flat glass and fabricated glass products, continuous-strand fiberglass, and industrial and specialty chemicals. Founded in 1883. **Corporate headquarters location:** Pittsburgh PA. **International locations:** Worldwide. **Listed on:** New York Stock Exchange. **Stock exchange symbol:** PPG. **Annual sales/revenues:** More than $100 million.

ROHM & HAAS COMPANY
P.O. Box 904, Spring House PA 19477-0904. 215/641-7000. **Physical address:** 727 Norristown Road, Spring House PA. **Contact:** Human Resources Department. **World Wide Web address:** http://www.rohmhaas.com. **Description:** This location is a research facility. Overall, Rohm & Haas is a specialty chemicals company operating in four industry segments: Polymers, Resins, and Monomers; Plastics; Industrial Chemicals; and Agricultural Chemicals. The company is also engaged in nonchemical industries such as forestry products, carpet production, and biomedical testing. **Corporate headquarters location:** Philadelphia PA. **Listed on:** New York Stock Exchange. **Stock exchange symbol:** ROH. **Annual sales/revenues:** More than $100 million.

ROHM & HAAS COMPANY
100 Independence Mall West, Philadelphia PA 19106-2399. 215/592-3000. **Contact:** Corporate Staffing. **World Wide Web address:** http://www.rohmhaas.com. **Description:** A specialty chemicals company that produces polymers, resins, and monomers; plastics; industrial chemicals; and agricultural chemicals. Rohm & Haas Company is also engaged in nonchemical industries such as forestry products, carpet production, and biomedical testing. **Corporate headquarters location:** This location. **Listed on:** New York Stock Exchange. **Stock exchange symbol:** ROH. **Annual sales/revenues:** More than $100 million.

ROHM & HAAS COMPANY

P.O. Box 584, Bristol PA 19007. 215/785-8000. **Physical address:** Route 413 and State Road, Bristol PA 19007. **Contact:** Human Resources Department. **World Wide Web address:** http://www.rohmhaas.com. **Description:** This location manufactures acrylic plastics used by the automotive industry to make taillights. Overall, Rohm & Haas is a specialty chemicals company operating in four business segments: Polymers, Resins, and Monomers; Plastics; Industrial Chemicals; and Agricultural Chemicals. Rohm & Haas is also engaged in nonchemical industries such as forestry products, carpet production, and biomedical testing. **Corporate headquarters location:** Philadelphia PA. **Listed on:** New York Stock Exchange. **Stock exchange symbol:** ROH. **Annual sales/revenues:** More than $100 million.

SETON COMPANY

1000 Madison Avenue, Norristown PA 19403. 610/666-9600. **Contact:** Human Resources. **E-mail address:** hr@setonco.com. **World Wide Web address:** http://www.setonleather.com. **Description:** This location manufactures leather car seats. Overall, Seton's operations are conducted primarily through two business segments: Leather is involved in tanning, finishing, and distributing of whole-hide cattle leathers for the automotive and furniture upholstery industries; cattle hide side leathers for the footwear, handbag, and other markets; and cattle hide products for collagen, rawhide pet items, and other applications; and Chemicals and Coated Products is engaged in the manufacture and distribution of epoxy and urethane chemicals, specialty leather finishes, industrial and medical tapes, foams, films, and laminates.

STRICK CORPORATION

225 Lincoln Highway, Fairless Hills PA 19030. 215/949-3600. **Contact:** Human Resources. **World Wide Web address:** http://www.strickcorp.com. **Description:** A manufacturer of trailers, flatbeds, and chassis. **Common positions include:** Accountant/Auditor; Buyer; Computer Programmer; Designer; Human Resources Representative; Industrial Engineer; Industrial Production Manager; Materials Engineer; Mechanical Engineer; Operations/Production Manager; Purchasing Agent/Manager; Quality Control Supervisor; Structural Engineer; Systems Analyst. **Corporate headquarters location:** Monroe IN. **Other U.S. locations:** IN. **Operations at this facility include:** Administration; Research and Development; Sales; Service. **Listed on:** Privately held. **Number of employees at this location:** 65. **Number of employees nationwide:** 1,000.

SUBARU OF AMERICA
2235 Route 70 West, Cherry Hill NJ 08046. 856/488-8500.
Fax: 856/488-3196. **Contact:** Scott Mogren, Vice President of
Human Resources Department. **World Wide Web address:**
http://www.subaru.com. **Description:** This location houses
administrative offices. Overall, Subaru of America
manufactures cars and trucks.

UNITED DEFENSE
P.O. Box 15512, York PA 17405-1512. 717/225-8000.
Contact: Human Resources. **World Wide Web address:**
http://www.uniteddefense.com. **Description:** Manufactures
military tracked vehicles and personnel carriers. **Common
positions include:** Accountant/Auditor; Electrical/Electronics
Engineer; Financial Analyst; Mechanical Engineer; Systems
Analyst; Technical Writer/Editor. **Corporate headquarters
location:** Arlington VA. **Operations at this facility include:**
Manufacturing. **Listed on:** New York Stock Exchange. **Stock
exchange symbol:** UDI. **Number of employees nationwide:**
2,000.

BANKING/SAVINGS AND LOANS

You can expect to find the following types of companies in this chapter:

Banks • Bank Holding Companies and Associations • Lending Firms/Financial Services Institutions

BANK OF GLOUCESTER COUNTY
100 Park Avenue, Woodbury NJ 08096. 856/845-0700. **Fax:** 856/415-1347. **Contact:** Human Resources. **E-mail address:** humanresources@thebankofgc.com. **World Wide Web address:** http://www.thebankofgc.com. **Description:** A bank. Founded in 1989. **Common positions include:** Administrative Assistant; Assistant Manager; Bank Officer/Manager; Bank Teller; Branch Manager; Credit Manager; Customer Service Representative; Financial Analyst; Management Trainee. **Office hours:** Monday - Friday, 8:30 a.m. - 5:00 p.m. **Corporate headquarters location:** This location. **Parent company:** Fulton Financial Corporation. **Listed on:** NASDAQ. **Stock exchange symbol:** FULT. **Number of employees at this location:** 200.

BENEFICIAL SAVINGS BANK
530 Walnut, Philadelphia PA 19106. 215/864-6000. **Contact:** Joseph Vetter, Personnel Manager. **World Wide Web address:** http://www.beneficialbank.com. **Description:** A full-service savings bank that also offers home mortgaging.

BRYN MAWR BANK CORPORATION
801 Lancaster Avenue, Bryn Mawr PA 19010-3396. 610/525-1700. **Contact:** Human Resources. **World Wide Web address:** http://www.bmtc.com. **Description:** A holding company. **Subsidiaries include:** Bryn Mawr Trust operates 14 banks throughout Eastern Pennsylvania. **Listed on:** NASDAQ. **Stock exchange symbol:** BMTC.

CITIZENS BANK
8 West Market Street, Wilkes-Barre PA 18711. 570/826-2611. **Contact:** Human Resources. **World Wide Web address:** http://www.mellon.com. **Description:** A bank. As part of the Northeastern Region, this location serves consumer and small to mid-sized commercial markets in northeastern Pennsylvania. **Corporate headquarters location:** Providence RI. **Other U.S. locations:** Northeast. **Listed on:** NASDAQ. **Stock exchange symbol:** CBCF. **Number of employees nationwide:** 20,000.

CITIZENS NATIONAL BANK OF SOUTHERN PENNSYLVANIA

35 North Carlisle Street, Greencastle PA 17225. 717/597-2191. **Contact:** Human Resources. **World Wide Web address:** http://www.citizensbsp.com. **Description:** A full-service bank. **Parent company:** Susquehanna Bancshares, Inc. is a multifinancial institution. Since 1982, Susquehanna has grown from one bank serving one county with 14 offices to six banks serving eight counties with 83 offices. The company also operates a leasing company whose market encompasses Pennsylvania, Maryland, New Jersey, Virginia, West Virginia, and Delaware.

COMMERCE BANK

17000 Horizon Way, Mount Laurel NJ 08054. 856/751-9000. **Contact:** Human Resources Department. **World Wide Web address:** http://www.commerceonline.com. **Description:** This location is the operations center. Overall, Commerce Bank is a full-service bank offering a variety of services including Commerce Capital, an in-house stocks and bonds investment program. Commerce Bank, along with its affiliates Commerce Bank NJ, Commerce Bank Shore, Commerce Bank Harrisburg, and Independence Bank, constitutes the Commerce Network. **Listed on:** New York Stock Exchange. **Stock exchange symbol:** CBH.

COMMONWEALTH BANK

P.O. Box 2100, Valley Forge PA 19482-2100. 610/313-1600. **Toll-free phone:** 800/327-9885. **Fax:** 610/313-1509. **Contact:** Human Resources Department. **E-mail address:** hrrecruit@commonwealthbank.com. **World Wide Web address:** http://www.commonwealthbank.com. **Description:** A full-service community bank serving retail and small business customers in northeast Pennsylvania. Founded in 1924. **NOTE:** Part-time jobs are offered. **Common positions include:** Accountant; Assistant Manager; Auditor; Bank Officer/Manager; Branch Manager; Customer Service Representative; Sales Manager; Sales Representative. **Special programs:** Training; Summer Jobs. **Corporate headquarters location:** This location. **Listed on:** NASDAQ. **Stock exchange symbol:** CMSB.

EQUITY NATIONAL BANK

8000 Sagemore Drive, Suite 8101, Marlton NJ 08053. 856/983-4000. **Contact:** Human Resources. **Description:** A full-service bank whose operations include commercial and investment banking services.

FIRST NATIONAL BANK OF CHESTER COUNTY
P.O. Box 523, West Chester PA 19381-0523. 610/692-3000.
Contact: Human Resources. **World Wide Web address:**
http://www.1st-national.com. **Description:** A full-service bank.

FIRST UNION NATIONAL BANK
220 South Broad Street, Woodbury NJ 08096. 856/845-3000.
Contact: Human Resources Department. **World Wide Web
address:** http://www.firstunion.com. **Description:** A bank.
Common positions include: Bank Officer/Manager; Bank
Teller; Branch Manager; Customer Service Representative;
Loan Officer. **Parent company:** First Union Corporation
(Charlotte NC) is one of the nation's largest bank holding
companies with subsidiaries that operate over 1,330 full-
service bank branches in the south Atlantic states. These
subsidiaries provide retail banking, retail investment, and
commercial banking services. The corporation provides other
financial services including mortgage banking, home equity
lending, leasing, insurance, and securities brokerage services
from 222 branch locations. The corporation also operates one
of the nation's largest ATM networks. **Listed on:** New York
Stock Exchange. **Stock exchange symbol:** FUR. **Number of
employees at this location:** 800.

FIRST UNION NATIONAL BANK
50 Huntington Pike, Rockledge PA 19046. 215/379-8777.
Contact: Human Resources. **World Wide Web address:**
http://www.firstunion.com. **Description:** A bank. **Parent
company:** First Union Corporation (Charlotte NC) is one of the
nation's largest bank holding companies with subsidiaries
operating over 1,330 full-service bank branches in the south
Atlantic states. These subsidiaries provide retail banking, retail
investment, and commercial banking services. The corporation
provides other financial services including mortgage banking,
home equity lending, leasing, insurance, and securities
brokerage services from 222 branch locations. The corporation
also operates one of the nation's largest ATM networks.

FIRST UNION NATIONAL BANK
2560 Huntingdon Pike, Huntingdon Valley PA 19006.
215/947-3700. **Contact:** Human Resources. **World Wide Web
address:** http://www.firstunion.com. **Description:** A bank.
Parent company: First Union Corporation (Charlotte NC) is
one of the nation's largest bank holding companies with
subsidiaries operating over 1,330 full-service bank branches in
the south Atlantic states. These subsidiaries provide retail
banking, retail investment, and commercial banking services.

The corporation provides other financial services including mortgage banking, home equity lending, leasing, insurance, and securities brokerage services from 222 branch locations. The corporation also operates one of the nation's largest ATM networks.

FIRST UNION NATIONAL BANK
1500 Market Street, Philadelphia PA 19102. 215/786-5980. **Contact:** Human Resources. **World Wide Web address:** http://www.firstunion.com. **Description:** A bank. **Parent company:** First Union Corporation (Charlotte NC) is one of the nation's largest bank holding companies with subsidiaries that operate over 1,330 full-service bank branches in the south Atlantic states. These subsidiaries provide retail banking, retail investment, and commercial banking services. The corporation provides other financial services including mortgage banking, home equity lending, leasing, insurance, and securities brokerage services from 222 branch locations. The corporation also operates one of the nation's largest ATM networks.

FLEET BANK
1503 Linden Street, Bethlehem PA 18017. 610/865-8467. **Contact:** Human Resources. **World Wide Web address:** http://www.fleet.com. **Description:** A full-service financial institution that serves corporate, retail, and private markets.

FULTON FINANCIAL CORPORATION
FULTON BANK
One Penn Square, P.O. Box 4887, Lancaster PA 17602. 717/291-2467. **Fax:** 717/295-4783. **Contact:** Human Resources. **World Wide Web address:** http://www.fult.com. **Description:** A bank holding company. **Common positions include:** Bank Officer/Manager; Branch Manager; Management Trainee. **Corporate headquarters location:** This location. **Subsidiaries include:** Fulton Bank (also at this location).

HUDSON UNITED BANK
222 Haddon Avenue, Westmont NJ 08108. 856/869-7900. **Contact:** Human Resources Department. **E-mail address:** career@hudsonunitedbank.com. **World Wide Web address:** http://www.hudsonunitedbank.com. **Description:** A full-service bank. **NOTE:** Please send resumes to 1000 MacArthur Boulevard, Mahwah NJ 07430. **Parent company:** Hudson United Bancorp.

HUDSON UNITED BANK

Lafayette Building, Fifth & Chestnut Streets, Philadelphia PA 19106. 215/861-7000. **Toll-free phone:** 800/482-5465. **Contact:** Manager of Human Resources Department. **E-mail address:** career@hudsonunitedbank.com. **World Wide Web address:** http://www.hudsonunitedbank.com. **Description:** A full-service bank. **Parent company:** Hudson United Bancorp. **Listed on:** New York Stock Exchange. **Stock exchange symbol:** HU.

HUDSON UNITED BANK

United Engineers Building, 31 South 18th Street, Philadelphia PA 19103. 800/482-5465. **Contact:** Personnel. **E-mail address:** career@hudsonunitedbank.com. **World Wide Web address:** http://www.hudsonunitedbank.com. **Description:** A full-service bank. **Parent company:** Hudson United Bancorp. **Listed on:** New York Stock Exchange. **Stock exchange symbol:** HU.

LEBANON VALLEY FARMERS BANK

555 Willow Street, P.O. Box 1285, Lebanon PA 17042-1285. 717/274-6871. **Fax:** 717/274-6838. **Contact:** Human Resources Department. **World Wide Web address:** http://www.lvfb.com. **Description:** A full-service bank. **Common positions include:** Accountant/Auditor; Agricultural Scientist; Bank Officer/Manager; Branch Manager; Computer Programmer; Financial Analyst; Management Trainee; Systems Analyst; Underwriter/Assistant Underwriter. **Special programs:** Internships. **Corporate headquarters location:** This location. **Parent company:** Fulton Financial Corporation. **Operations at this facility include:** Administration; Sales; Service. **Number of employees at this location:** 325.

M&T BANK

One South Centre Street, Pottsville PA 17901-7150. 570/622-4200. **Contact:** Christine Pfeiffenberger, Personnel. **World Wide Web address:** http://www.mandtbank.com. **Description:** A full-service banking institution. **Corporate headquarters location:** Horsham PA.

M&T BANK

15 South Franklin Street, Wilkes-Barre PA 18711. 570/821-7168. **Fax:** 570/831-8810. **Contact:** Rita Bartol, Director of Human Resources Department. **World Wide Web address:** http://www.mandtbank.com. **Description:** A bank.

M&T BANK

601 Dresher Road, Horsham PA 19044. **Toll-free phone:** 800/724-2440. **Fax:** 215/956-7122. **Contact:** Personnel. **World Wide Web address:** http://www.mandtbank.com. **Description:** A full-service banking institution. **Common positions include:** Accountant/Auditor; Bank Officer/Manager; Customer Service Representative. **Corporate headquarters location:** This location.

MADISON BANK

Madison Bank Building, 1767 Sentry Parkway West, Blue Bell PA 19422. 215/641-1111. **Contact:** Personnel. **World Wide Web address:** http://www.madisonbank.com. **Description:** A retail and commercial bank. The bank offers a broad range of consumer and commercial deposit banking services including both commercial and consumer deposit accounts. The bank places an emphasis on serving the needs of individuals, small and medium-sized businesses, executives, professionals, and professional organizations. **Corporate headquarters location:** This location. **Other area locations:** Conshohocken PA.

NATIONAL PENN BANK

P.O. Box 547, Boyertown PA 19512. 610/367-6001. **Toll-free phone:** 800/822-3321. **Fax:** 610/369-6676. **Contact:** Earl Houseknecht, Senior Vice-President of Human Resources. **World Wide Web address:** http://www.natpennbank.com. **Description:** A bank. **Parent company:** National Penn Bancshares, Inc. is a $2.1 billion bank holding company. Other subsidiaries of National Penn Bancshares include Investors Trust Company.

NAZARETH NATIONAL BANK AND TRUST COMPANY

44 East Broad Street, Bethlehem PA 18018. 610/861-7843. **Contact:** Human Resources. **World Wide Web address:** http://www.nazbank.com. **Description:** An independent community bank providing full financial services through 14 local branches. **Corporate headquarters location:** This location. **Parent company:** First Colonial Group is a bank holding company. The company also operates First C.G. Company, Inc. (Wilmington DE), established to invest in various types of securities.

PNC BANK

11 West Market Street, Wilkes-Barre PA 18768. 570/961-7222. **Recorded jobline:** 800/PNC-JOBS. **Fax:** 800/267-3755. **Contact:** Human Resources Department. **E-mail address:** resumes@pncbank.com. **World Wide Web address:**

http://www.pncbank.com. **Description:** A bank. **Parent company:** PNC Bank Corporation is one of the nation's largest financial services companies. The company's major divisions include Corporate Banking, Consumer Banking, PNC Mortgage, and PNC Asset Management Group. With nearly 500 offices across Delaware, Indiana, Kentucky, Ohio, and Pennsylvania, PNC is one of the largest banking franchises in the Midwest and Mid-Atlantic. **Listed on:** New York Stock Exchange. **Stock exchange symbol:** PNC.

PNC BANK
18 South Bryn Mawr Avenue, Bryn Mawr PA 19010. 610/520-5151. **Recorded jobline:** 800/PNC-JOBS. **Fax:** 800/267-3755. **Contact:** Human Resources Department. **E-mail address:** resumes@pncbank.com. **World Wide Web address:** http://www.pncbank.com. **Description:** A bank. **Parent company:** PNC Bank Corporation is one of the nation's largest financial services companies. The company's major divisions include Corporate Banking, Consumer Banking, PNC Mortgage, and PNC Asset Management Group. With nearly 500 offices across Delaware, Indiana, Kentucky, Ohio, and Pennsylvania, PNC is one of the largest banking franchises in the Midwest and Mid-Atlantic. **Listed on:** New York Stock Exchange. **Stock exchange symbol:** PNC.

PHILADELPHIA FEDERAL CREDIT UNION
12800 Townsend Road, Philadelphia PA 19154-1003. 215/934-3500. **Contact:** Human Resources. **World Wide Web address:** http://www.pfcu.com. **Description:** This location is a service center. Overall, Philadelphia Credit Union offers a variety of financial services including checking and savings accounts, share certificates, bill payment services, loans, and a Visa credit card.

PROGRESS BANK
P.O. Box 3036, 4 Sentry Parkway, Blue Bell PA 19422-2311. 610/825-8800. **Physical address:** 4 Sentry Parkway, Suite 200, Blue Bell PA 19422. **Contact:** Human Resources. **World Wide Web address:** http://www.progressbank.com. **Description:** A federally chartered stock savings bank that conducts community banking throughout Eastern Pennsylvania. **Corporate headquarters location:** This location. **Other area locations:** Conshohocken PA; Jeffersonville PA; King of Prussia PA; Norristown PA; Philadelphia PA; Plymouth Meeting PA; Rosemont PA. **Listed on:** NASDAQ. **Stock exchange symbol:** PFNC.

ROYAL BANK OF PENNSYLVANIA
732 Montgomery Avenue, Narberth PA 19072. 610/668-4700.
Fax: 610/668-3670. **Contact:** Human Resources Department.
E-mail address: careers@royalbankpa.com. **World Wide Web
address:** http://www.royalbankpa.com. **Description:** A
community bank operating through 14 branches in the
Philadelphia area.

SOVEREIGN BANK
100 Berlin Road, Clementon NJ 08021. 856/783-5700.
Contact: Human Resources. **World Wide Web address:**
http://www.sovereignbank.com. **Description:** A bank. **Parent
company:** Sovereign Bancorp is one of the largest thrift holding
companies, with community banking and loan offices serving
New England, eastern Pennsylvania, New Jersey, and northern
Delaware.

SOVEREIGN BANK
P.O. Box 12646, Reading PA 19612. 610/320-8400. **Physical
address:** 1130 Berkshire Boulevard, Wyomissing PA 19610.
Fax: 610/376-8379. **Contact:** Recruiting. **World Wide Web
address:** http://www.sovereignbank.com. **Description:** A full-
service banking institution serving the Mid-Atlantic and
Northeast regions. **Common positions include:** Accountant;
Administrative Assistant; Attorney; Auditor; Bank
Officer/Manager; Branch Manager; Budget Analyst; Chief
Financial Officer; Computer Engineer; Controller; Customer
Service Representative; Database Manager; Editorial Assistant;
Finance Director; Financial Analyst; Fund Manager; Graphic
Artist; Graphic Designer; Human Resources Manager; Internet
Services Manager; Management Trainee; Market Research
Analyst; Marketing Manager; Marketing Specialist;
Network/Systems Administrator; Paralegal; Purchasing
Agent/Manager; Secretary; Systems Analyst; Systems Manager;
Webmaster. **Special programs:** Internships; Training; Summer
Jobs. **Corporate headquarters location:** This location. **Other
U.S. locations:** DE; NJ. **Listed on:** New York Stock Exchange.
Stock exchange symbol: SOV. **Number of employees
nationwide:** 4,000.

SUSQUEHANNA BANCSHARES, INC.
701 South Broadstreet Street, Lititz PA 17543. 717/626-4721.
Fax: 717/625-0555. **Contact:** Human Resources. **World Wide
Web address:** http://www.susq.com. **Description:** A
multifinancial institution that operates six banks serving eight
counties with 83 offices. The company also operates a leasing
company. Its market encompasses Pennsylvania, Maryland,

New Jersey, Virginia, West Virginia, and Delaware. Founded in 1982. **Subsidiaries include:** Citizens National Bank of Southern Pennsylvania, Greencastle PA; Farmers and Merchants Bank & Trust, Hagerstown MD; Farmers First Bank, Lititz PA; First National Trust Bank, Sunbury PA; Spring Grove National Bank, Spring Grove PA; Williamsport National Bank, Williamsport PA. **Listed on:** NASDAQ. **Stock exchange symbol:** SUSQ.

UNIVEST CORPORATION OF PENNSYLVANIA
10 West Broad Street, Souderton PA 18964. 215/721-2400. **Fax:** 215/721-2427. **Contact:** Human Resources. **E-mail address:** univest@rpc.webhire.com. **World Wide Web address:** http://www.univest-corp.com. **Description:** A holding company. **Subsidiaries include:** Fin-Plan Group is a financial services group offering asset management, financial planning, insurance, and investments. George Becker Associates is a full-service insurance company. Pennview Savings Bank is a full-service bank. Union National Bank is a full-service bank. **Common positions include:** Account Manager; Account Representative; Accountant; Administrative Assistant; Administrative Manager; Advertising Clerk; Advertising Executive; AS400 Programmer Analyst; Assistant Manager; Auditor; Bank Officer/Manager; Chief Financial Officer; Clerical Supervisor; Computer Operator; Computer Programmer; Computer Support Technician; Controller; Credit Manager; Customer Service Representative; Economist; Event Planner; Finance Director; Financial Analyst; General Manager; Human Resources Manager; Management Analyst/Consultant; Management Trainee; Marketing Manager; Marketing Specialist; MIS Specialist; Operations Manager; Public Relations Specialist; Sales Executive; Sales Manager; Sales Representative; Secretary. **Special programs:** Summer Jobs. **Number of employees at this location:** 455.

WAYPOINT BANK
449 Eisenhower Boulevard, Harrisburg PA 17111. 866/929-7646. **Fax:** 717/909-7457. **Contact:** Personnel. **World Wide Web address:** http://www.waypointbank.com. **Description:** A savings and loan association. **Common positions include:** Accountant/Auditor; Bank Officer/Manager; Branch Manager; Customer Service Representative; Human Resources Manager; Underwriter/Assistant Underwriter. **Other U.S. locations:** MD. **Parent company:** York Financial Corporation. **Operations at this facility include:** Administration; Divisional Headquarters; Sales. **Listed on:** NASDAQ. **Stock exchange symbol:** WYPT.

BIOTECHNOLOGY, PHARMACEUTICALS, AND SCIENTIFIC R&D

You can expect to find the following types of companies in this chapter:

Clinical Labs • Lab Equipment Manufacturers
Pharmaceutical Manufacturers and Distributors

AMERISOURCEBERGEN CORPORATION
1300 Morris Drive, Suite 100, Chesterbrook PA 19087-5594. 610/727-7000. **Fax:** 610/727-3611. **Contact:** Lisa Hickman, Human Resources Manager. **World Wide Web address:** http://www.amerisourcebergen.net. **Description:** A large pharmaceutical distribution company serving hospitals, nursing homes, clinics, and pharmacy chains. The company also provides health and beauty aids, general merchandise, inventory control, emergency delivery, and marketing and promotional services. **Corporate headquarters location:** This location. **Listed on:** New York Stock Exchange. **Stock exchange symbol:** ABC. **Annual sales/revenues:** More than $100 million.

AVENTIS PASTEUR
Discovery Drive, Box 187, Swiftwater PA 18370-0187. 570/839-7187. **Fax:** 570/839-0561. **Contact:** Human Resources Department. **World Wide Web address:** http://www.aventispasteur.com. **Description:** A pharmaceutical manufacturing firm with an emphasis on developing vaccines to prevent diseases such as Lyme disease, AIDS, and malaria.

BIO-IMAGING TECHNOLOGIES, INC.
826 Newtown-Yardley Road, Newtown PA 18940-1721. 267/757-1360. **Fax:** 267/757-1361. **Contact:** Maria Kraus, Controller. **E-mail address:** careers@bioimaging.com. **World Wide Web address:** http://www.bioimaging.com. **Description:** Processes and analyzes data for clinics and labs. The company receives lab data from clinical tests, including MRIs and ultrasounds, and then digitizes the information.

BIOSIS
2 Commerce Square, 2001 Market Street, Suite 700, Philadelphia PA 19103-7095. 215/587-4800. **Toll-free phone:** 800/523-4806. **Fax:** 215/587-4938. **Contact:** Dana Felt, Senior Human Resources Generalist. **World Wide Web address:** http://www.biosis.org. **Description:** A nonprofit educational

organization. Its mission is to foster the growth, communication, and use of biological knowledge. BIOSIS offers one of the world's largest collections of abstracts and bibliographical references of biological and medical literature available for public use. Founded in 1926. **NOTE:** Entry-level positions are offered. **Common positions include:** Biological Scientist; Computer Programmer; Marketing Specialist; MIS Specialist; Systems Analyst; Technical Writer/Editor. **Corporate headquarters location:** This location. **International locations:** Worldwide. **Subsidiaries include:** BIOSIS (UK). **Operations at this facility include:** Administration; Marketing; Production; Sales. **President:** John E. Anderson. **Annual sales/revenues:** $21-$50 million. **Number of employees at this location:** 250.

B. BRAUN BIOTECH, INC., USA
999 Postal Road, Allentown PA 18103. 610/266-6262. **Fax:** 610/266-9319. **Contact:** Human Resources Department. **World Wide Web address:** http://www.bbraunbiotech.com. **Description:** Manufactures custom-built fermentation/cell culture bioreactor systems. B. Braun Biotech also produces a line of accessory products for laboratories including shakers, homogenizers, freeze-dryers, and heating/cooling circulator baths.

CENTOCOR, INC.
200 Great Valley Parkway, Malvern PA 19355. 610/651-6000. **Contact:** Frances Littlewood, Human Resources Department. **World Wide Web address:** http://www.centocor.com. **Description:** Develops biopharmaceutical therapeutics and diagnostic products for cardiovascular, inflammatory, and infectious diseases, and cancer. Centocor concentrates on research, development, and manufacturing with a technological focus on monoclonal antibodies, peptides, and nucleic acids. **NOTE:** On-line applications can be made via the Johnson and Johnson Careers Website. **Corporate headquarters location:** This location. **Subsidiaries include:** Centocor B.V. (the Netherlands); Centocor U.K. Limited (England); and Nippon Centocor K.K. (Japan). **Parent company:** Johnson & Johnson. **Listed on:** New York Stock Exchange. **Stock exchange symbol:** JNJ.

CEPHALON, INC.
145 Brandywine Parkway, West Chester PA 19380. 610/344-0200. **Contact:** Ms. Pat Vandenberg, Recruiting. **World Wide Web address:** http://www.cephalon.com. **Description:** Develops, manufactures, and markets pharmaceutical products for the treatment of neurological disorders, sleep disorders,

and cancer. **Corporate headquarters location:** This location. **Subsidiaries include:** Cephalon Development Corporation; Cephalon International Holdings, Inc.; Cephalon Investments, Inc.; Cephalon Property Management, Inc.; Cephalon Technology, Inc. **Listed on:** NASDAQ. **Stock exchange symbol:** CEPH.

ECOGEN, INC.
2000 West Cabot Boulevard, Suite 170, Langhorne PA 19047-1811. 215/757-1590. **Fax:** 215/752-2461. **Contact:** Human Resources Department. **World Wide Web address:** http://www.ecogeninc.com. **Description:** An agricultural biotechnology company. Ecogen seeks environmentally compatible solutions to agricultural pest problems through the development of biologically derived pesticides.

GENAERA CORPORATION
5110 Campus Drive, Plymouth Meeting PA 19462. 610/941-4020. **Fax:** 610/941-5399. **Contact:** Human Resources Department. **E-mail address:** resumes@genaera.com. **World Wide Web address:** http://www.genaera.com. **Description:** A biopharmaceutical company engaged in the development of medicine for infectious and genetic diseases. The company's clinical development efforts are focused on oncology with ongoing research efforts in respiratory and infectious diseases. **Listed on:** NASDAQ. **Stock exchange symbol:** GENR. **Number of employees at this location:** 40.

GLAXOSMITHKLINE CORPORATION
One Franklin Plaza, P.O. Box 7929, Philadelphia PA 19101-7929. 215/751-4000. **Contact:** Personnel Department. **World Wide Web address:** http://www.gsk.com. **Description:** This location is the U.S. headquarters. Overall, GlaxoSmithKline Corporation is a health care company engaged in the research, development, manufacture, and marketing of ethical pharmaceuticals, animal health products, ethical and proprietary medicines, and eye care products. The company's principal divisions include GlaxoSmithKline Pharmaceuticals, GlaxoSmithKline Animal Health, and GlaxoSmithKline Consumer Healthcare. The company is also engaged in many other aspects of the health care field including the production of medical and electronic instruments. Through its subsidiary, Menley & James Laboratories, the company also manufactures proprietary medicines including Contac Cold Capsules, Sine-Off sinus medicine, Love cosmetics, and Sea & Ski outdoor products. **Corporate headquarters location:** This location.

Listed on: New York Stock Exchange. **Stock exchange symbol:** GSK. **Number of employees nationwide:** 20,000.

IGI, INC.

105 Lincoln Avenue, P.O. Box 687, Buena NJ 08310. 856/697-1441. **Contact:** Sherri DiPasquale, Human Resources Director. **World Wide Web address:** http://www.askigi.com. **Description:** A diversified company engaged in three business segments: animal health products, cosmetic and consumer products, and biotechnology. The animal health products business produces and markets poultry vaccines, veterinary products, nutritional supplements, and grooming aids. The cosmetic and consumer products business produces and markets dermatologic, cosmetic, and consumer products. The biotechnology business develops and markets various applications of IGI's lipid encapsulation technology, primarily for human medicines and vaccines. Founded in 1977. **Corporate headquarters location:** This location.

McNEIL CONSUMER HEALTH CARE
JOHNSON & JOHNSON MERCK CONSUMER PHARMACEUTICALS CO.

7050 Camp Hill Road, Fort Washington PA 19034-2292. 215/273-7000. **Contact:** Human Resources. **World Wide Web address:** http://www.tylenol.com. **Description:** Manufactures and markets a wide range of consumer pharmaceutical products, including Tylenol. Johnson & Johnson Merck Consumer Pharmaceuticals Company (also at this location) develops and markets a variety of over-the-counter items. **NOTE:** All hiring is done through the corporate office. Interested jobseekers should direct resumes to Johnson & Johnson Headquarters, Shared Services Recruiting, Johnson Hall JH-215, New Brunswick NJ 08901. **Common positions include:** Accountant/Auditor; Buyer; Chemical Engineer; Chemist; Claim Representative; Computer Programmer; Credit Manager; Customer Service Representative; Human Resources Manager; Industrial Engineer; Manufacturer's/Wholesaler's Sales Rep.; Marketing Specialist; Mechanical Engineer; Operations/Production Manager; Purchasing Agent/Manager; Quality Control Supervisor; Statistician; Systems Analyst; Transportation/Traffic Specialist. **Parent company:** Johnson & Johnson (New Brunswick NJ).

MERCK & COMPANY, INC.

P.O. Box 4, West Point PA 19486. 215/652-5000. **Physical address:** 770 Sumneytown Pike, West Point PA 19486. **Contact:** Human Resources. **World Wide Web address:**

http://www.merck.com. **Description:** This location researches and manufactures prescription drugs, and performs administrative and human resources functions. Overall, Merck & Company is a worldwide organization engaged primarily in the business of discovering, developing, producing, and marketing products for the maintenance of health and the environment. Products include human and animal pharmaceuticals and chemicals sold to the health care, oil exploration, food processing, textile, and paper industries. Merck also runs an ethical drug, mail-order marketing business. **Corporate headquarters location:** Whitehouse Station NJ.

ORASURE TECHNOLOGIES, INC.
150 Webster Street, Bethlehem PA 18015. 610/882-1820. **Fax:** 610/882-1830. **Contact:** Wade Smedley, Human Resources Director. **World Wide Web address:** http://www.orasure.com. **Description:** Produces biomedical diagnostic products. **Corporate headquarters location:** Beaverton OR.

ORTHO-McNEIL PHARMACEUTICAL
Welsh Road at McKean Road, Spring House PA 19477-0776. 215/628-5000. **Contact:** Employment Manager. **World Wide Web address:** http://www.ortho-mcneil.com. **Description:** Develops and sells pharmaceutical products including women's health, infectious disease, and wound healing products. **NOTE:** Jobs are posted on the Johnson & Johnson corporate Website: http://www.jnj.com. **Common positions include:** Accountant/Auditor; Chemical Engineer; Computer Programmer; Electrical/Electronics Engineer; Financial Analyst; Human Resources Manager; Industrial Engineer; Manufacturer's/Wholesaler's Sales Rep.; Mechanical Engineer; Statistician; Technical Writer/Editor. **Corporate headquarters location:** This location. **Parent company:** Johnson & Johnson (New Brunswick NJ). **Operations at this facility include:** Administration; Manufacturing; Research and Development.

PFIZER
400 West Lincoln Avenue, Lititz PA 17543. 717/626-2011. **Fax:** 717/627-9548. **Contact:** Human Resources. **World Wide Web address:** http://www.pfizer.com. **Description:** This location is a manufacturing and distribution facility. Overall, Pfizer is a leading pharmaceutical company that distributes products concerning cardiovascular health, central nervous system disorders, infectious diseases, and women's health worldwide. The company's brand-name products include Benadryl, Ben Gay, Cortizone, Desitin, Halls, Listerine,

Sudafed, and Zantac 75. **Corporate headquarters location:** New York NY.

QUEST DIAGNOSTICS INCORPORATED
400 Egypt Road, Norristown PA 19403. 610/631-4200. **Contact:** Human Resources Department. **World Wide Web address:** http://www.questdiagnostics.com. **Description:** One of the largest clinical laboratories in North America, providing a broad range of clinical laboratory services to health care clients that include physicians, hospitals, clinics, dialysis centers, pharmaceutical companies, and corporations. The company offers and performs tests on blood, urine, and other bodily fluids and tissues to provide information for health and well-being. **Other U.S. locations:** Nationwide.

REPRODUCTIVE SCIENCE INSTITUTE
950 West Valley Road, Suite 2401, Wayne PA 19087. 610/964-9663. **Fax:** 610/964-0536. **Contact:** Personnel. **World Wide Web address:** http://www.ihr.com/rsi. **Description:** A medical laboratory specializing in hormonal studies and endocrinology research.

VWR SCIENTIFIC PRODUCTS
1310 Goshen Parkway, West Chester PA 19380. 610/431-1700. **Fax:** 610/436-1763. **Contact:** Human Resources. **E-mail address:** hrwc@vwr.com. **World Wide Web address:** http://www.vwrsp.com. **Description:** Provides laboratory equipment, chemicals, and supplies to the scientific marketplace worldwide. VWR Scientific is organized into five operating units that are aligned to serve specific market niche opportunities both in North America and overseas. VWR Scientific, the company's main domestic operating unit, is a full-line distributor of scientific supplies, laboratory chemicals and apparatus, and research equipment. VWR Scientific Products serves customers in a wide variety of markets including pharmaceuticals, biotechnology, chemicals, environmental testing, food, electronics, and education. VWR Canada provides the Canadian marketplace with a single coast-to-coast supplier. VWR International exports scientific equipment and supplies to more than 54 countries worldwide. Bender & Hobein is a joint venture with E. Merck of Germany and is one of the largest scientific distributors in the German marketplace. Sargent-Welch Scientific sells scientific instruments to the education market for the teaching of science in public and private schools throughout the United States. **Corporate headquarters location:** This location. **Number of employees nationwide:** 1,635.

WEST PHARMACEUTICAL SERVICES

101 Gordon Drive, P.O. 645, Lionville PA 19341-0645. 610/594-2900. **Fax:** 610/594-3011. **Contact:** Human Resources Department. **World Wide Web address:** http://www.westpharma.com. **Description:** Researches and develops drug molecule delivery systems; designs and manufactures packaging components, systems, and devices that deliver and differentiate drugs and health care products; provides contract laboratory services; and performs commercialization processes for the manufacturing, filling, and packaging of drug and health care products. Founded in 1923. **Common positions include:** Account Manager; Account Representative; Administrative Assistant; Auditor; Chemist; Computer Operator; Customer Service Representative; Financial Analyst; Market Research Analyst; Mechanical Engineer; Network/Systems Administrator; Purchasing Agent/Manager. **Corporate headquarters location:** This location. **International locations:** Worldwide. **Listed on:** New York Stock Exchange. **Stock exchange symbol:** WST. **Annual sales/revenues:** More than $100 million. **Number of employees at this location:** 300. **Number of employees nationwide:** 2,500. **Number of employees worldwide:** 5,000.

WISTAR INSTITUTE OF ANATOMY AND BIOLOGY

3601 Spruce Street, Philadelphia PA 19104. 215/898-3700. **Fax:** 215/898-2204. **Contact:** Jo-Ann Mendel, Human Resources Director. **World Wide Web address:** http://www.wistar.upenn.edu. **Description:** A nonprofit, biomedical research facility. As a federally designated Basic Cancer Research Center, the institute emphasizes cancer studies in addition to searching for ways to prevent and cure other devastating diseases. Wistar Institute develops model systems and tools for biomedical research, such as cell lines, monoclonal antibodies, viral vectors, and other products of genetic engineering. General areas of research include molecular genetics, molecular virology, cell and developmental biology, cell and molecular immunology, and structural biology. **Common positions include:** Research Technician.

WYETH-AYERST PHARMACEUTICALS

611 East Nield Street, West Chester PA 19382. 610/696-3100. **Contact:** Personnel Director. **World Wide Web address:** http://www.ahp.com/ahp/wyeth.htm. **Description:** Produces a wide range of pharmaceutical products and proprietary medicines. **NOTE:** Entry-level positions are offered. **Common positions include:** Accountant; Administrative Assistant;

Biochemist; Chemist; Controller; Draftsperson; Electrician; Environmental Engineer; Human Resources Manager; Licensed Practical Nurse; Mechanical Engineer; Network Engineer; Network/Systems Administrator; Operations Manager; Production Manager; Project Manager; Purchasing Agent/Manager; Quality Assurance Engineer; Systems Analyst. **Special programs:** Summer Jobs. **Corporate headquarters location:** Radnor PA.

WYETH-AYERST PHARMACEUTICALS
31 Morehell Road, Frazer PA 19355. 610/902-4100. **Contact:** Human Resources Department. **World Wide Web address:** http://www.ahp.com/ahp/wyeth.htm. **Description:** This location houses administrative offices as well as all other divisions of Wyeth-Ayerst including Wyeth-Ayerst Laboratories; Wyeth-Ayerst International; Wyeth-Ayerst Pharmaceuticals; and Wyeth-Ayerst Research. Overall, the company produces a wide range of pharmaceutical products and proprietary medicines. **Parent company:** American Home Products.

BUSINESS SERVICES AND NON-SCIENTIFIC RESEARCH

You can expect to find the following types of companies in this chapter:

Adjustment and Collection Services • Cleaning, Maintenance, and Pest Control Services • Credit Reporting • Detective, Guard, and Armored Car Services • Miscellaneous Equipment Rental and Leasing • Secretarial and Court Reporting Services

ALLIED SECURITY INC.

3606 Horizon Drive, King of Prussia PA 19406. 610/239-1100. **Toll-free phone:** 800/334-2038. **Fax:** 610/239-1109. **Contact:** Human Resources Department. **World Wide Web address:** http://www.alliedsecurity.com. **Description:** One of the largest national contract security officer companies in the United States. Allied Security provides loss prevention services to private businesses and government agencies. **Common positions include:** Branch Manager; Client Services Representative; Computer Programmer; Customer Service Representative; Human Service Worker; Investigator; Management Trainee; Sales Representative. **Special programs:** Internships. **Office hours:** Monday - Friday, 8:00 a.m. - 5:00 p.m. **Corporate headquarters location:** This location. **Subsidiaries include:** Allsafe Security Inc. **Operations at this facility include:** Administration; Sales; Service. **Listed on:** Privately held. **Annual sales/revenues:** More than $100 million. **Number of employees at this location:** 45. **Number of employees nationwide:** 8,000.

ARAMARK CORPORATION
ARAMARK LEISURE SERVICES GROUP

ARAMARK Tower, 1101 Market Street, Philadelphia PA 19107. 215/238-3000. **Contact:** Personnel. **World Wide Web address:** http://www.aramark.com. **Description:** One of the world's leading providers of managed services. The company operates in all 50 states and 10 foreign countries, offering a broad range of services to businesses of all sizes including most *Fortune* 500 companies and thousands of universities; hospitals; and municipal, state, and federal government facilities. ARAMARK Corporation is employee-owned. The company is among the market leaders in all of its businesses, which are: Food, Leisure and Support Services, including Campus Dining Services, School Nutrition Services, Leisure Services, Business Dining Services, International Services,

Healthcare Support Services, Conference Center Management, and Refreshment Services; Facility Services; Correctional Services; Industrial Services; Uniform Services, which includes Wearguard, a direct marketer of work clothing; Health and Education Services, including Spectrum Healthcare Services and Children's World Learning Centers; and Book and Magazine Services. **Listed on:** New York Stock Exchange. **Stock exchange symbol:** RMK. **Corporate headquarters location:** This location. **Annual sales/revenues:** More than $100 million. **Number of employees nationwide:** 150,000.

ARAMARK FACILITY SERVICES
ARAMARK Tower, 1101 Market Street, Philadelphia PA 19107. 215/238-2000. **Contact:** Human Resources. **World Wide Web address:** http://www.aramark.com. **Description:** Provides housekeeping and maintenance services. **Corporate headquarters location:** This location. **Parent company:** ARAMARK Corporation is one of the world's leading providers of managed services. The company operates in all 50 states and 10 foreign countries, offering a broad range of services to businesses of all sizes, including most *Fortune* 500 companies and thousands of universities; hospitals; and municipal, state, and federal government facilities. ARAMARK is employee-owned. The company is among the market leaders in all of its businesses, which are: Food, Leisure and Support Services, including Campus Dining Services, School Nutrition Services, Leisure Services, Business Dining Services, International Services, Healthcare Support Services, Conference Center Management, and Refreshment Services; Facility Services; Correctional Services; Industrial Services; Uniform Services, which includes Wearguard, a direct marketer of work clothing; Health and Education Services including Spectrum Healthcare Services and Children's World Learning Centers; and Book and Magazine Services. **Listed on:** New York Stock Exchange. **Stock exchange symbol:** RMK. **Annual sales/revenues:** More than $100 million. **Number of employees nationwide:** 150,000.

ASSOCIATED CREDIT BUREAU SERVICES INC.
5910 Hamilton Boulevard, Allentown PA 18106. 610/398-7300. **Contact:** Human Resources. **World Wide Web address:** http://www.acbsi.com. **Description:** A full-service business information company providing consumer credit information and employment reports to a variety of businesses, state and local governments, retailers, and schools. Founded in 1916. **Corporate headquarters location:** This location.

AUTOMATIC DATA PROCESSING (ADP)

1125 Virginia Drive, Fort Washington PA 19034. 215/283-4113. **Contact:** Human Resources. **World Wide Web address:** http://www.adp.com. **Description:** Provides computerized transaction processing, record keeping, data communications, and information services. ADP helps more than 300,000 clients improve their business performance by providing services such as payroll, payroll tax, and human resource information management; brokerage industry market data, back office, and proxy services; industry-specific services to auto and truck dealers; and computerized auto repair and replacement estimating for auto insurance companies and body repair shops. Employer Services, Brokerage Services, Dealer Services, and Claims Services are the company's four largest businesses. **Corporate headquarters location:** Roseland NJ. **Listed on:** New York Stock Exchange. **Stock exchange symbol:** ADP. **Number of employees at this location:** 250.

BOEKEL SCIENTIFIC

855 Pennsylvania Boulevard, Feasterville PA 19053. 215/396-8200. **Toll-free phone:** 800/336-6929. **Contact:** Human Resources Department. **World Wide Web address:** http://www.boekelsci.com. **Description:** Provides abstracting and indexing services for biological and medical research. The company also provides access to life sciences literature worldwide, offering more than 90 products and services including several online databases.

DAY & ZIMMERMANN, INC.

1818 Market Street, Philadelphia PA 19103. 215/299-8000. **Contact:** Human Resources. **World Wide Web address:** http://www.dayzim.com. **Description:** Provides a wide range of professional services including engineering design, construction, and procurement; clean room design and validation; construction management; technical services; automation and data processing consulting; mass real estate appraisal; security guard services; munitions manufacturing services; naval ship alterations; and logistical support. **Common positions include:** Accountant/Auditor; Attorney; Biomedical Engineer; Chemical Engineer; Computer Programmer; Designer; Draftsperson; Electrical/Electronics Engineer; Employment Interviewer; Financial Manager; Human Resources Manager; Industrial Engineer; Mechanical Engineer; Payroll Clerk; Sales Executive; Secretary; Systems Analyst. **Corporate headquarters location:** This location. **Operations at this facility include:** Administration; Sales; Service. **Number of**

employees at this location: 200. **Number of employees nationwide:** 12,000.

FAULKNER INFORMATION SERVICES
114 Cooper Center, 7905 Browning Road, Pennsauken NJ 08109-4319. 856/662-2070. **Toll-free phone:** 800/843-0460. **Fax:** 856/662-3380. **Contact:** Betsey Wilson, Operations/Human Resources Administrator. **E-mail address:** faulkner@faulkner.com. **World Wide Web address:** http://www.faulkner.com. **Description:** An independent publishing and research company specializing in providing technical information to end users and communication and IT professionals. Faulkner Information Services publishes more than a dozen standard information services in both print and electronic formats. The company provides comprehensive intelligence on products, vendors, technological advancements, and management issues associated with a wide range of technologies from open systems and client/server to enterprise networking, workgroup computing, and telecommunications. Faulkner also offers custom research and publication capabilities in such areas as market studies, customer satisfaction surveys, competitive analysis reports, and custom databases. **Common positions include:** Accountant/Auditor; Customer Service Representative; Human Resources Manager; Systems Analyst; Technical Writer/Editor. **Corporate headquarters location:** This location. **Operations at this facility include:** Administration; Research and Development; Sales; Service. **Number of employees at this location:** 45.

HEALTHCARE SERVICES GROUP
3220 Tillman Drive, Suite 300, Bensalem PA 19020. 215/639-8191. **Toll-free phone:** 800/363-4274. **Contact:** Human Resources. **E-mail address:** jobs@hcsgcorp.com. **World Wide Web address:** http://www.hcsgcorp.com. **Description:** Provides cleaning and laundering services for nursing homes and hospitals. **Other area locations:** Doylestown PA. **Corporate headquarters location:** This location.

HOSPITAL CENTRAL SERVICES INC.
2171 28th Street SW, Allentown PA 18103. 610/791-2222. **Fax:** 610/791-2919. **Contact:** Human Resources Department. **E-mail address:** hr@hcsc.org. **World Wide Web address:** http://www.hcsc.org. **Description:** Provides management services for hospitals including laundry services, physician billing, and the operation of blood centers.

MACINTOSH LINEN AND UNIFORM RENTAL

1202 West Allen Street, Allentown PA 18102. 610/437-5435. **Contact:** Human Resources. **Description:** Rents linen and uniforms to a variety of industries including restaurants, hospitals, and nursing homes.

NCO GROUP, INC.

50 Prudential Road, Horsham PA 19044. 215/441-3000. **Contact:** Human Resources. **World Wide Web address:** http://www.ncogroup.com. **Description:** Provides accounts-receivable and delinquency management, collection services, billing, market research, and telemarketing services to a variety of businesses. Founded in 1926. **Corporate headquarters location:** This location. **Listed on:** NASDAQ. **Stock exchange symbol:** NCOG.

PAYCHEX, INC.

7450 Tilghman Street, Suite 107, Allentown PA 18106. 610/398-7518. **Contact:** Human Resources. **World Wide Web address:** http://www.paychex.com. **Description:** A payroll processing and payroll tax preparation company for small to medium-sized businesses. **Corporate headquarters location:** Rochester NY. **Other U.S. locations:** Nationwide. **Number of employees nationwide:** 3,300.

CHARITIES AND SOCIAL SERVICES

You can expect to find the following types of organizations in this chapter:

Social and Human Service Agencies • Job Training and Vocational Rehabilitation Services • Nonprofit Organizations

ARTHRITIS FOUNDATION
219 North Broad Street, 2nd Floor, Philadelphia PA 19107. 215/564-9800. **Contact:** Branch Director. **World Wide Web address:** http://www.arthritis.org. **Description:** This location is a branch office of the Eastern Pennsylvania chapter of the Arthritis Foundation. The Arthritis Foundation is a nonprofit organization that is engaged in research to find a cure for arthritis and to educate those who have the disease. Founded in 1948. **NOTE:** The foundation encourages applicants for volunteer positions. **Common positions include:** Administrative Assistant; Executive Director. **Office hours:** Monday - Friday, 8:30 a.m. - 4:30 p.m. **Corporate headquarters location:** Atlanta GA. **Number of employees nationwide:** 650.

BIG BROTHERS/BIG SISTERS OF AMERICA
230 North 13th Street, Philadelphia PA 19107. 215/567-7000. **Fax:** 215/567-0394. **Contact:** Human Resources. **E-mail address:** nationalcareers@bbbsa.org. **World Wide Web address:** http://www.bbbsa.org. **Description:** The National Office of Big Brothers/Big Sisters of America. Provides volunteer and professional services to assist children and youth in achieving their highest potential as they grow. There are over 505 Big Brothers/Big Sisters agencies nationwide where more than 75,000 children are matched with adult volunteers. The agency also provides counseling, referral, and family support services to parents and children in more 110,000 families each year. Additional programs focus on children with special needs including physical or learning disabilities, as well as those who are abused, neglected, or have dropped out of school. Special prevention and intervention programs at many agencies address the problems of drug abuse, teen pregnancy, foster care, and juvenile delinquency. Founded in 1904. **Other U.S. locations:** Nationwide.

HOPE ENTERPRISES INC.
136 Catawissa Avenue, P.O. Box 1837, Williamsport PA 17703-1837. 570/326-3745. **Fax:** 570/326-1258. **Contact:** Human Resources Department. **World Wide Web address:**

http://www.heionline.org. **Description:** Offers workshop training for individuals with mental disabilities. Hope Enterprises also operates over 20 group homes, a preschool, and an adult training facility that teaches domestic skills and personal hygiene.

KEYSTONE AREA COUNCIL OF THE BOY SCOUTS OF AMERICA

P.O. Box 389, One Baden-Powell Lane, Mechanicsburg PA 17055. 717/766-1591. **Fax:** 717/795-8721. **Contact:** Human Resources Department. **World Wide Web address:** http://www.keystonebsa.org. **Description:** The national scouting organization for young adults. The Boy Scouts of America has 340 local councils nationwide. **Corporate headquarters location:** Irving TX.

SOUTHERN HOME SERVICES

3149 Germantown Avenue, Philadelphia PA 19133. 215/221-1700. **Contact:** Personnel. **Description:** Operates a child and family treatment center. Southern Home Services provides children's services including after-school programs, foster care, and residential care. **NOTE:** Entry-level positions and second and third shifts are offered. **Common positions include:** Clerical Supervisor; Controller; Mental Health Worker; Psychologist; Secretary; Social Worker; Typist/Word Processor. **Listed on:** Privately held. **Annual sales/revenues:** $5 - $10 million. **Number of employees at this location:** 160.

SUNCOM INDUSTRIES INC.

P.O. Box 46, Northumberland PA 17857. 570/473-8352. **Physical address:** 128 Water Street, Northumberland PA 17857. **Fax:** 570/473-0159. **Contact:** Peggy Vitale, Chief Executive Officer. **World Wide Web address:** http://www.suncom.org. **Description:** Operates a workshop for people with physical and mental disabilities. **Facilities Manager:** Roger Dietz.

YOUTH ADVOCATE PROGRAM

127 West Market Street, Suite 200, York PA 17401. 717/845-8731. **Contact:** Human Resources. **World Wide Web address:** http://www.yapinc.com. **Description:** Dedicated to promoting the rights and well-being of youths on a worldwide basis. The organization pays particular attention to needy youths.

CHEMICALS/RUBBER AND PLASTICS

You can expect to find the following types of companies in this chapter:

*Adhesives, Detergents, Inks, Paints, Soaps, Varnishes •
Agricultural Chemicals and Fertilizers • Carbon and Graphite
Products •* Chemical Engineering Firms• Industrial Gases

AIR PRODUCTS AND CHEMICALS, INC.
7201 Hamilton Boulevard, Allentown PA 18195. 610/481-4911. **Contact:** Human Resources. **World Wide Web address:** http://www.airproducts.com. **Description:** Manufactures industrial gases, process equipment, and chemicals. The company's products include cryogenic equipment, air separation systems, hydrogen purification devices, and nitrogen rejection equipment. In addition, the company provides engineering services, and is involved in landfill gas recovery, waste management, waste-to-energy ventures, flue gas desulfurization, and cogeneration operations. **Common positions include:** Chemical Engineer; Financial Analyst; Mechanical Engineer. **Special programs:** Internships. **Corporate headquarters location:** This location. **Other U.S. locations:** Nationwide. **International locations:** Worldwide. **Listed on:** New York Stock Exchange. **Stock exchange symbol:** APD. **Annual sales/revenues:** More than $100 million.

AIRGAS, INC.
259 North Radnor-Chester Road, Suite 100, Radnor PA 19087. 610/687-5253. **Fax:** 610/687-5611. **Contact:** Personnel. **E-mail address:** employment@airgas.com. **World Wide Web address:** http://www.airgas.com. **Description:** Airgas, Inc. distributes industrial, medical, and specialty gases; protective equipment; and welding accessories. **Listed on:** New York Stock Exchange. **Stock exchange symbol:** ARG. **Number of employees nationwide:** 2,800.

ALCOA FLEXIBLE PACKAGING
441 County Line Road, Gilbertsville PA 19525. 610/367-2991. **Contact:** Human Resources. **Description:** This location manufactures polyethylene. Overall, ALCOA is engaged in all aspects of the aluminum industry including mining, refining, smelting, fabricating, and recycling. ALCOA also manufactures ceramic packaging for the semiconductor industry, alumina chemicals, plastic bottle closures, vinyl siding, packaging machinery, and electrical distribution systems for automobiles. **Corporate headquarters location:** This location. **Other U.S.**

locations: Nationwide. **International locations:** Worldwide. **Listed on:** New York Stock Exchange. **Stock exchange symbol:** AA. **Annual sales/revenues:** More than $100 million. **Number of employees worldwide:** 86,200.

ASHLAND CHEMICAL COMPANY
400 Island Park Road, Easton PA 18042-6899. 610/258-9135. **Contact:** Human Resources. **World Wide Web address:** http://www.ashland.com. **Description:** Manufactures, markets, and distributes a wide variety of chemical products through facilities worldwide. **Corporate headquarters location:** Dublin OH. **Parent company:** Ashland Oil, Inc. **Listed on:** New York Stock Exchange. **Stock exchange symbol:** ASH.

ATOFINA CHEMICALS, INC.
2000 Market Street, Philadelphia PA 19103-3222. 215/419-7000. **Contact:** Human Resources Department. **World Wide Web address:** http://www.atofinachemicals.com. **Description:** A chemical manufacturer with products that include polymers, fluorochemicals, carbons, and specialty chemicals. The company also produces petroleum products. **Corporate headquarters location:** This location. **Other U.S. locations:** Nationwide. **International locations:** Worldwide. **Parent company:** Elf Atochem S.A. **Listed on:** New York Stock Exchange. **Stock exchange symbol:** TOT. **Annual sales/revenues:** More than $100 million. **Number of employees worldwide:** 6,000.

M.A. BRUDER & SONS INC.
600 Reed Road, Broomall PA 19008. 610/353-5100. **Toll-free phone:** 800/MAB-1899. **Fax:** 610/325-2718. **Contact:** Randy McCullough, Director of Human Resources. **World Wide Web address:** http://www.mabpaints.com. **Description:** A national manufacturer and marketer of paint, operating over 250 retail and wholesale locations. Founded in 1899. **Corporate headquarters location:** This location.

CONSOLIDATED CONTAINER COMPANY
6831 Ruppsville Road, Allentown PA 18106. 610/481-0655. **Fax:** 610/481-0658. **Contact:** Human Resources. **Description:** A manufacturer of blow-molded custom and stock plastic containers.

E.I. DUPONT DE NEMOURS & COMPANY
Route 130, Deepwater NJ 08023. 856/299-5000. **Contact:** Human Resources. **World Wide Web address:** http://www.dupont.com. **Description:** This location is a

chemical manufacturing plant. Overall, E.I. DuPont de Nemours & Company's activities include the manufacturing of biomedical, industrial, and consumer products (such as photographic, data-recording, and video devices); the production of manmade fiber products (with applications in a variety of consumer and commercial industries), polymer products (such as plastic resins, elastomers, and films), and agricultural and industrial chemicals (such as herbicides and insecticides, pigments, fluorochemicals, petroleum additives, and mineral acids); the exploration and production of crude oil and natural gas; the refining, marketing, and downstream transportation of petroleum; and the mining and distribution of steam and metallurgical coals. Industries served include aerospace, agriculture, apparel, transportation, health care, and printing and publishing. **Corporate headquarters location:** Wilmington DE. **Listed on:** New York Stock Exchange. **Stock exchange symbol:** DD. **Chairman/CEO:** Charles O. Holliday, Jr. **Annual sales/revenues:** More than $100 million. **Number of employees worldwide:** 94,000.

DYNASIL CORPORATION OF AMERICA
385 Cooper Road, West Berlin NJ 08091-9145. 856/767-4600. **Fax:** 856/767-6813. **Contact:** John Kane, President. **World Wide Web address:** http://www.dynasil.com. **Description:** Manufactures synthetic fused silica and fused quartz products. Founded in 1960. **Corporate headquarters location:** This location. **Annual sales/revenues:** $5 - $10 million. **Number of employees at this location:** 35. **Number of employees nationwide:** 40.

FMC CORPORATION
Mellon Bank Building, 1735 Market Street, Philadelphia PA 19103. 215/299-6000. **Fax:** 215/299-6618. **Contact:** Human Resources. **World Wide Web address:** http://www.fmc.com. **Description:** A diversified manufacturer of specialty, industrial, and agricultural chemicals; defense-related systems; and industrial machinery. The company is also engaged in the processing of gold, silver, and petroleum. **NOTE:** Part-time jobs are offered. **Common positions include:** Account Manager; Account Representative; Accountant; Administrative Assistant; Computer Programmer; Customer Service Representative; Electrical/Electronics Engineer; Human Resources Manager; Industrial Engineer; Intellectual Property Lawyer; Marketing Manager; Mechanical Engineer; Network/Systems Administrator; Operations Manager; Paralegal; Production Manager; Project Manager; Sales Manager; Sales Representative; Secretary; Systems Analyst;

Systems Manager; Transportation/Traffic Specialist. **Special programs:** Co-ops. **Office hours:** Monday - Friday, 8:30 a.m. - 5:00 p.m. **Corporate headquarters location:** Chicago IL. **International locations:** Worldwide. **Operations at this facility include:** Administration; Divisional Headquarters; Financial Offices; Legal/Legal Research; Regional Headquarters; Sales. **Listed on:** New York Stock Exchange. **Stock exchange symbol:** FMC. **Annual sales/revenues:** More than $100 million. **Number of employees at this location:** 500. **Number of employees worldwide:** 20,000.

FOAMEX INTERNATIONAL, INC.

1000 Columbia Avenue, Linwood PA 19061-3997. 610/859-3000. **Contact:** Human Resources. **World Wide Web address:** http://www.foamex.com. **Description:** One of the nation's largest manufacturers of flexible polyurethane foam products. Foamex products are classified into four groups: Cushion Foams are used for mattresses, quilting and borders, home and office furniture, computer and electronics packaging, and padding foams for health care; Carpet Cushions include prime, bonded, sponge rubber, felt carpet cushion, synthetic grass turf, and a variety of textured carpeting and wall coverings; Automotive Foams include foams for cushioning and seating, acoustical foams, headliner foams, trim foams, and foams for door panel parts; Technical Foams include those for filtration, reservoiring, sound absorption and transmission, carburetors, high-speed inkjet printers, speaker grilles, oxygenators, and EKG pads, as well as cosmetic applicators, mop heads, paint brushes, and diapers. **Corporate headquarters location:** This location. **Other U.S. locations:** Nationwide. **Listed on:** NASDAQ. **Stock exchange symbol:** FMXI. **Annual sales/revenues:** More than $100 million. **Number of employees worldwide:** 3,600.

GE BETZ

4636 Somerton Road, Trevose PA 19053. 215/953-2472. **Fax:** 215/953-5552. **Contact:** Michael Cuff, Employment Specialist. **E-mail address:** michael.e.cuff@gebetz.com. **World Wide Web address:** http://www.gebetz.com. **Description:** Manufactures and markets a variety of specialty chemical products used in the chemical treatment of water, wastewater, and process systems. GE Betz operates in a variety of industrial and commercial applications, with particular emphasis on the chemical, petroleum refining, paper, automotive, electrical utility, and steel industries. The company's chemical treatment programs are used in boilers, cooling towers, heat exchangers, paper and petroleum process streams, and both influent and effluent systems. **Common positions include:** Chemical Engineer; Chemist; Electrical/Electronics Engineer; Human Resources Manager; Research Scientist. **Corporate headquarters location:** This location. **Parent company:** General Electric Company. **Number of employees worldwide:** 3,000.

GFC FOAM INC.
Valmont Industrial Park, 25 Jaycee Drive, West Hazleton PA 18201. 570/455-4931. **Contact:** Personnel. **Description:** Manufactures polyurethane products. **Corporate headquarters location:** Paramus NJ. **Operations at this facility include:** Manufacturing; Research and Development.

GOODALL RUBBER COMPANY
790 Birney Highway, Aston PA 19014. 610/361-0800. **Contact:** Personnel. **Description:** Manufactures, distributes, and sells rubber through 45 U.S. and Canadian sales and service centers. Products include hoses, belting products, lined pipes, and fittings. **Corporate headquarters location:** This location.

ICI PAINTS
301 Bern Street, Reading PA 19601. 610/373-4111. **Contact:** Gary Noll, Human Resources Manager. **World Wide Web address:** http://www.icidecorativepaints.com. **Description:** Manufactures and distributes a complete range of paints, varnishes, lacquers, rust inhibitors, and other protective coatings. **Common positions include:** Accountant/Auditor; Administrator; Blue-Collar Worker Supervisor; Branch Manager; Buyer; Chemical Engineer; Chemist; Civil Engineer; Claim Representative; Credit Manager; Customer Service Representative; Financial Analyst; General Manager; Human Resources Manager; Industrial Engineer; Management Trainee; Manufacturer's/Wholesaler's Sales Rep.; Marketing Specialist; Mechanical Engineer; Operations/Production Manager; Purchasing Agent/Manager; Quality Control Supervisor; Transportation/Traffic Specialist. **International locations:** Worldwide.

INOLEX CHEMICAL COMPANY
Jackson & Swanson Streets, Philadelphia PA 19148-3497. **Toll-free phone:** 800/246-6539. **Fax:** 215/271-2621. **Contact:** Human Resources. **World Wide Web address:** http://www.inolex.com. **Description:** Manufactures specialty chemicals for the cosmetics, lubricants, and polyurethane industries. **Common positions include:** Accountant/Auditor;

Administrative Manager; Budget Analyst; Chemical Engineer; Chemist; Clerical Supervisor; Computer Programmer; Credit Manager; Customer Service Representative; Financial Analyst; Human Resources Manager; Operations/Production Manager; Quality Control Supervisor; Services Sales Representative; Systems Analyst. **Corporate headquarters location:** This location. **Operations at this facility include:** Administration; Manufacturing; Research and Development; Sales; Service. **Listed on:** Privately held.

LYONDELL CHEMICAL
3801 West Chester Pike, Newtown Square PA 19073. 610/359-2000. **Contact:** Human Resources. **World Wide Web address:** http://www.lyondell.com. **Description:** A chemical manufacturer and marketer specializing in plastics, foams, fuel additives, and other intermediate chemicals. **Common positions include:** Chemical Engineer; Chemist; Electrical/Electronics Engineer; Metallurgical Engineer. **Corporate headquarters:** Houston TX. **Listed on:** New York Stock Exchange. **Stock exchange symbol:** LYO.

OCCIDENTAL CHEMICAL CORPORATION
375 Arm and Hammer Boulevard, P.O. Box 699, Pottstown PA 19464. 610/327-6400. **Contact:** Human Resources. **World Wide Web address:** http://www.oxychem.com. **Description:** Manufactures a wide range of PVC resins, compounds, and fabricated products. **Corporate headquarters location:** Dallas TX. **Parent company:** Occidental Petroleum Corporation is a natural resources company engaged in the exploration for and the development of oil and natural gas in the United States.

PPG INDUSTRIES, INC.
400 Park Drive, Carlisle PA 17013. 717/486-3366. **Contact:** Human Resources. **World Wide Web address:** http://www.ppg.com. **Description:** This location manufactures flat glass. Overall, PPG Industries is a diversified global manufacturer supplying products for manufacturing, building, automotive, processing, and numerous other world industries. The company makes decorative and protective coatings, flat glass and fabricated glass products, continuous-strand fiberglass, and industrial and specialty chemicals. Founded in 1883. **Corporate headquarters location:** Pittsburgh PA. **International locations:** Worldwide. **Listed on:** New York Stock Exchange. **Stock exchange symbol:** PPG. **Annual sales/revenues:** More than $100 million.

POLYONE CORPORATION

P.O. Box 400, Pedricktown NJ 08067. 856/299-8659. **Physical address:** Route 130 & Porcupine Road, Pedricktown NJ 08067. **Contact:** Human Resources Department. **World Wide Web address:** http://www.polyone.com. **Description:** Manufactures and develops thermoplastic compounds, specialty resins, engineered films, color and additive systems, specialty polymers, rubber compounding, and vinyl compounds. **Corporate headquarters location:** Cleveland OH. **Other U.S. locations:** Nationwide. **International locations:** Worldwide. **Listed on:** New York Stock Exchange. **Stock exchange symbol:** POL. **Annual sales/revenues:** More than $100 million.

QUADRANT

2120 Fairmount Avenue, P.O. Box 14235, Reading PA 19612-4235. 610/320-6600. **Fax:** 610/320-6817. **Contact:** Frank Luff, Human Resources Department. **World Wide Web address:** http://www.quadrantepp.com. **Description:** Manufactures and markets engineering plastics. Founded in 1946. **Common positions include:** Accountant/Auditor; Chemical Engineer; Computer Programmer; Customer Service Representative; Manufacturer's Sales Representative; Operations/Production Manager. **Corporate headquarters location:** This location. **International locations:** Worldwide.

QUAKER CHEMICAL CORPORATION

One Quaker Park, 901 Hector Street, Conshohocken PA 19428. 610/832-4000. **Fax:** 610/832-4282. **Contact:** James Geiere, Vice President of Human Resources Department. **World Wide Web address:** http://www.quakerchem.com. **Description:** Manufactures rolling lubricants for steel and nonferrous metals; corrosion preventives; machining, grinding, and drawing compounds; hydraulic fluids; metal finishing compounds; and other products. Quaker Chemical Corporation also provides chemical management services to industrial customers. **Common positions include:** Chemical Engineer; Chemist; Customer Service Representative; Industrial Engineer; Mechanical Engineer; Systems Analyst. **Corporate headquarters location:** This location. **Other U.S. locations:** Savannah GA; Detroit MI. **Listed on:** New York Stock Exchange. **Listed on:** KWR. **Annual sales/revenues:** More than $100 million. **Number of employees at this location:** 230. **Number of employees worldwide:** 925.

RHODIA INC.

2300 South Pennsylvania Avenue, Morrisville PA 19067. 215/295-9319. **Contact:** Human Resources. **E-mail address:**

Rhodia@rpc.webhire.com. **World Wide Web address:** http://www.us.rhodia.com. **Description:** Supplies specialty and intermediate chemicals for consumer and industrial applications. **Other U.S. locations:** Nationwide. **Parent company:** Rhone-Poulenc.

ROHM & HAAS COMPANY
P.O. Box 904, Spring House PA 19477-0904. 215/641-7000. **Physical address:** 727 Norristown Road, Spring House PA. **Contact:** Human Resources Department. **World Wide Web address:** http://www.rohmhaas.com. **Description:** This location is a research facility. Overall, Rohm & Haas is a specialty chemicals company operating in four industry segments: Polymers, Resins, and Monomers; Plastics; Industrial Chemicals; and Agricultural Chemicals. The company is also engaged in nonchemical industries such as forestry products, carpet production, and biomedical testing. **Corporate headquarters location:** Philadelphia PA. **Listed on:** New York Stock Exchange. **Stock exchange symbol:** ROH. **Annual sales/revenues:** More than $100 million.

ROHM & HAAS COMPANY
100 Independence Mall West, Philadelphia PA 19106-2399. 215/592-3000. **Contact:** Corporate Staffing. **World Wide Web address:** http://www.rohmhaas.com. **Description:** A specialty chemicals company that produces polymers, resins, and monomers; plastics; industrial chemicals; and agricultural chemicals. Rohm & Haas Company is also engaged in nonchemical industries such as forestry products, carpet production, and biomedical testing. **Corporate headquarters location:** This location. **Listed on:** New York Stock Exchange. **Stock exchange symbol:** ROH. **Annual sales/revenues:** More than $100 million.

ROHM & HAAS COMPANY
P.O. Box 584, Bristol PA 19007. 215/785-8000. **Physical address:** Route 413 and State Road, Bristol PA 19007. **Contact:** Human Resources Department. **World Wide Web address:** http://www.rohmhaas.com. **Description:** This location manufactures acrylic plastics used by the automotive industry to make taillights. Overall, Rohm & Haas is a specialty chemicals company operating in four business segments: Polymers, Resins, and Monomers; Plastics; Industrial Chemicals; and Agricultural Chemicals. Rohm & Haas is also engaged in nonchemical industries such as forestry products, carpet production, and biomedical testing. **Corporate headquarters location:** Philadelphia PA. **Listed on:** New York

Stock Exchange. **Stock exchange symbol:** ROH. **Annual sales/revenues:** More than $100 million.

SUN CHEMICAL/GENERAL PRINTING INC.
3301 Hunting Park Avenue, Philadelphia PA 19132. 215/223-8220. **Contact:** Mr. Louis A. Schiliro, Director of Human Resources Department. **World Wide Web address:** http://www.sunchemical.com. **Description:** Manufactures printing ink and graphic arts coatings.

SUNOCO CHEMICALS
Margaret & Bermuda Streets, Philadelphia PA 19137. 215/533-3000. **Contact:** Human Resources Department. **World Wide Web address:** http://www.sunocochem.com. **Description:** This location produces a variety of chemical products including synthetic phenol, acetone, alpha methyl styrene, and cumene hydroperoxide. **Common positions include:** Accountant/Auditor; Chemical Engineer; Chemist; Industrial Engineer. **Special programs:** Internships. **Corporate headquarters location:** Philadelphia PA. **Parent company:** Sunoco Inc. **Listed on:** New York Stock Exchange. **Stock exchange symbol:** SUN.

U.S. FILTER WALLACE & TIERNAN
1901 West Garden Road, Vineland NJ 08360. 856/507-9000. **Contact:** Human Resources Administrator. **World Wide Web address:** http://www.usfwt.com. **Description:** A manufacturer of chlorinates for water and wastewater treatment. **Corporate headquarters location:** This location.

WHEATON USA
1101 Wheaton Avenue, Millville NJ 08332. 856/825-1400. **Contact:** Human Resources Department. **World Wide Web address:** http://www.wheaton.com. **Description:** Manufactures glass and plastic tubes and containers used in the pharmaceutical and cosmetic industries. **Parent company:** Alcan Packaging.

COMMUNICATIONS: TELECOMMUNICATIONS AND BROADCASTING

You can expect to find the following types of companies in this chapter:

Cable/Pay Television Services • Communications Equipment • Radio and Television Broadcasting Systems • Telephone, Telegraph, and other Message Communications

AM COMMUNICATIONS
1900 AM Drive, Quakertown PA 18951-2107. 215/536-1354. **Fax:** 215/538-8779. **Contact:** Patricia Eynon, Human Resources. **E-mail address:** careers@amcomm.com. **World Wide Web address:** http://www.amcomm.com. **Description:** One of the world's leading suppliers of network status and performance monitoring systems for hybrid fiber/coaxial telecommunications networks. Products are sold directly to cable system operators and through original equipment manufacturers. Founded in 1974. **Corporate headquarters location:** This location.

AGERE SYSTEMS
2525 North 12th Street, Reading PA 19605. 610/939-7011. **Contact:** Mike Deloretta, Director of Human Resources. **World Wide Web address:** http://www.agere.com. **Description:** Manufactures communications products including switching, transmission, fiber-optic cable, wireless systems, and operations systems, to supply the needs of telephone companies and other communications service providers. **Listed on:** New York Stock Exchange. **Stock exchange symbol:** AGR.

CTI DATA SOLUTIONS INC.
2550 Eisenhower Avenue, Norristown PA 19403. 610/666-1700. **Fax:** 610/666-7707. **Contact:** Human Resources. **E-mail address:** hrdirector@ctigroup.com. **World Wide Web address:** http://www.ctigroup.com. **Description:** Through its subsidiaries, CTI Group Holdings designs, develops, and markets software and systems for the telecommunications industry. Founded in 1968. **Corporate headquarters location:** Indianapolis IN. **Parent company:** CTI Group.

CAPSULE COMMUNICATIONS
2 Greenwood Square, 3331 Street Road, Suite 275, Bensalem PA 19020-2052. 215/633-9400. **Contact:** Human Resources. **World Wide Web address:** http://www.capsulecom.com.

Description: A switch-based interexchange carrier providing long-distance telephone communications primarily to small and medium-sized businesses. The company also provides inbound 800 long-distance services, as well as other telecommunications services, such as calling cards, cellular, paging, dedicated access, data services, and debit cards. The company uses its own switching facilities to originate, transport, and terminate calls for customers generally located between Boston MA, Norfolk VA, and Pittsburgh PA. For calls originating or terminating outside the company's own network, the company uses services provided by other long-distance companies. **Parent company:** Covista. **Listed on:** NASDAQ. **Stock exchange symbol:** CVST.

COMCAST CORPORATION
1500 Market Street, Philadelphia PA 19102. 215/665-1700. **Contact:** Human Resources Department. **World Wide Web address:** http://www.comcast.com. **Description:** A cable television system operator that also distributes Muzak and provides cellular phone services. **Common positions include:** Accountant/Auditor; Administrator; Customer Service Representative; Financial Analyst; General Manager; Operations/Production Manager; Purchasing Agent/Manager. **Corporate headquarters location:** This location. **Listed on:** New York Stock Exchange. **Stock exchange symbol:** CCZ. **Annual sales/revenues:** More than $100 million. **Number of employees nationwide:** 17,000.

CONESTOGA ENTERPRISES, INC.
202 East First Street, Birdsboro PA 19508. 610/582-8711. **Fax:** 610/582-6469. **Contact:** Elton Butler, Human Resources. **E-mail address:** hrmail@ceni.com. **World Wide Web address:** http://www.ceni.com. **Description:** A holding company for several communications firms. **Corporate headquarters location:** This location. **Subsidiaries include:** Conestoga Telephone and Telegraph Company furnishes both regulated and nonregulated telecommunications services to an area in Pennsylvania that includes parts of Berks, Chester, Lancaster, and Montgomery Counties; Northern Communications, Inc. resells long-distance services; Conestoga Mobile Systems, Inc. provides paging communication services. **Listed on:** NASDAQ. **Stock exchange symbol:** CENI.

DENVER & EPHRATA TELEPHONE AND TELEGRAPH COMPANY (D&E)
124 East Main Street, P.O. Box 458, Ephrata PA 17522-0458. 717/738-8603. **Fax:** 717/859-4803. **Contact:** Recruiter. **E-mail**

address: hr@decommunications.com. **World Wide Web address:** http://www.decommunications.com. **Description:** Furnishes telephone service to an estimated population of 100,000 in parts of Berks, Lancaster, and Lebanon Counties in Pennsylvania. Two host switching centers are owned and operated in the boroughs of Ephrata and Lititz. The company also owns and operates 25 remote digital dial tone facilities throughout its service area. Local, national, and international telephone services are furnished through these facilities and interconnections with the facilities of other companies. The company also provides videoconferencing services and one-way tone, display, and wide-area paging services. **Subsidiaries include:** Red Rose Systems, Inc. sells, installs, and maintains telecommunications equipment, and provides long-distance telephone services; D&E Marketing Corporation provides residential and business telecommunications services in Hungary.

EMCEE BROADCAST PRODUCTS, INC.
P.O. Box 68, White Haven PA 18661-0068. 570/443-9575. **Toll-free phone:** 800/233-6193. **Fax:** 570/443-9257. **Contact:** Ms. Nelda Seibel, Human Resources Department. **World Wide Web address:** http://www.emceebrd.com. **Description:** Manufactures and sells Multichannel Multipoint Distribution Service (MMDS) microwave transmitters for the wireless cable industry and low-power television translators and transmitters for the television broadcast industry. The company also provides all services relative to the design, procurement, and installation of television broadcast stations, with the exception of licensing submissions. **Corporate headquarters location:** This location. **Subsidiaries include:** Pro-Community TV, Inc. (PA); EMCEE Cellular Inc. (DE); EMCEE Export Sales Company, Inc. (DE); and R.F. Systems, Inc. (DE). **Listed on:** NASDAQ. **Stock exchange symbol:** ECIN. **Number of employees at this location:** 90.

GREATER PHILADELPHIA RADIO GROUP
One Bala Plaza, Suite 424, Bala-Cynwyd PA 19004. 610/771-0933. **Fax:** 610/771-9610. **Contact:** Human Resources. **Description:** Operates four radio stations in the Philadelphia area: MAX 95.7; WMGK-FM; WMMR-FM; and WPEN-AM. **Parent company:** Greater Media Inc.

MOTOROLA, INC.
BROADBAND COMMUNICATIONS SECTOR
101 Tournament Drive, Horsham PA 19044. 215/323-1000. **Contact:** Human Resources. **World Wide Web address:**

http://www.motorola.com. **Description:** This location houses the administrative offices of the Broadband Communications Sector. Overall, Motorola provides applied research, development, manufacturing, and marketing of high-tech systems and components for industry and government in the fields of electronics, communications, automotive, controls, semiconductor, information systems, and office information. Motorola manufactures communications equipment and electronic products including car radios, cellular phones, semiconductors, computer systems, cellular infrastructure equipment, pagers, cordless phones, and LANs.

NBC 10-WCAU
10 Monument Road, Bala-Cynwyd PA 19004-1771. 610/668-5510. **Contact:** Human Resources Department. **World Wide Web address:** http://www.nbc10.com. **Description:** An NBC-affiliated television station. This location is also home to WOGL-FM Oldies 98 and WGMD-AM 'The Game.'

POPVISION CABLE COMPANY
2510 Metropolitan Drive, Trevose PA 19053. 215/396-9400. **Contact:** Human Resources. **World Wide Web address:** http://www.worldcom.com. **Description:** Operates a wireless cable system and markets a package of 30 channels of programming, consisting of 24 wireless cable channels, five local off-air VHF/UHF broadcast channels, and one special pay-per-view channel. Basic programs include CNN, ESPN, Lifetime, MTV, Nickelodeon, USA Network, and The Weather Channel. Premium programs include The Disney Channel, HBO, Pay-Per-View, and Showtime. **Parent company:** MCI Worldcom.

QVC NETWORK, INC.
1365 Enterprise Drive, West Chester PA 19380. 610/431-8463. **Contact:** Human Resources Manager. **World Wide Web address:** http://www.qvc.com. **Description:** A leader in electronic retailing with shopping available via television 24 hours per day. The retail programming is transmitted to over 55 million U.S. households. Founded in 1986. **Common positions include:** Accountant/Auditor; Administrative Assistant; Broadcast Technician; Budget Analyst; Buyer; Computer Programmer; Customer Service Representative; Financial Analyst; Graphic Designer; Human Resources Manager; Industrial Engineer; Librarian; Market Research Analyst; Marketing Specialist; MIS Specialist; Project Manager; Public Relations Specialist; Purchasing Agent/Manager; Quality Control Supervisor; Radio/TV Announcer/Broadcaster; Sales

Executive; Secretary; Software Engineer; Systems Analyst; Systems Manager; Telecommunications Manager; Video Production Coordinator. **Special programs:** Internships. **Internship information:** The company has internships in a variety of areas including broadcasting, merchandising, customer service, distribution, guest relations, information systems and technology, finance, and creative services. Please send a resume and cover letter to the College Relations Department. Applications are accepted on a rolling basis. **Corporate headquarters location:** This location. **Other U.S. locations:** DE; TX; VA. **International locations:** Germany; United Kingdom. **Parent company:** Comcast Corporation. **Listed on:** Privately held. **Annual sales/revenues:** More than $100 million. **Number of employees at this location:** 2,500. **Number of employees nationwide:** 8,000. **Number of employees worldwide:** 8,500.

VERIZON COMMUNICATIONS
1717 Arch Street, 17th Floor, Philadelphia PA 19103. 215/963-6000. **Contact:** Human Resources Department. **World Wide Web address:** http://www.verizon.com. **Description:** A full-service communications services provider. Residential customers are offered local and long-distance phone services; dial-up and high-speed Internet access; wireless service plans and equipment; and additional phone services and accessories. Commercial customers are offered data services; local and long-distance phone services; dial-up and high-speed Internet access; payphones; and additional telecommunications equipment and services. Verizon Communications also offers a full range of services and equipment for government clients, and sells its products and services wholesale to other long-distance and wireless service providers. **Corporate headquarters location:** New York NY. **Listed on:** New York Stock Exchange. **Stock exchange symbol:** VZ.

WBEB-FM
10 Presidential Boulevard, Bala-Cynwyd PA 19004. 610/667-8400. **Fax:** 610/667-6795. **Contact:** Human Resources. **World Wide Web address:** http://www.b101radio.com. **Description:** WBEB-FM is a radio station featuring adult contemporary music.

COMPUTER HARDWARE, SOFTWARE, AND SERVICES

You can expect to find the following types of companies in this chapter:

Computer Components and Hardware Manufacturers • Consultants and Computer Training Companies • Internet and Online Service Providers • Networking and Systems Services • Repair Services/Rental and Leasing • Resellers, Wholesalers, and Distributors • Software Developers/Programming Services • Web Technologies

AJILON SERVICES INC.
5 Tower Bridge, Suite 550, 300 Bar Harbor Drive, Conshohocken PA 19428. 610/834-8290. **Contact:** Recruiting. **World Wide Web address:** http://www.ajilon.com. **Description:** Provides computer consulting services, project support, and end user services. **Other U.S. locations:** Nationwide.

ALTEC LANSING TECHNOLOGIES, INC.
Route 6 & 209, P.O. Box 277, Milford PA 18337-0277. 570/296-4434. **Toll-free phone:** 800/258-3288. **Fax:** 570/296-1528. **Contact:** Human Resources Department. **E-mail address:** resumes@alteclansing.com. **World Wide Web address:** http://www.altecmm.com. **Description:** Manufactures speakers and surround sound systems for computers. **NOTE:** Entry-level positions are offered. **Common positions include:** Account Manager; Customer Service Representative; Design Engineer; Draftsperson; Electrical/Electronics Engineer; Graphic Artist; Graphic Designer; Internet Services Manager; Marketing Manager; Mechanical Engineer; MIS Specialist; Multimedia Designer; Project Manager; Sales Engineer; Sales Executive; Sales Representative; Secretary; Software Engineer; Webmaster. **Special programs:** Internships; Co-ops. **Office hours:** Monday - Friday, 8:30 a.m. - 5:00 p.m. **Corporate headquarters location:** This location. **Other U.S. locations:** Nationwide. **International locations:** Worldwide. **Listed on:** Privately held. **Number of employees at this location:** 130.

ASTEA INTERNATIONAL INC.
455 Business Center Drive, Horsham PA 19044-3415. 215/682-2500. **Toll-free phone:** 800/347-7334. **Contact:** Lisa Nagle, Human Resources. **E-mail address:** hr@astea.com. **World Wide Web address:** http://www.astea.com.

Description: Develops, markets, and supports a variety of applications for client/server and host-based environments that permit organizations of various sizes across a wide range of industries to automate and integrate field service and customer support functions. Astea also offers a full range of consulting, training, and customer support services. **NOTE:** Entry-level positions are offered. **Common positions include:** Computer Programmer; Customer Service Representative; Software Engineer; Technical Writer/Editor. **Corporate headquarters location:** This location. **Other U.S. locations:** San Mateo CA; Denver CO; Bedford MA. **Listed on:** NASDAQ. **Stock exchange symbol:** ATEA. **Annual sales/revenues:** $21 - $50 million. **Number of employees at this location:** 200. **Number of employees nationwide:** 450.

AVERCOM, INC.
607 Louis Drive, Warminster PA 18974-2863. 215/674-2913. **Contact:** Personnel Department. **World Wide Web address:** http://www.avercom.net. **Description:** This location engineers software. Overall, AverCom provides software systems, services, and products to a broad base of customers around the world. The company's expertise includes language design and programmer productivity tools; digital signal processing tools and applications; hardware and system simulation; computer and network security products; guidance, navigation, and control products; and information systems integration. The products and services are used by major corporations and government agencies for applications in such fields as transportation, financial management and decision support, automotive, communications, manned space flight, air traffic control, antisubmarine warfare, and command and control. Along with building programming tools and environments, the company responds directly to customer needs by developing software system solutions; analyzing system requirements; performing rapid prototyping; performing integration, verification, and validation testing; re-engineering systems; maintaining operational software; and providing training and support. **Corporate headquarters location:** Woodbridge NJ. **Parent company:** Titan Corporation. **Number of employees at this location:** 600.

BENTLEY SYSTEMS INC.
685 Stockton Drive, Exton PA 19341. 610/458-5000. **Contact:** Human Resources Department. **World Wide Web address:** http://www.bentley.com. **Description:** Develops CAD software for universities, students, and engineers.

BRODART AUTOMATION
500 Arch Street, Williamsport PA 17705. **Toll-free phone:** 800/233-8467. **Contact:** Human Resources Department. **World Wide Web address:** http://www.brodart.com. **Description:** A leading provider of automated library services including computer-based bibliographic maintenance. Founded in 1975. **Parent company:** Brodart Company.

COMPUTER ASSOCIATES INTERNATIONAL, INC.
2000 Midlantic Drive, Suite 300, Mount Laurel NJ 08054. 856/273-9100. **Contact:** Human Resources Department. **E-mail address:** joinCA@ca.com. **World Wide Web address:** http://www.cai.com. **Description:** This location sells software and offers technical support. Overall, Computer Associates International is one of the world's leading developers of client/server and distributed computing software. The company develops, markets, and supports enterprise management, database and applications development, business applications, and consumer software products for a broad range of mainframe, midrange, and desktop computers. Computer Associates International serves major business, government, research, and educational organizations. Founded in 1976. **NOTE:** Mail resumes to: CAI Inc., One Computer Associates Plaza, Islandia NY 11749. **Special programs:** Internships. **Corporate headquarters location:** Islandia NY. **Other U.S. locations:** Nationwide. **Listed on:** New York Stock Exchange. **Stock exchange symbol:** CA. **Annual sales/revenues:** More than $100 million.

COMPUTER ASSOCIATES INTERNATIONAL, INC.
220 West Germantown Pike, Plymouth Meeting PA 19462. 610/940-9900. **Contact:** Human Resources. **World Wide Web address:** http://www.cai.com. **Description:** One of the world's leading developers of client/server and distributed computing software. The company develops, markets, and supports enterprise management, database and applications development, business applications, and consumer software products for a broad range of mainframe, midrange, and desktop computers. Computer Associates International serves major business, government, research, and educational organizations. Founded in 1976. **Corporate headquarters location:** Islandia NY. **Other U.S. locations:** Nationwide. **Listed on:** New York Stock Exchange. **Stock exchange symbol:** CA.

COMPUTER HARDWARE SERVICE COMPANY (CHSC)

11 Vincent Circle, Ivyland PA 18974. 215/443-9220. **Contact:** Human Resources. **World Wide Web address:** http://www.chscinc.com. **Description:** Provides computer network maintenance and repair services.

COMPUTER SCIENCES CORPORATION

304 West Route 38, P.O. Box 1038, Moorestown NJ 08057-0902. 856/234-1166. **Contact:** Human Resources. **World Wide Web address:** http://www.csc.com. **Description:** This location develops software. Overall, Computer Sciences Corporation is comprised of four sectors: the Systems Group Division designs, engineers, and integrates computer-based systems and communications systems, providing all the hardware, software, training, and related elements necessary to operate such a system; the Consulting Division includes consulting and technical services in the development of computer and communication systems to nonfederal organizations; the Industry Services Group provides service to the health care, insurance, and financial services industries, as well as providing large-scale claim processing and other insurance-related services; CSC Health Care and CSC Enterprises make up the CSC Divisions. CSC Health Care markets business systems and services to the managed health care industry, clinics, and physicians. CSC Enterprises provides consumer credit reports and account management services to credit grantors. **Corporate headquarters location:** El Segundo CA. **Other U.S. locations:** Nationwide.

COMTREX SYSTEMS CORPORATION

102 Executive Drive, Suite 1, Moorestown NJ 08057. 856/778-0090. **Fax:** 856/778-9322. **Contact:** Personnel. **World Wide Web address:** http://www.comtrex.com. **Description:** Designs, develops, assembles, and markets computer software electronics terminals, which provide retailers with transaction processing, in-store controls, and management information capabilities. The company primarily serves the food service and hospitality industries. Founded in 1981. **Corporate headquarters location:** This location. **Listed on:** NASDAQ. **Stock exchange symbol:** COMX.

CRADEN PERIPHERALS CORPORATION

7860 Airport Highway, Pennsauken NJ 08109. 856/488-0700. **Fax:** 856/488-0925. **Contact:** Human Resources. **World Wide Web address:** http://www.craden.com. **Description:** Manufactures and markets printers under the Craden brand name.

CYBERTECH INC.
935 Horsham Road, Suite I, Horsham PA 19044. 215/957-6220. **Contact:** Human Resources. **World Wide Web address:** http://www.cbrtech.com. **Description:** Manufactures specialty printers for corporate customers.

DAISY DATA INC.
2850 Lewisberry Road, York Haven PA 17370. 717/932-9999. **Fax:** 717/932-8000. **Contact:** Human Resources. **E-mail address:** shefetv@daisydata.com. **World Wide Web address:** http://www.daisydata.com. **Description:** Manufactures rugged computers for industrial environments.

DATA-CORE SYSTEMS INC.
3700 Science Center, Philadelphia PA 19104. 215/243-1990. **Fax:** 215/243-1978. **Contact:** Human Resources Department. **World Wide Web address:** http://www.dclgroup.com. **Description:** Develops database applications software. **Parent company:** DC Kuljian Group is a diversified holding company engaged in engineering, construction management, software, communications, chemicals, and health care.

DATACAP SYSTEMS, INC.
100 New Britain Boulevard, Chalfont PA 18914. 215/997-8989. **Contact:** Human Resources. **World Wide Web address:** http://www.dcap.com. **Description:** Develops software and point-of-sale systems.

DAY-TIMER, INC.
One Willow Lane, East Texas PA 18046. 610/398-1151. **Toll-free phone:** 800/225-5005. **Contact:** Human Resources. **World Wide Web address:** http://www.daytimer.com. **Description:** Designs and manufactures personal and organizational calendars, accessories, and software. **Corporate headquarters location:** This location.

DECISIONONE
50 East Swedesford Road, Frazer PA 19355. 610/296-6000. **Toll-free phone:** 800/860-1647. **Contact:** Human Resources. **World Wide Web address:** http://www.decisionone.com. **Description:** An international supplier of plug-compatible computer equipment and accessories. Products include disk and tape storage devices, terminals, intelligent workstations and systems, controllers, printers, airline reservation systems, and a comprehensive range of computer supplies. **Corporate headquarters location:** This location. **International locations:** Nationwide.

DENDRITE
701 Main Street, Stroudsburg PA 18360. 570/420-0800. **Fax:** 570/420-0818. **Contact:** Human Resources. **World Wide Web address:** http://www.dendrite.com. **Description:** Develops sales force automation software. Founded in 1986. **Common positions include:** Account Manager; Computer Programmer; Customer Service Representative; Database Manager; Sales Executive; Software Engineer; Systems Analyst; Systems Manager; Technical Writer/Editor; Telecommunications Manager. **Special programs:** Internships. **Corporate headquarters location:** Morristown NJ. **Listed on:** NASDAQ. **Stock exchange symbol:** DRTE. **Annual sales/revenues:** $11 - $20 million. **Number of employees at this location:** 190.

EGAMES, INC.
2000 Cabot Boulevard West, Suite 110, Langhorne PA 19047-1811. 215/750-6606. **Fax:** 215/750-3722. **Contact:** Human Resources. **E-mail address:** jobs@egames.com. **World Wide Web address:** http://www.egames.com. **Description:** Publishes and distributes CD-ROM software containing a variety of games. Founded in 1992.

EPLUS, INC.
130 Futura Drive, P.O. Box 479, Pottstown PA 19464. 610/495-7800. **Contact:** Human Resources. **World Wide Web address:** http://www.eplus.com. **Description:** Leases and sells computers and other IT equipment. ePlus also develops online software products that provide supply chain management solutions including electronic procurement, e-financing, and e-asset management. **Corporate headquarters location:** Herndon VA. **Other U.S. locations:** Scottsdale AZ; Sacramento CA; San Diego CA; Lenexa KS; Columbia MD; Minneapolis MN; Greenville NC; Raleigh NC; Waxhaw NC; Wilmington NC; West Chester PA; Harrisburg PA; Dallas TX; Austin TX. **Listed on:** NASDAQ. **Stock exchange symbol:** PLUS.

EPLUS, INC.
130 Futura Drive, Pottstown PA 19464. 610/495-7800. **Contact:** Human Resources. **World Wide Web address:** http://www.eplus.com. **Description:** Leases and sells computers and other IT equipment. ePlus also develops online software products that provide supply chain management solutions including electronic procurement, e-financing, and e-asset management. **Common positions include:** Administrative Assistant; Applications Engineer; Computer Animator; Computer Operator; Design Engineer; MIS Specialist; Sales Engineer; Sales Executive; Sales Representative. **Corporate**

headquarters location: Herndon VA. **Other U.S. locations:** Scottsdale AZ; Sacramento CA; San Diego CA; Lenexa KS; Columbia MD; Minneapolis MN; Greenville NC; Raleigh NC; Waxhaw NC; Wilmington NC; West Chester PA; Harrisburg PA; Dallas TX; Austin TX. **Listed on:** NASDAQ. **Stock exchange symbol:** PLUS.

EXECUTIVE IMAGING SYSTEMS INC.
P.O. Box 2380, One Allison Drive, Cherry Hill NJ 08034. 856/424-5898. **Fax:** 856/424-7848. **Contact:** Human Resources Department. **World Wide Web address:** http://www.executiveimaging.com. **Description:** Resells computers, facsimiles, printers, and peripherals.

FORMATION, INC.
121 Whittendale Drive, Moorestown NJ 08057. 856/234-5020. **Toll-free phone:** 800/220-1200. **Fax:** 856/234-8543. **Contact:** Human Resources Department. **E-mail address:** resume@formation.com. **World Wide Web address:** http://www.formation.com. **Description:** Designs and manufactures communications products and real-time, high-performance storage and retrieval systems. The company's products are capable of integrating a number of inputs including video, audio, data/text, and radar, and can employ a variety of communications protocols. The company supplies an open systems storage system using Redundant Array of Independent Disks (RAID) technology. Formation also supplies plug-compatible data storage systems for IBM AS/400 computers, as well as data storage systems to open systems computer manufacturers and systems integrators. **Common positions include:** Computer Engineer; Electrical/Electronics Engineer; Mechanical Engineer; Software Engineer. **Corporate headquarters location:** This location. **Operations at this facility include:** Administration; Manufacturing; Research and Development; Sales; Service. **Number of employees at this location:** 75.

GE ENERGY SERVICES
2849 Sterling Drive, Hatfield PA 19440. 215/996-9200. **Fax:** 215/996-9201. **Contact:** Human Resources. **World Wide Web address:** http://www.enertec.com. **Description:** Formerly KVB-Enertec Inc., now a division of GE Power Systems. A manufacturer of SNIFFER computerized CEM (continuous emissions monitoring) systems used to test for state and EPA compliance for pollutant-emitting sources such as incinerators, boilers, turbines, and cogeneration plants. **Parent company:**

General Electric Company. **Listed on:** New York Stock Exchange. **Stock exchange symbol:** GE.

GLOBAL SPORTS, INC.
GLOBAL SPORTS INTERACTIVE
1075 First Avenue, King of Prussia PA 19406. 610/491-7000. **Fax:** 610/265-0736. **Contact:** Melissa Reinish, Human Resources Director. **E-mail address:** jobs@globalsports.com. **World Wide Web address:** http://www.globalsports.com. **Description:** Designs and maintains Websites that allow sporting good retailers to sell and distribute products. Founded in 1991. **Common positions include:** Account Manager; Account Representative; Accountant; Administrative Assistant; AS400 Programmer Analyst; Buyer; Chief Financial Officer; Controller; Credit Manager; Customer Service Representative; Graphic Designer; Human Resources Manager; Marketing Manager; Network/Systems Administrator; Public Relations Specialist; Sales Executive; Transportation/Traffic Specialist. **Special programs:** Internships. **Office hours:** Monday - Friday, 8:30 a.m. - 5:30 p.m. **Corporate headquarters location:** This location. **Listed on:** NASDAQ. **Stock exchange symbol:** GSPT. **CEO:** Michael Rubin. **Annual sales/revenues:** More than $100 million. **Number of employees at this location:** 85. **Number of employees nationwide:** 95. **Number of employees worldwide:** 140.

HMW ENTERPRISES INC.
207 North Franklin Street, Waynesboro PA 17268. 717/765-4690. **Contact:** Human Resources. **World Wide Web address:** http://www.hmwent.com. **Description:** Manufactures industrial computers.

HEWLETT-PACKARD MIDDLEWARE
6000 Irwin Road, Mount Laurel NJ 08054-4128. 856/638-6000. **Fax:** 856/638-6170. **Contact:** Monique McLaughlin, Recruiter. **E-mail address:** hpmdinfo@hp.com. **World Wide Web address:** http://www.hpmiddleware.com. **Description:** Develops computer technology programs and provides user training. Offers Web-based software including dynamic Web applications and GUIs. **NOTE:** Entry-level positions are offered. **Common positions include:** Administrative Assistant; Marketing Specialist; MIS Specialist; Sales Engineer; Sales Representative; Software Engineer. **Special programs:** Training. **Corporate headquarters location:** Palo Alto CA. **Other U.S. locations:** Nationwide. **Listed on:** New York Stock Exchange. **Stock exchange symbol:** HWP.

INSTITUTE FOR SCIENTIFIC INFORMATION

3501 Market Street, Philadelphia PA 19104. 215/386-0100. **Fax:** 215/387-4231. **Contact:** Brian Richards, Employment/Employee Relations Manager. **World Wide Web address:** http://www.isinet.com. **Description:** Supplies researchers and scientists with needed information in electronic formats. Institute for Scientific Information produces indexes and databases that provide information from journals, books, and other significant materials published in the sciences, social sciences, and arts and humanities. The company also offers online services and technical support. **Common positions include:** Accountant/Auditor; Computer Programmer; Customer Service Representative; Database Manager; Editor; Financial Analyst; Indexer; Marketing Specialist; Operations/Production Manager; Proofreader; Quality Control Supervisor; Systems Analyst; Technical Writer/Editor; Translator. **Corporate headquarters location:** This location. **Other area locations:** Cherry Hill NJ; Mount Laurel NJ. **Parent company:** Thomson Company. **Number of employees at this location:** 450. **Number of employees nationwide:** 750.

KEANE, INC.

460 Norristown Road, Suite 200, Blue Bell PA 19422. 610/260-0640. **Contact:** Human Resources Department. **World Wide Web address:** http://www.keane.com. **Description:** Offers businesses a variety of computer consulting services. Keane also develops, markets, and manages software for its clients and assists in project management. **Corporate headquarters location:** Boston MA. **Listed on:** American Stock Exchange. **Stock exchange symbol:** KEA.

KEYSTONE COMPUTER ASSOCIATES

1055 Virginia Drive, Fort Washington PA 19034. 215/643-3800. **Fax:** 215/643-0115. **Contact:** Human Resources. **World Wide Web address:** http://www.keystoneca.com. **Description:** A computer consulting firm.

MAXWELL SYSTEMS, INC.

2500 DeKalb Pike, Norristown PA 19401. 610/277-3515. **Contact:** Human Resources. **World Wide Web address:** http://www.maxwellsystems.com. **Description:** This location is a computer training facility. Overall, Maxwell Systems sells software for construction, service, and related industries. **Corporate headquarters location:** This location.

McKESSONHBOC

700 East Gate Drive, Suite 500, Mount Laurel NJ 08054-3808. 856/234-4041. **Contact:** Human Resources. **E-mail address:** job.infosolutions@mckesson.com. **World Wide Web address:** http://www.hboc.com. **Description:** This location offers sales and technical support. Overall, McKessonHBOC provides networking solutions and software by supplying physicians, hospitals, and other health care facilities with network service and support. **NOTE:** All resumes should be sent to Human Resources, McKesson InfoSolutions, 5995 Windward Parkway, Alpharetta GA 30005. 404/338-6000. **Corporate headquarters location:** San Francisco CA. **Listed on:** New York Stock Exchange. **Stock exchange symbol:** MCK.

McKESSONHBOC

5 Country View Road, Malvern PA 19355-1421. 610/296-3838. **Contact:** Human Resources. **World Wide Web address:** http://www.mckhboc.com. **Description:** Provides information systems and technology to health care enterprises including hospitals, integrated delivery networks, and managed care organizations. McKessonHBOC's primary products are Pathways 2000, a family of client/server-based applications that allow the integration and uniting of health care providers; STAR, Series, and HealthQuest transaction systems; TRENDSTAR decision support system; and QUANTUM enterprise information system. The company also offers outsourcing services that include strategic information systems planning, data center operations, receivables management, business office administration, and major system conversions. **Common positions include:** Accountant/Auditor; Computer Programmer; Dental Assistant/Dental Hygienist; Dentist; Department Manager; Employment Interviewer; Human Resources Manager; Licensed Practical Nurse; Medical Records Technician; Payroll Clerk; Sales Executive; Surgical Technician; Systems Analyst. **Corporate headquarters location:** San Francisco CA. **Other U.S. locations:** Boston MA. **Operations at this facility include:** Administration; Divisional Headquarters; Research and Development; Sales; Service. **Number of employees at this location:** 155. **Number of employees nationwide:** 175.

NEOWARE SYSTEMS, INC.

400 Feheley Drive, King of Prussia PA 19406. 610/277-8300. **Contact:** Human Resources. **World Wide Web address:** http://www.neoware.com. **Description:** Designs, manufactures, and markets a family of desktop computing devices including multimedia capable X Window stations.

OKI DATA AMERICAS, INC.
2000 Bishops Gate Boulevard, Mount Laurel NJ 08054. 856/235-2600. **Contact:** Human Resources. **World Wide Web address:** http://www.okidata.com. **Description:** Manufactures computer printers and fax machines. **Corporate headquarters location:** This location. **International locations:** Worldwide.

PDS INC. (PERSONNEL DATA SYSTEMS)
650 Sentry Parkway, Blue Bell PA 19422. 610/828-4294. **Fax:** 610/828-5193. **Contact:** Human Resources Department. **World Wide Web address:** http://www.pdssoftware.com. **Description:** PDS designs and develops human resources and payroll systems software for PC networks, IBM mainframes, and operating environments with strong emphasis on client/server technology. **Common positions include:** Administrative Assistant; Computer Programmer; Controller; Database Manager; Human Resources Manager; Marketing Manager; MIS Specialist; Sales Executive; Sales Manager; Sales Representative; Systems Analyst.

PENTAMATION ENTERPRISE INC.
225 Marketplace, Bethlehem PA 18018. 610/691-3616. **Contact:** Human Resources Department. **World Wide Web address:** http://www.pentamation.com. **Description:** Develops software and computer systems for school districts and government facilities.

PERIPHERAL DYNAMICS INC. (PDI)
5150 Campus Drive, Plymouth Meeting PA 19462-1197. 610/825-7090. **Contact:** Human Resources. **World Wide Web address:** http://www.pdiscan.com. **Description:** Manufactures scanners, optical readers, and other peripherals used in computer data entry.

PRESCIENT SYSTEMS, INC.
1247 Ward Avenue, Suite 200, West Chester PA 19380. 610/719-1600. **Toll-free phone:** 888/610-1800. **Fax:** 610/719-8575. **Contact:** Human Resources. **World Wide Web address:** http://www.prescientsystems.com. **Description:** A developer and supplier of forecasting and logistics software solutions. The company's supply chain management software provides a solution for demand forecasting, inventory planning, and continuous replenishment. This software is used by manufacturers, distributors, and retailers worldwide. **Common positions include:** Accountant/Auditor; Administrative Manager; Computer Programmer; Human Resources Manager; Operations/Production Manager; Purchasing Agent/Manager;

Quality Control Supervisor; Software Engineer; Systems Analyst; Technical Writer/Editor. **Corporate headquarters location:** This location. **Operations at this facility include:** Administration; Research and Development; Sales; Service. **Listed on:** Privately held. **Annual sales/revenues:** Less than $5 million. **Number of employees at this location:** 30. **Number of employees nationwide:** 45.

PRIMAVERA SYSTEMS INC.
3 Bala Plaza West, Suite 700, Bala-Cynwyd PA 19004. 610/667-8600. **Fax:** 610/949-6761. **Contact:** Joanne McCool, Vice President of Human Resources Department. **E-mail address:** jobs@primavera.com. **World Wide Web address:** http://www.primavera.com. **Description:** Develops and supports an array of project management software for assisting clients in risk analysis, large-scale projects, contract management, team communication, and remote real-time updating. Founded in 1983. **NOTE:** Entry-level positions are offered. **Common positions include:** Administrative Assistant; Computer Programmer; Database Manager; Marketing Manager; Sales Engineer; Sales Representative; Secretary; Software Engineer. **Special programs:** Internships; Co-ops. **Office hours:** Monday - Friday, 8:00 a.m. - 5:00 p.m. **Corporate headquarters location:** This location. **Other U.S. locations:** Nationwide. **International locations:** Worldwide. **Listed on:** Privately held. **Annual sales/revenues:** $21 - $50 million. **Number of employees at this location:** 180. **Number of employees nationwide:** 230. **Number of employees worldwide:** 260.

PROPHET 21 INC.
19 West College Avenue, Yardley PA 19067. 215/493-8900. **Contact:** Human Resources. **World Wide Web address:** http://www.p21.com. **Description:** Supplies software solutions to the distribution industry. Founded in 1967. **Listed on:** NASDAQ. **Stock exchange symbol:** PXXI.

QAD INC.
10000 Midlantic Drive, Suite 200, Mount Laurel NJ 08054. 856/273-1717. **Contact:** Human Resources. **World Wide Web address:** http://www.qad.com. **Description:** This location serves as a technical support branch and regional sales office. Overall, QAD develops MFG/PRO, a software package designed to aid in supply and distribution management for large companies. **Corporate headquarters location:** Carpinteria CA. **Listed on:** NASDAQ. **Stock exchange symbol:** QADI.

RAINMAKER SOFTWARE, INC.
475 Sentry Parkway, Suite 4000, Blue Bell PA 19422. 610/567-3400. **Contact:** Kim Robinson, Human Resources. **E-mail address:** krobinson@rainmakerlegal.com. **World Wide Web address:** http://www.rainmakerlegal.com. **Description:** Develops computer applications for the legal industry. **Corporate headquarters location:** Framingham MA. **Parent company:** ASA International Ltd. designs and develops proprietary vertical market software and installs software on a variety of computers and networks.

SAP AMERICA, INC.
3999 West Chester Pike, Newtown Square PA 19073. 610/355-2500. **Contact:** Human Resources. **World Wide Web address:** http://www.sap.com. **Description:** Develops a variety of client/server computer software packages including programs for finance, human resources, and materials management applications. **Corporate headquarters location:** This location. **Other U.S. locations:** Nationwide. **International locations:** Germany. **Parent company:** SAP AG. **Number of employees nationwide:** 3,000. **Number of employees worldwide:** 13,000.

SCT CORPORATION
4 Country View Road, Malvern PA 19355. **Toll-free phone:** 800/223-7036. **Fax:** 800/578-5102. **Contact:** Human Resources Department. **World Wide Web address:** http://www.sctcorp.com. **Description:** Develops software and offers computer-related services to the higher education, local government, utility, and manufacturing communities. The company operates through the following divisions: Information Resource Management (IRM); Software & Technology Services (STS); SCT Public Sector, Inc.; and SCT Utility Systems, Inc. **NOTE:** Entry-level positions are offered. **Common positions include:** Accountant/Auditor; Budget Analyst; Computer Programmer; Human Resources Specialist; Management Analyst/Consultant; Management Trainee; MIS Specialist; Systems Analyst; Technical Writer/Editor. **Corporate headquarters location:** This location. **Annual sales/revenues:** More than $100 million.

SAFEGUARD SCIENTIFICS, INC.
800 Safeguard Building, 435 Devon Park Drive, Wayne PA 19087. 610/293-0600. **Fax:** 610/293-0601. **Contact:** Human Resources Department. **World Wide Web address:** http://www.safeguard.com. **Description:** A strategic information systems holding company. **Corporate**

headquarters location: This location. **Subsidiaries include:** Cambridge Technology Partners; ChromaVision Medical Systems; CompuCom Systems, Inc.; Diamond Technology Partners; DocuCorp International; OAD Technology Solutions; Sanchez Computer Association; Tangram Enterprise Solutions; and USDATA Corporation. **Listed on:** New York Stock Exchange. **Stock exchange symbol:** SFE.

SIEMENS MEDICAL SOLUTIONS HEALTH SERVICES CORPORATION

51 Valley Stream Parkway, Malvern PA 19355. 610/219-6300. **Fax:** 610/219-3124. **Contact:** Human Resources. **World Wide Web address:** http://www.smed.com. **Description:** A leading provider of health information and service solutions to hospitals, multi-entity health care corporations, integrated health networks, physician groups, and other health care providers in North America and Europe. The company also provides a full complement of solutions for the newly-emerging community health information networks, which include payers and employers as well as providers. Shared Medical Systems offers a comprehensive line of health care information systems including clinical, financial, administrative, ambulatory, and decision support systems for both the public and private health care sectors. These systems are offered on computers operating at the customer site, at the SMS Information Services Center, or as part of a distributed network. Shared Medical Systems also provides a portfolio of professional services including systems installation, support, and education. In addition, the company provides specialized consulting services for the design and integration of software and networks, facilities management, information systems planning, and systems-related process reengineering. Founded in 1969. **NOTE:** Entry-level positions are offered. **Common positions include:** Accountant; Computer Programmer; Licensed Practical Nurse; MIS Specialist; Network Engineer; Pharmacist; Project Manager; Radiological Technologist; Registered Nurse; Software Engineer; Systems Analyst; Technical Writer/Editor. **Special programs:** Internships. **Corporate headquarters location:** This location. **Other U.S. locations:** Nationwide. **Operations at this facility include:** Administration; Research and Development; Sales; Service. **Listed on:** New York Stock Exchange. **Stock exchange symbol:** SMS. **Annual sales/revenues:** More than $100 million. **Number of employees at this location:** 3,200. **Number of employees worldwide:** 5,000.

SOFTMART, INC.
450 Acorn Lane, Downingtown PA 19335. 610/518-4058. **Fax:** 610/518-3014. **Contact:** Recruiting Manager. **World Wide Web address:** http://www.softmart.com. **Description:** Resells computer software and hardware to government and commercial clients. Founded in 1983. **NOTE:** Entry-level positions and second and third shifts are offered. **Common positions include:** Account Manager; Account Representative; Accountant; Administrative Assistant; Advertising Clerk; Advertising Executive; Assistant Manager; Attorney; Budget Analyst; Buyer; Clerical Supervisor; Computer Operator; Computer Programmer; Controller; Credit Manager; Customer Service Representative; Database Manager; Editor; Financial Analyst; Graphic Artist; Graphic Designer; Human Resources Manager; Marketing Manager; Marketing Specialist; MIS Specialist; Multimedia Designer; Production Manager; Project Manager; Quality Control Supervisor; Sales Executive; Sales Manager; Sales Representative; Secretary; Software Engineer; Systems Analyst; Systems Manager; Technical Writer/Editor; Telecommunications Manager; Webmaster. **Special programs:** Internships; Training; Summer Jobs. **Office hours:** Monday - Friday, 8:30 a.m. - 5:30 p.m. **Corporate headquarters location:** This location. **Listed on:** Privately held. **President:** Elliot Levine. **Annual sales/revenues:** More than $100 million. **Number of employees at this location:** 490.

STORAGE TECHNOLOGY CORPORATION
6 Tower Bridge, Suite 400, 181 Washington Street, Conshohocken PA 19428. 484/530-4100. **Contact:** Human Resources Department. **World Wide Web address:** http://www.storagetek.com. **Description:** Manufactures, sells, and services data storage devices. Overall, Storage Technology Corporation manufactures high-performance computer information storage and retrieval systems for mainframe and mid-frame computers and networks. Products include automated cartridge systems, random access subsystems, and fault-tolerant disk arrays. The company also distributes equipment; sells new peripherals, software, and hardware; and offers support services. **Corporate headquarters location:** Louisville CO.

SUNGARD ASSET MANAGEMENT SYSTEMS, INC.
40 General Warren Boulevard, Suite 200, Malvern PA 19355. 610/251-1813. **Fax:** 610/251-6585. **Contact:** Teresa Urban, Human Resources Coordinator. **World Wide Web address:** http://www.sungard.com. **Description:** Develops, markets, and supports software for the financial industry. **NOTE:** Entry-level

positions are offered. **Common positions include:** Software Engineer. **Special programs:** Internships; Training. **Corporate headquarters location:** This location. **Other U.S. locations:** Nationwide. **Operations at this facility include:** Administration; Sales; Service. **Listed on:** Privately held. **Annual sales/revenues:** $21 - $50 million.

SUNGARD DATA SYSTEMS INC./SUNGARD RECOVERY SERVICES

1285 Drummers Lane, Wayne PA 19087. 610/341-8700. **Contact:** Anne Beeson, Vice President of Human Resources. **World Wide Web address:** http://www.sungard.com. **Description:** Provides specialized computer services including proprietary investment support systems for the financial services industry and computer disaster planning/recovery services. SunGard Data Systems Inc.'s investment accounting and portfolio systems maintain the books and records of large investment portfolios including those managed by banks and mutual funds. The company's disaster recovery services include alternate-site backup, testing, and recovery services for IBM, Prime, Stratus, Tandem, and Unisys computer installations. The company's computer service unit provides remote-access IBM computer processing, direct marketing, and automated mailing services. SunGard Data Systems Inc. also provides computer software, data processing, programming, and repair services. SunGard Recovery Systems (also at this location) provides business recovery services for both mainframe and mid-range computer platforms. **Corporate headquarters location:** This location. **Number of employees at this location:** 2,100.

TENEX SYSTEMS INC.

2011 Renaissance Boulevard, Suite 100, King of Prussia PA 19406. 610/239-9988. **Fax:** 610/239-9995. **Contact:** Human Resources Department. **World Wide Web address:** http://www.tenexsys.com. **Description:** Provides administrative software development and support services for school districts. **Common positions include:** Administrative Assistant; AS400 Programmer Analyst. **Office hours:** Monday - Friday, 7:30 a.m. - 4:30 p.m. **President:** Ron Cranford.

TRIVERSITY INC.

311 Sinclair Street, Bristol PA 19007. 215/785-4321. **Contact:** Personnel. **E-mail address:** triversity@rpc.webhire.com. **World Wide Web address:** http://www.triversity.com. **Description:** Provides transaction processing and customer relationship

management solutions for physical, catalog, and online retailers. **Corporate headquarters location:** Toronto, Canada.

ULTICOM INC.
1020 Briggs Road, Mount Laurel NJ 08054. 856/787-2700. **Contact:** Human Resources. **World Wide Web address:** http://www.ulticom.com. **Description:** Develops Signal Ware brand telecommunications software and hardware.

UNISYS CORPORATION
Unisys Way, Blue Bell PA 19424. 215/986-3501. **Fax:** 215/986-6732. **Contact:** Recruiting and Staffing. **E-mail address:** jobs@unisys.com. **World Wide Web address:** http://www.unisys.com. **Description:** Provides information services, technology, and software. Unisys specializes in developing critical business solutions based on open information networks. The company's Enabling Software Team creates a variety of software projects that facilitate the building of user applications and the management of distributed systems. The company's Platforms Group is responsible for UNIX Operating Systems running across a wide range of multiple processor server platforms including all peripheral and communication drivers. The Unisys Commercial Parallel Processing Team develops microkernel-based operating systems, I/O device drivers, ATM hardware, diagnostics, and system architectures. The System Management Group is in charge of the overall management of development programs for UNIX desktop and entry-server products. **NOTE:** Entry-level positions and part-time jobs are offered. **Common positions include:** Account Manager; Account Representative; Administrative Assistant; Applications Engineer; AS400 Programmer Analyst; Computer Engineer; Computer Programmer; Computer Scientist; Computer Support Technician; Computer Technician; Content Developer; Customer Service Representative; Database Administrator; Database Manager; Finance Director; Financial Analyst; General Manager; Help-Desk Technician; Human Resources Manager; Internet Services Manager; Intranet Developer; Market Research Analyst; Marketing Specialist; MIS Specialist; Network Engineer; Network Manager; Network/Systems Administrator; Online Sales Manager; Project Manager; Purchasing Agent/Manager; Sales Executive; Sales Manager; Sales Representative; Software Engineer; SQL Programmer; Systems Analyst; Systems Manager; Technical Support Manager; Webmaster; Website Developer. **Special programs:** Internships; Training; Co-ops; Summer Jobs. **Corporate headquarters location:** This location. **Other U.S. locations:**

Nationwide. **International locations:** Worldwide. **Listed on:** New York Stock Exchange. **Stock exchange symbol:** UIS. **CEO:** Larry Weinbach. **Annual sales/revenues:** More than $100 million. **Number of employees at this location:** 2,500. **Number of employees nationwide:** 37,000. **Number of employees worldwide:** 49,000.

UNISYS CORPORATION
2476 Swedesford Road, Malvern PA 19355. 610/648-4000. **Contact:** Human Resources. **World Wide Web address:** http://www.unisys.com. **Description:** This location is a software engineering facility. Overall, Unisys Corporation provides information services, technology, and software. Unisys specializes in developing critical business solutions based on open information networks. The company's Enabling Software Team creates a variety of software projects that facilitate the building of user applications and the management of distributed systems. The company's Platforms Group is responsible for UNIX Operating Systems running across a wide range of multiple processor server platforms including all peripheral and communication drivers. The Unisys Commercial Parallel Processing Team develops microkernel-based operating systems, I/O device drivers, ATM hardware, diagnostics, and system architectures. The System Management Group is in charge of the overall management of development programs for UNIX desktop and entry-server products. **Corporate headquarters location:** Blue Bell PA. **Other U.S. locations:** Nationwide. **International locations:** Worldwide. **Listed on:** New York Stock Exchange. **Stock exchange symbol:** UIS. **CEO:** Larry Weinbach. **Annual sales/revenues:** More than $100 million. **Number of employees nationwide:** 37,000. **Number of employees worldwide:** 49,000.

VECTOR ESP, INC.
676 East Swedesford Road, Suite 200, Philadelphia PA 19087. 610/995-8420. **Toll-free phone:** 800/852-3658. **Fax:** 610/995-8448. **Contact:** Recruiting. **World Wide Web address:** http://www.vector.com. **Description:** Offers computer consulting services to a variety of businesses. **Common positions include:** Account Representative; Administrative Assistant; Applications Engineer; Computer Engineer; Computer Programmer; Computer Support Technician; Database Administrator; Database Manager; Human Resources Manager; Internet Services Manager; Multimedia Designer; Network/Systems Administrator; Software Engineer; SQL Programmer; Systems Analyst; Systems Manager; Webmaster.

Corporate headquarters location: Houston TX. **Listed on:** Privately held.

VERTEX SYSTEMS INC.
1041 Old Cassatt Road, Berwyn PA 19312. 610/640-4200. **Contact:** Human Resources. **World Wide Web address:** http://www.vertexinc.com. **Description:** Provides corporate clients with tax manuals and tax reference products and software.

XEROX CONNECT, INC.
411 Eagleview Boulevard, Exton PA 19341. 610/458-5500. **Toll-free phone:** 800/884-4736. **Contact:** Sherri Haines, Human Resources Administrator. **World Wide Web address:** http://www.xeroxconnect.com. **Description:** Offers systems integration services. The company operates in three service groups: Consulting and Design Services, Systems Integration, and Operations and Support Services. **Common positions include:** Computer Programmer; Database Manager; Systems Analyst; Systems Manager. **Parent company:** Xerox Corporation. **COO:** Tim Wallace.

EDUCATIONAL SERVICES

You can expect to find the following types of facilities in this chapter:

*Business/Secretarial/Data Processing Schools •
Colleges/Universities/Professional Schools • Community
Colleges/Technical Schools/Vocational Schools • Elementary
and Secondary Schools • Preschool and Child Daycare
Services*

BUCKS COUNTY COMMUNITY COLLEGE
Tyler Hall, Room 130, 275 Swamp Road, Newtown PA 18940.
215/968-8000. **Fax:** 215/504-8506. **Contact:** Human
Resources. **World Wide Web address:** http://www.bucks.edu.
Description: A public, two-year community college offering
certificates and associate's degrees in more than 50 academic
disciplines.

CALIFORNIA UNIVERSITY OF PENNSYLVANIA
Dixon Hall, Room 408, 250 University Avenue, California PA
15419. 724/938-4427. **Contact:** Office of Human Resources.
E-mail address: cupjobs@cup.edu. **World Wide Web address:**
http://www.cup.edu. **Description:** A university offering two-
year, four-year, and graduate programs leading to associate's,
bachelor's, and master's degrees. Enrollment includes
approximately 6,000 undergraduates and 700 graduate
students.

CAMDEN COUNTY COLLEGE
College Road, P.O. Box 200, Blackwood NJ 08012. 856/227-
7200. **Contact:** Human Resources Department. **E-mail address:**
hr@camdencc.edu. **World Wide Web address:**
http://www.camdencc.edu. **Description:** A community college
with more than 11,500 students enrolled in over 80 academic
areas.

COMMUNITY COLLEGE OF PHILADELPHIA
1700 Spring Garden Street, Room M2-3, Philadelphia PA
19130. 215/751-8035. **Fax:** 215/972-6307. **Contact:** Human
Resources Department. **World Wide Web address:**
http://www.ccp.cc.pa.us. **Description:** A two-year community
college offering certificates and associate's degrees.
Approximately 40,000 students attend Community College of
Philadelphia.

DESALES UNIVERSITY

2755 Station Avenue, Center Valley PA 18034. 610/282-1100. **Fax:** 610/282-3206. **Contact:** Judi Shaughnessy, Employment and Benefits Manager. **World Wide Web address:** http://www.desales.edu. **Description:** A small, Catholic liberal arts college. **NOTE:** Formerly known as Allentown College.

DREXEL UNIVERSITY

3141 Chestnut Street, Philadelphia PA 19104. 215/895-2850. **Physical address:** 3201 Arch Street, 4th Floor, Suite 430, Philadelphia PA 19104. **Recorded jobline:** 215/895-2562. **Fax:** 215/895-5813. **Contact:** Human Resources Department. **E-mail address:** hrdept@drexel.edu. **World Wide Web address:** http://www.drexel.edu. **Description:** A four-year university offering bachelor's and master's degrees including MBAs. Approximately 8,000 undergraduate and 3,700 graduate students attend Drexel University.

FRANKLIN AND MARSHALL COLLEGE

P.O. Box 3003, Lancaster PA 17604-3003. 717/291-3911. **Fax:** 717/291-3969. **Contact:** Human Resources. **World Wide Web address:** http://www.fandm.edu. **Description:** A small, private, four-year college. **NOTE:** Job opportunities are posted on the above Website. No phone calls or walk-ins.

THOMAS JEFFERSON UNIVERSITY

201 South 11th Street, The Martin Building, Philadelphia PA 19107. 215/955-6000. **Fax:** 215/503-2183. **Contact:** Office of Employee Selection & Placement. **World Wide Web address:** http://www.tju.edu. **Description:** An academic medical university. Thomas Jefferson University includes one of the largest private medical schools in the United States, a hospital, and graduate programs in the biomedical sciences.

KUTZTOWN UNIVERSITY

P.O. Box 730, Kutztown PA 19530-0730. 610/683-1353. **Physical address:** Personnel Office, Stratton Administration Center, Room 109, Kutztown PA 19530. **Fax:** 610/683-4641. **Contact:** Personnel Department. **World Wide Web address:** http://www.kutztown.edu. **Description:** A four-year university offering bachelor's and master's degrees including MBAs. Approximately 7,000 undergraduate and 800 graduate students attend Kutztown University.

LA SALLE UNIVERSITY

1900 West Olney Avenue, Philadelphia PA 19141. 215/951-1013. **Contact:** Human Resources. **World Wide Web address:**

http://www.lasalle.edu. **Description:** A four-year university offering bachelor's and master's degrees including MBAs. Approximately 3,600 undergraduate and 900 graduate students attend La Salle University.

LACKAWANNA JUNIOR COLLEGE
501 Vine Street, Scranton PA 18509. 570/961-7841. **Contact:** Human Resources Department. **World Wide Web address:** http://www.ljc.edu. **Description:** A junior college.

LEHIGH UNIVERSITY
428 Brodhead Avenue, Bethlehem PA 18015-1687. 610/758-3900. **Fax:** 610/758-6226. **Contact:** Human Resources. **World Wide Web address:** http://www.lehigh.edu. **Description:** A four-year university offering bachelor's, master's (including MBAs), and doctoral degrees. Approximately 4,400 undergraduate and 2,000 graduate students attend Lehigh University. **Common positions include:** Accountant/Auditor; Administrator; Biological Scientist; Buyer; Civil Engineer; Computer Programmer; Draftsperson; Electrical/Electronics Engineer; Geologist/Geophysicist; Human Resources Manager; Industrial Engineer; Mechanical Engineer; Metallurgical Engineer; Reporter; Systems Analyst; Technical Writer/Editor; Transportation/Traffic Specialist. **Corporate headquarters location:** This location. **Operations at this facility include:** Service.

MILLERSVILLE UNIVERSITY OF PENNSYLVANIA
Dilworth Building, P.O. Box 1002, Millersville PA 17551-0302. 717/872-3011. **Contact:** Human Resources. **World Wide Web address:** http://muweb.millersv.edu. **Description:** A four-year university offering associate's, bachelor's, and master's degrees to approximately 7,500 students.

MORAVIAN COLLEGE
MORAVIAN THEOLOGICAL SEMINARY
1200 Main Street, Bethlehem PA 18018. 610/861-1527. **Physical address:** Colonial Hall, 3rd Floor, Main Street and Elizabeth Avenue, Bethlehem PA 18018. **Fax:** 610/625-7883. **Contact:** Human Resources Department. **E-mail address:** employment@moravian.edu. **World Wide Web address:** http://www.moravian.edu. **Description:** A four-year college offering bachelor's degrees and MBAs to approximately 1,200 students. Moravian Theological Seminary (also at this location) is a graduate-professional school of theology. **Common positions include:** Accountant/Auditor; Computer Programmer; Counselor; Editor; Education Administrator; General Manager;

Health Services Manager; Human Resources Manager; Librarian; Library Technician; Psychologist; Registered Nurse; Systems Analyst; Teacher/Professor. **Operations at this facility include:** Administration; Service. **Number of employees at this location:** 400.

MUHLENBERG COLLEGE
2400 Chew Street, Allentown PA 18104-5586. 484-664-3165. **Fax:** 484/664-3107. **Contact:** Human Resources. **World Wide Web address:** http://www.muhlenberg.edu. **Description:** A four-year, undergraduate, liberal arts college. Founded in 1848. **Common positions include:** Secretary; Teacher/Professor. **President:** Arthur R. Taylor. **Number of employees at this location:** 500.

NOBEL LEARNING COMMUNITIES
1615 West Chester Pike, West Chester PA 19382. 484/947-2000. **Contact:** Human Resources. **World Wide Web address:** http://www.nobellearning.com. **Description:** Provides for the care and education of children from infancy through eighth grade. The daycare and early developmental programs are provided by the Rocking Horse Child Care division, which consists of 40 centers, while the preschool through eighth grade educational programs are provided through Merryhill Country Schools in California; and Chesterbrook Academy in Pennsylvania, New Jersey, North Carolina, and Illinois. Founded in 1982.

PHILADELPHIA UNIVERSITY
School House & Henry Avenue, Philadelphia PA 19144. 215/951-2969. **Contact:** Human Resources Department. **E-mail address:** humanresources@philau.edu. **World Wide Web address:** http://www.philau.edu. **Description:** A four-year college offering bachelor's and master's degrees including MBAs. Approximately 3,100 undergraduate and graduate students attend Philadelphia University.

ROWAN UNIVERSITY
201 Mullica Hill Road, Linden Hall, 1st Floor, Glassboro NJ 08028. 856/256-4134. **Contact:** Human Resources. **World Wide Web address:** http://www.rowan.edu. **Description:** A four-year, state college offering bachelor's and master's degrees (including MBAs). Approximately 9,000 students attend Rowan University.

SHIPPENSBURG UNIVERSITY
1871 Old Main Drive, Shippensburg PA 17257-2299. 717/477-1124. **Fax:** 717/477-4037. **Contact:** Office of Human Resources. **E-mail address:** hr@ship.edu. **World Wide Web address:** http://www.ship.edu. **Description:** A four-year university offering bachelor's and master's degrees. Approximately 5,200 undergraduates and 1,200 graduate students attend Shippensburg University.

SWARTHMORE COLLEGE
500 College Avenue, Swarthmore PA 19081. 610/328-7797. **Fax:** 610/690-2040. **Recorded jobline:** 610/328-8494. **Contact:** Human Resources. **E-mail address:** jobapps@swarthmore.edu. **World Wide Web address:** http://www.swarthmore.edu. **Description:** Swarthmore College is a small, private, liberal arts college.

TEMPLE UNIVERSITY
University Services Building, 1601 North Broad Street, USB Room 202, Philadelphia PA 19122. 215/204-7174. **Contact:** Human Resources Department. **World Wide Web address:** http://www.temple.edu. **Description:** A four-year university offering bachelor's, master's (including MBAs), first professional, and doctoral degrees. Approximately 22,000 undergraduate and 9,400 graduate students attend Temple University. **Common positions include:** Clinical Lab Technician; Computer Programmer; Counselor; Dental Assistant/Dental Hygienist; Education Administrator; Health Services Manager; Librarian; Library Technician; Licensed Practical Nurse; Nuclear Medicine Technologist; Occupational Therapist; Physical Therapist; Registered Nurse; Secretary; Typist/Word Processor. **Corporate headquarters location:** This location. **Number of employees at this location:** 9,000.

UNIVERSITY OF PENNSYLVANIA
3401 Walnut Street, Suite 527A, Philadelphia PA 19104-6228. 215/898-7281. **Contact:** Human Resources. **World Wide Web address:** http://www.hr.upenn.edu/jobs. **Description:** An Ivy League university offering undergraduate and graduate degrees. **NOTE:** Resumes must be submitted online. Please check the Website for more information. Entry-level positions are offered. **Common positions include:** Account Manager; Accountant; Administrative Assistant; Administrative Manager; Advertising Clerk; Advertising Executive; Architect; Assistant Manager; Auditor; Biomedical Engineer; Broadcast Technician; Budget Analyst; Buyer; Certified Nurses Aide; Clerical Supervisor; Computer Operator; Computer Programmer;

Counselor; Customer Service Representative; Database Manager; Editor; Editorial Assistant; Financial Analyst; Graphic Designer; Human Resources Manager; Internet Services Manager; Librarian; Licensed Practical Nurse; Managing Editor; Market Research Analyst; Marketing Manager; Marketing Specialist; Mechanical Engineer; MIS Specialist; Operations Manager; Production Manager; Project Manager; Purchasing Agent/Manager; Registered Nurse; Secretary; Systems Analyst; Systems Manager; Technical Writer/Editor; Telecommunications Manager; Typist/Word Processor; Veterinarian. **Special programs:** Internships; Training.

UNIVERSITY OF SCRANTON
St. Thomas Hall, Room 104, Scranton PA 18510. 570/941-7452. **Fax:** 570/941-5937. **Contact:** Human Resources. **World Wide Web address:** http://www.uofs.edu. **Description:** A four-year university offering certificates, associate's, bachelor's, and master's degrees (including MBAs). Approximately 3,950 undergraduate and 700 graduate students attend the University of Scranton.

VILLANOVA UNIVERSITY
800 Lancaster Avenue, Villanova PA 19085-1699. 610/519-7900. **Fax:** 610/519-6667. **Contact:** Barbara Kearns, Employment Coordinator. **E-mail address:** hr@villanova.edu. **World Wide Web address:** http://www.villanova.edu. **Description:** A Catholic university serving approximately 6,000 full-time undergraduates and 4,000 graduate and part-time students in the Colleges of Arts & Sciences, Engineering, Commerce & Finance, Nursing, and Law, as well as an MBA program. Founded in 1842. **Common positions include:** Accountant; Administrative Assistant; Blue-Collar Worker Supervisor; Budget Analyst; Buyer; Chemist; Chief Financial Officer; Clerical Supervisor; Computer Animator; Computer Operator; Computer Programmer; Controller; Cost Estimator; Counselor; Database Manager; Electrician; Financial Analyst; Graphic Artist; Graphic Designer; Human Resources Manager; Librarian; MIS Specialist; Psychologist; Public Relations Specialist; Purchasing Agent/Manager; Registered Nurse; Secretary; Systems Analyst; Systems Manager; Teacher/Professor; Telecommunications Manager; Typist/Word Processor. **Corporate headquarters location:** This location. **President:** Reverend Edmund J. Dobbin. **Annual sales/revenues:** More than $100 million. **Number of employees at this location:** 1,500.

WEST CHESTER UNIVERSITY
201 Carter Drive, West Chester PA 19383. 610/436-2800. **Fax:** 610/436-3464. **Recorded jobline:** 610/436-3464. **Contact:** Office of Human Resources. **World Wide Web address:** http://www.wcupa.edu. **Description:** A four-year university offering certificates, associate's, bachelor's, and master's degrees (including MBAs). Approximately 9,300 undergraduate and 1,800 graduate students attend West Chester University.

WIDENER UNIVERSITY
One University Place, Chester PA 19013-5792. 610/499-4278. **Contact:** Human Resources Department. **World Wide Web address:** http://www.widener.edu. **Description:** A four-year university offering bachelor's, master's (including MBAs), and doctoral degrees. Approximately 4,900 undergraduate and 3,000 graduate students attend Widener.

WILKES UNIVERSITY
P.O. Box 111, Wilkes-Barre PA 18766. 570/831-4630. **Contact:** Human Resources Department. **World Wide Web address:** http://www.wilkes.edu. **Description:** A four-year university offering bachelor's and master's degrees. Approximately 1,900 undergraduate and 800 graduate students attend Wilkes University.

YORK COLLEGE OF PENNSYLVANIA
Country Club Road, York PA 17405-7199. 717/846-7788. **Contact:** Human Resources Department. **World Wide Web address:** http://www.ycp.edu. **Description:** A four-year college offering associate's, bachelor's, and master's degrees including MBAs. Approximately 4,900 undergraduate and 50 graduate students attend York College.

ELECTRONIC/INDUSTRIAL ELECTRICAL EQUIPMENT

You can expect to find the following types of companies in this chapter:

Electronic Machines and Systems • Semiconductor Manufacturers

ABB INSTRUMENTATION CO.
125 East County Line Road, Warminster PA 18974. 215/674-6000. **Contact:** Ms. Aimee Watson, Manager of Employee Relations. **World Wide Web address:** http://www.abb.com. **Description:** Engaged in the design, manufacture, sale, and service of electronic and pneumatic instruments, specific process analyzers, and analog and digital systems that measure and control flow temperatures, pressure, and level. **Listed on:** New York Stock Exchange. **Stock exchange symbol:** ABB.

ACCU-SORT SYSTEMS, INC.
511 School House Road, Telford PA 18969. 215/723-0981. **Toll-free phone:** 800/BAR-CODE. **Fax:** 215/799-1774. **Contact:** Roxanne Detweiler, Human Resources. **E-mail address:** jobs@accusort.com. **World Wide Web address:** http://www.accusort.com. **Description:** A leading manufacturer of bar code scanners and other material handling systems. **NOTE:** Entry-level positions and part-time jobs are offered. **Company slogan:** Solutions with vision. **Common positions include:** Account Manager; Accountant; Administrative Assistant; Customer Service Representative; Design Engineer; Draftsperson; Electrical/Electronics Engineer; Human Resources Manager; Manufacturing Engineer; Marketing Specialist; Mechanical Engineer; MIS Specialist; Quality Assurance Engineer; Sales Representative; Software Engineer. **Special programs:** Internships; Training; Co-ops; Summer Jobs. **Office hours:** Monday - Friday, 8:00 a.m. - 5:30 p.m. **Corporate headquarters location:** This location. **Other U.S. locations:** Nationwide. **International locations:** Worldwide. **Number of employees nationwide:** 500.

ACTION MANUFACTURING COMPANY
100 East Erie Avenue, Philadelphia PA 19134. 215/739-6400. **Contact:** Mr. Toni Capella, Human Resources. **World Wide Web address:** http://www.action-mfg.com. **Description:** A manufacturer of precision electromechanical instruments and ordnance products. **Common positions include:** Accountant/Auditor; Administrator; Chemist; Computer

Programmer; Financial Analyst; Geologist/Geophysicist; Mechanical Engineer. **Corporate headquarters location:** This location. **Operations at this facility include:** Administration; Manufacturing; Regional Headquarters.

ADVANCED ENERGY
1007 Laurel Oak Road, Voorhees NJ 08043. 856/627-6100. **Fax:** 856/627-6159. **Contact:** Human Resources. **World Wide Web address:** http://www.advanced-energy.com. **Description:** Designs, develops, manufactures, and markets ion-beam sources, plasma abatement systems, power conversion and control system solutions, and process monitoring and control tools. Founded in 1981. **NOTE:** For employment information, contact the Advanced Energy World Headquarters: 1625 Sharp Point Drive, Fort Collins CO 80525. 800/446-9167. **Corporate headquarters location:** Fort Collins CO.

ALLEGRO MICROSYSTEMS
3900 Welsh Road, Willow Grove PA 19090-2995. 215/657-8400. **Contact:** Human Resources. **E-mail address:** allegro@rpc.webhire.com. **World Wide Web address:** http://www.allegromicro.com. **Description:** Manufactures semiconductors and mixed-signal integrated circuits. **Parent company:** Sanken Electric Company Ltd.

AMETEK DREXELBROOK
205 Keith Valley Road, Horsham PA 19044. 215/674-1234. **Contact:** Personnel Department. **World Wide Web address:** http://www.drexelbrook.com. **Description:** A manufacturer of level control and level measurement instrumentation for the process control industry. **Corporate headquarters location:** This location.

AMETEK, INC.
900 Clymer Avenue, Sellersville PA 18960. 215/257-6531. **Contact:** Human Resources. **World Wide Web address:** http://www.ametek.com. **Description:** This location manufactures various types of gauges. Overall, AMETEK is a global manufacturing company that serves a variety of industrial and commercial markets through its Electromechanical, Precision Instruments, and Industrial Materials Groups. The Electromechanical Group has a leading market share in the production of electric motors for vacuum cleaners and floor care products, with a growing business in technical motor products for computer, medical, and other markets. The company operates more than 30 manufacturing facilities in 12 states. **Corporate headquarters location:** Paoli

PA. **International locations:** Denmark; England; Italy; Mexico. **Listed on:** New York Stock Exchange. **Stock exchange symbol:** AME. **Number of employees worldwide:** 6,200.

AMETEK, INC.
37 North Valley Road, Building 4, P.O. Box 1764, Paoli PA 19301. 610/647-2121. **Toll-free phone:** 800/473-1286. **Fax:** 610/296-3412. **Contact:** Human Resources. **World Wide Web address:** http://www.ametek.com. **Description:** A global manufacturing company that serves a variety of industrial and commercial markets through its Electromechanical, Precision Instruments, and Industrial Materials Groups. **Common positions include:** Accountant/Auditor; Financial Analyst; Human Resources Manager; Management Trainee; Public Relations Specialist; Purchasing Agent/Manager; Travel Agent. **Corporate headquarters location:** This location. **Other U.S. locations:** Nationwide. **International locations:** Denmark; England; Italy; Mexico. **Listed on:** New York Stock Exchange. **Stock exchange symbol:** AME. **Number of employees at this location:** 90. **Number of employees worldwide:** 6,200.

AMKOR TECHNOLOGIES
1345 Enterprise Drive, West Chester PA 19380-5964. 610/431-9600. **Contact:** Mr. Chris Roberts, Recruiting. **World Wide Web address:** http://www.amkor.com. **Description:** Provides semiconductor packaging and test service. Founded in 1968. **Common positions include:** Computer Programmer; Customer Service Representative; Electrical/Electronics Engineer; Sales Representative; Systems Analyst. **Corporate headquarters location:** This location.

BAE SYSTEMS
305 Richardson Road, Lansdale PA 19446. 215/996-2000. **Fax:** 215/996-2081. **Contact:** Kim Lundy, Human Resources. **World Wide Web address:** http://www.baesystems.com. **Description:** A leading supplier of electronic countermeasure systems and developer of electronic warfare systems that provide protection for aircraft, ships, and tanks from various missile threats.

C.W. INDUSTRIES, INC.
130 James Way, Southampton PA 18966. 215/355-7080. **Fax:** 215/355-1088. **Contact:** Human Resources. **World Wide Web address:** http://www.cwind.com. **Description:** Produces a wide range of electrical switches and connectors.

CHECKPOINT METO

101 Wolf Drive, Thorofare NJ 08086. 856/848-1800. **Fax:** 856/848-0937. **Contact:** Robert Holloway, Manager of Personnel. **E-mail address:** hresources@checkpt.com. **World Wide Web address:** http://www.checkpointsystems.com. **Description:** Develops, manufactures, and markets Electronic Article Surveillance systems to control shoplifting in retail stores and protect books and materials in libraries and universities; electronic access control systems to secure buildings and areas within buildings; and closed circuit television systems and solutions to control shoplifting and internal theft. **Corporate headquarters location:** This location.

CRANE NUCLEAR, INC.

2600 Eisenhower Avenue, Trooper PA 19403. 610/650-0330. **Fax:** 770/429-4754. **Contact:** Human Resources Department. **E-mail address:** careers@cranenuclear.com. **World Wide Web address:** http://www.cranenuclear.com. **Description:** Provides diagnostic, condition monitoring, and nondestructive testing systems and services to customers in the power and process industries worldwide. **NOTE:** Mail employment correspondence to: Corporate Headquarters, 2825 Cobb International Boulevard, Kennesaw GA 30152-4352. 770/424-6343.

FAIRCHILD SEMICONDUCTOR

125 Crestwood Road, Mountain Top PA 18707. 570/474-6761. **Fax:** 207/775-8045. **Contact:** Human Resources. **E-mail address:** corporate.resume@fairchildsemi.com. **World Wide Web address:** http://www.fairchildsemi.com. **Description:** Manufactures semiconductors. **NOTE:** Mail resumes to: Mail Stop 35-1D, 82 Running Hill Road, South Portland ME 04106. **Listed on:** New York Stock Exchange. **Stock exchange symbol:** FCS.

FINCOR ELECTRONICS
IMO INDUSTRIES, INC.

3750 East Market Street, York PA 17402. 717/751-4200. **Toll-free phone:** 800/334-3024. **Fax:** 717/751-4372. **Contact:** Human Resources Department. **World Wide Web address:** http://www.fincor.net. **Description:** Produces electronic controls for industrial and graphic arts uses. **Common positions include:** Electrical/Electronics Engineer. **Corporate headquarters location:** Lawrenceville NJ. **Operations at this facility include:** Manufacturing. **Listed on:** New York Stock Exchange. **Number of employees at this location:** 250. **Number of employees nationwide:** 6,200.

GENERAL ELECTRIC COMPANY

6901 Elmwood Avenue, Philadelphia PA 19142. 215/726-2626. **Contact:** Joanne McGroarty, Human Resources. **World Wide Web address:** http://www.ge.com. **Description:** This location is the switchgear division, manufacturing components and parts. Overall, General Electric operates in the following areas: aircraft engines including jet engines, replacement parts, and repair services for commercial, military, executive, and commuter aircraft; appliances; broadcasting through NBC; industrial including lighting products, electrical distribution and control equipment, transportation systems products, electric motors and related products, a broad range of electrical and electronic industrial automation products, and a network of electrical supply houses; materials including plastics, ABS resins, silicones, superabrasives, and laminates; power systems including products for the generation, transmission, and distribution of electricity; technical products and systems including medical systems and equipment, as well as a full range of computer-based information and data interchange services for both internal use and external commercial and industrial customers; and capital services including consumer services, financing, and specialty insurance. **Listed on:** New York Stock Exchange. **Stock exchange symbol:** GE. **Number of employees worldwide:** 230,000.

HONEYWELL INC.

P.O. Box 934, York PA 17405. 717/771-8100. **Contact:** Human Resources Department. **World Wide Web address:** http://www.honeywell.com. **Description:** This location manufactures industrial and programmable controls for a wide range of manufacturers. Overall, Honeywell is engaged in the research, development, manufacture, and sale of advanced technology products and services in the fields of chemicals, electronics, automation, and controls. The company's major businesses are home and building automation and control, performance polymers and chemicals, industrial automation and control, space and aviation systems, and defense and marine systems. **Listed on:** New York Stock Exchange. **Stock exchange symbol:** HON.

INTEGRATED CIRCUIT SYSTEMS, INC.

2435 Boulevard of the Generals, Norristown PA 19403. 610/630-5300. **Fax:** 610/630-5399. **Contact:** Human Resources. **World Wide Web address:** http://www.icst.com. **Description:** Integrated Circuit Systems, Inc. designs, develops, and markets innovative, very large-scale integrated (VSLI) circuits including standard and custom application-specific integrated circuit (ASIC) products, using mixed analog/digital technology. Products are marketed to original equipment manufacturers for use in video graphics display products, CPU (central processing unit) systems, PC multimedia, and portable device battery charging applications. **Corporate headquarters location:** This location. **Listed on:** NASDAQ. **Stock exchange symbol:** ICST.

KULICKE & SOFFA INDUSTRIES, INC. (K&S)
2101 Blair Mill Road, Willow Grove PA 19090. 215/784-6000. **Toll-free phone:** 800/523-1321. **Fax:** 215/659-7588. **Contact:** Human Resources Department. **E-mail address:** hr@kns.com. **World Wide Web address:** http://www.kns.com. **Description:** A leader in semiconductor assembly systems and services. The company designs, manufactures, markets, and supports equipment for IC and MCM/hybrid semiconductor manufacturers worldwide. Kulicke & Soffa Industries, Inc.'s product lines include wafer and hard materials dicing, die bonding and wire bonding equipment, service and spare parts, and the Micro-Swiss line of bonding and dicing tools and production accessories. With sales and service operations in 15 countries, K&S is one of the largest suppliers of semiconductor assembly equipment in the world, as well as one of the world's largest suppliers of automatic wire bonders. Founded in 1951. **Common positions include:** Account Manager; Accountant; Applications Engineer; Assembler; Blue-Collar Worker Supervisor; Buyer; Clerical Supervisor; Computer Programmer; Credit Manager; Customer Service Representative; Electrical/Electronics Engineer; Financial Analyst; Human Resources Manager; Manufacturing Engineer; Marketing Manager; Marketing Specialist; Mechanical Engineer; MIS Specialist; Production Manager; Purchasing Agent/Manager; Quality Control Supervisor; Sales Engineer; Secretary; Software Engineer; Systems Analyst; Systems Manager; Technical Writer/Editor; Typist/Word Processor. **Corporate headquarters location:** This location. **Other U.S. locations:** Santa Clara CA. **International locations:** Worldwide. **Operations at this facility include:** Administration; Manufacturing; Research and Development; Sales; Service. **Listed on:** NASDAQ. **Stock exchange symbol:** KLIC. **Annual sales/revenues:** More than $100 million. **Number of employees at this location:** 900. **Number of employees worldwide:** 2,400.

LOCKHEED MARTIN NAVAL ELECTRONICS & SURVEILLANCE SYSTEMS

459 Kennedy Drive, Archbald PA 18403. 570/803-2300. **Contact:** Personnel. **E-mail address:** jobs.lmco@lmco.com. **World Wide Web address:** http://www.lmco.com. **Description:** Manufactures instrumentation and controls for the U.S. Nuclear Reactor Program; fusing and sensor systems; expendable jammers; live-fire training missiles and rounds; and a complete line of thickness gages for the production of steel and aluminum worldwide. Overall, Lockheed Martin is an aerospace and technology company engaged in the design, manufacture, and management of systems and products in the fields of space, defense, electronics, communications, information management, energy, and materials. **Listed on:** New York Stock Exchange. **Stock exchange symbol:** LMT.

MARS ELECTRONICS INTERNATIONAL

1301 Wilson Drive, West Chester PA 19380. 610/430-2500. **Fax:** 610/430-2590. **Contact:** Human Resources Department. **World Wide Web address:** http://www.meiglobal.com. **Description:** Manufactures card-based cashless payment systems, electronic audit, and electronic coin/bill acceptors and change-giving machines for the amusement, gaming, retail, telecommunications, and transport industries. **Parent company:** Mars, Inc.

PEI-GENESIS

2180 Hornig Road, Philadelphia PA 19116-4289. 215/673-0400. **Toll-free phone:** 800/675-1214. **Fax:** 215/552-8022. **Contact:** Human Resources. **World Wide Web address:** http://www.pei-genesis.com. **Description:** A distributor of a variety of electronic parts. Founded in 1946.

POLY-PLANAR, INC.

P.O. Box 2578, Warminster PA 18974. 215/675-7805. **Physical address:** 1095 Mearns Road, Warminster PA 18974. **Contact:** Barbara Lange, Personnel Director. **World Wide Web address:** http://www.polyplanar.com. **Description:** Produces and distributes portable electronics products including all-weather loudspeakers for communications systems. Poly-Planar also manufactures consumer audio products, primarily speakers. **Corporate headquarters location:** This location.

PULSE SPECIALTY COMPONENTS

2 Pearl Buck Court, Bristol PA 19007-6812. 215/781-6400. **Contact:** Donna Ricciuti, Human Resources Manager. **World Wide Web address:** http://www.pulseeng.com. **Description:**

One of the world's leading suppliers of magnetic components. Overall, Pulse Engineering designs, manufactures, and markets a variety of electronic components and modules for original equipment manufacturers in the data processing, telecommunications networking, and power supply markets. **Common positions include:** Customer Service Representative. **Corporate headquarters location:** San Diego CA. **Parent company:** Technitrol.

SI HANDLING SYSTEMS INC.
PARAGON TECHNOLOGIES COMPANY
600 Kubler Road, Easton PA 18040. 610/252-7321. **Fax:** 610/250-9677. **Contact:** Human Resources. **World Wide Web address:** http://www.sihs.com. **Description:** Designs, manufactures, sells, and installs computer-directed, automated material-handling and automated order selection systems and equipment worldwide. **Common positions include:** Accountant/Auditor; Draftsperson; Electrical/Electronics Engineer; Industrial Engineer; Mechanical Engineer; Software Engineer. **Corporate headquarters location:** This location. **Parent company:** Paragon Technologies Company (also at this location). **Operations at this facility include:** Administration; Manufacturing; Research and Development; Sales; Service. **Number of employees at this location:** 175. **Number of employees nationwide:** 225.

SPD TECHNOLOGIES
13500 Roosevelt Boulevard, Philadelphia PA 19116. 215/677-4900. **Contact:** Jackie Taylor, Employee Relations Generalist. **World Wide Web address:** http://www.spdtech.com. **Description:** A world leader in the design, development, and manufacture of circuit breakers, switchgear, and related electrical protection systems for shipboard applications worldwide. **Common positions include:** Account Representative; Accountant; Administrative Assistant; Administrative Manager; Applications Engineer; Assistant Manager; Blue-Collar Worker Supervisor; Buyer; Chief Financial Officer; Clerical Supervisor; Computer Operator; Computer Programmer; Controller; Customer Service Representative; Database Manager; Design Engineer; Draftsperson; Electrical/Electronics Engineer; Electrician; Finance Director; Financial Analyst; Human Resources Manager; Industrial Engineer; Industrial Production Manager; Manufacturing Engineer; Marketing Manager; Marketing Specialist; Mechanical Engineer; MIS Specialist; Operations Manager; Production Manager; Project Manager; Purchasing Agent/Manager; Quality Control Supervisor; Sales Engineer;

Sales Executive; Sales Manager; Sales Representative; Secretary; Software Engineer; Systems Manager; Technical Writer/Editor; Transportation/Traffic Specialist. **Corporate headquarters location:** This location. **Subsidiaries include:** Henschel, Newburyport MA; Pac Ord, San Diego CA; SPD Switchgear, Montgomeryville PA. **Operations at this facility include:** Administration; Divisional Headquarters; Manufacturing; Research and Development; Sales. **Number of employees at this location:** 450. **Number of employees worldwide:** 800.

SPS TECHNOLOGIES
301 Highland Avenue, Jenkintown PA 19046. 215/572-3000. **Contact:** Human Resources Department. **World Wide Web address:** http://www.spstech.com. **Description:** Engaged in the design, manufacture, and marketing of high-tech fastener products, including precision components and computer-controlled tightening equipment and special materials. SPS Technologies maintains more than 15 manufacturing plants and sales offices located worldwide. **Common positions include:** Accountant/Auditor; Computer Programmer; Electrical/Electronics Engineer; Financial Analyst; Industrial Engineer; Marketing Specialist; Mechanical Engineer; Metallurgical Engineer; Operations/Production Manager. **Corporate headquarters location:** Newtown PA. **Subsidiaries include:** Henschel (Newburyport MA); Pac Ord (San Diego CA); SPD Switchgear (Montgomeryville PA). **Operations at this facility include:** Administration; Divisional Headquarters; Manufacturing; Research and Development; Sales; Service. **Listed on:** New York Stock Exchange. **Stock exchange symbol:** ST.

SIMKAR CORPORATION
700 Ramona Avenue, Philadelphia PA 19120-4691. 215/831-7700. **Fax:** 215/831-7703. **Contact:** Ken McArthur, Vice President of Human Resources. **World Wide Web address:** http://www.simkar.com. **Description:** Manufactures and markets H.I.D., fluorescent, and vandal-proof lighting fixtures for the industrial and consumer markets. **Common positions include:** Accountant/Auditor; Customer Service Representative; Management Trainee; Manufacturer's/Wholesaler's Sales Rep.; Manufacturing Engineer. **Corporate headquarters location:** This location.

TRITON ETD
3100 Charlotte Avenue, Easton PA 18044-0100. 610/252-7331. **Contact:** Dan Flannery, Director of Personnel. **World**

Wide Web address: http://www.tritonetd.com. **Description:** Manufactures and markets special-purpose electron tubes and integrated microwave subsystems for use in communications, defense, industrial, scientific, and medical applications. **Common positions include:** Accountant/Auditor; Buyer; Ceramics Engineer; Draftsperson; Electrical/Electronics Engineer; General Manager; Human Resources Manager; Industrial Engineer; Manufacturer's/Wholesaler's Sales Representative; Marketing Specialist; Mechanical Engineer; Operations/Production Manager; Purchasing Agent/Manager; Quality Control Supervisor; Systems Analyst. **Corporate headquarters location:** New York NY.

TYCO ELECTRONICS
2405 Maryland Road, Willow Grove PA 19090. 215/657-6202. **Fax:** 215/784-4514. **Contact:** Rick Whitehurst, Human Resources Director. **World Wide Web address:** http://www.tycoelectronics.com. **Description:** Tyco Electronics is a multinational company that designs, manufactures, and supports surface mount equipment and related peripherals and services used in the manufacture of printed circuit boards. **NOTE:** Entry-level positions are offered. **Common positions include:** Account Manager; Accountant; Administrative Assistant; Advertising Executive; Applications Engineer; Assistant Manager; Attorney; Controller; Electrical/Electronics Engineer; Finance Director; Human Resources Manager; Management Analyst/Consultant; Marketing Manager; Mechanical Engineer; MIS Specialist; Project Manager; Quality Control Supervisor; Secretary; Software Engineer. **Special programs:** Summer Jobs. **Corporate headquarters location:** This location. **Other U.S. locations:** Nationwide. **International locations:** Worldwide. **Listed on:** New York Stock Exchange. **Stock exchange symbol:** TYC. **Annual sales/revenues:** $51 - $100 million. **Number of employees at this location:** 280. **Number of employees worldwide:** 380.

ENVIRONMENTAL AND WASTE MANAGEMENT SERVICES

You can expect to find the following types of companies in this chapter:

Environmental Engineering Firms • Sanitary Services

AIR PRODUCTS AND CHEMICALS, INC.

7201 Hamilton Boulevard, Allentown PA 18195. 610/481-4911. **Contact:** Human Resources Department. **World Wide Web address:** http://www.airproducts.com. **Description:** Manufactures industrial gases, process equipment, and chemicals. The company's products include cryogenic equipment, air separation systems, hydrogen purification devices, and nitrogen rejection equipment. In addition, the company provides engineering services, and is involved in landfill gas recovery, waste management, waste-to-energy ventures, flue gas desulfurization, and cogeneration operations. **Common positions include:** Chemical Engineer; Financial Analyst; Mechanical Engineer. **Special programs:** Internships. **Corporate headquarters location:** This location. **Other U.S. locations:** Nationwide. **International locations:** Worldwide. **Listed on:** New York Stock Exchange. **Stock exchange symbol:** APD. **Annual sales/revenues:** More than $100 million.

CAMP DRESSER & McKEE, INC. (CDM)

205 Granite Run Drive, Suite 350, Lancaster PA 17601. 717/560-7500. **Contact:** Human Resources. **World Wide Web address:** http://www.cdm.com. **Description:** Camp Dresser & McKee is a worldwide provider of environmental engineering, scientific, planning, and management services. The company focuses on professional activities for the management of water resources, hazardous and solid wastes, wastewater, infrastructure, and environmental systems for industry and government. **Corporate headquarters location:** Cambridge MA.

CLEAN HARBORS, INC.

2301 Pennsylvania Avenue, Deptford NJ 08096. 856/589-5000. **Toll-free phone:** 800/544-3128. **Fax:** 856/227-9350. **Contact:** Human Resources Department. **World Wide Web address:** http://www.cleanharbors.com. **Description:** Clean Harbors, Inc., through its subsidiaries, provides comprehensive environmental services in 35 states in the Northeast, Midwest, Central, and Mid-Atlantic regions. Clean Harbors provides a wide range of hazardous waste management and environmental support services to a diversified customer base from over 40 locations. The company's hazardous waste management services include treatment, storage, recycling, transportation, risk analysis, site assessment, laboratory analysis, site closure, and disposal of hazardous materials through environmentally sound methods including incineration. Environmental remediation services include emergency response, surface remediation, groundwater restoration, industrial maintenance, and facility decontamination. **NOTE:** See Website for current job opportunities and contact information. **Corporate headquarters location:** Braintree MA. **Other U.S. locations:** Nationwide. **Number of employees nationwide:** 1,400.

DOOLAN INDUSTRIES, INC.
P.O. Box 73, Berlin NJ 08091. 856/791-9250. **Contact:** Tim Stein, President/CEO. **Description:** A holding company. Founded in 1938. **Common positions include:** Environmental Engineer; Sales Representative. **Subsidiaries include:** Doolan Environmental performs remediation and water filtration services. Doolan General Services provides contract facility management for maintenance and repair. Doolan Recovery Technologies recycles fluorescent lamps. Doolan Steel is a steel service center. Psycho Design provides truck lettering, signs, graphics, and striping. **Operations at this facility include:** Administration; Divisional Headquarters; Sales. **Listed on:** Privately held. **Annual sales/revenues:** $5 - $10 million. **Number of employees at this location:** 10. **Number of employees nationwide:** 45.

HARDING ESE
5205 Militia Hill Road, Plymouth Meeting PA 19462. 610/941-9700. **Contact:** Personnel Director. **World Wide Web address:** http://www.mactec.com. **Description:** Offers a full range of services in environmental and engineering consulting, laboratory analysis, asbestos management, industrial hygiene, engineering, and architecture for governmental, industrial, and commercial clients. **Parent company:** MACTEC, Inc. **Other U.S. locations:** Nationwide.

FABRICATED/PRIMARY METALS AND PRODUCTS

You can expect to find the following types of companies in this chapter:
Aluminum and Copper Foundries • Die-Castings • Iron and Steel Foundries • Steel Works, Blast Furnaces, and Rolling Mills

AMERICAN WIRE WORKS
3380 Tulip Street, Philadelphia PA 19134. 215/744-6600. **Contact:** Human Resources. **Description:** A wire manufacturer and processor. **Number of employees at this location:** 15.

BETHLEHEM LUKENS PLATE
ARC Building, 139 Modena Road, Box 3001, Coatesville PA 19320. 610/383-2000. **Contact:** Human Resources. **E-mail address:** careers@bethsteel.com. **World Wide Web address:** http://www.bethsteel.com. **Description:** Manufactures carbon, alloy, clad plate steel, stainless sheet, and strip plate. Customers include steel service centers, OEMs, and fabricators. **Common positions include:** Accountant/Auditor; Aircraft Mechanic/Engine Specialist; Attorney; Blue-Collar Worker Supervisor; Budget Analyst; Buyer; Ceramics Engineer; Chemical Engineer; Computer Programmer; Customer Service Representative; Electrical/Electronics Engineer; Human Resources Manager; Manufacturer's/Wholesaler's Sales Rep.; Materials Engineer; Mechanical Engineer; Metallurgical Engineer; Operations/Production Manager; Quality Control Supervisor; Statistician; Systems Analyst; Transportation/Traffic Specialist. **Listed on:** New York Stock Exchange. **Stock exchange symbol:** BS.

BETHLEHEM STEEL CORPORATION
1170 Eighth Avenue, Bethlehem PA 18016-7699. 610/694-2424. **Contact:** Leonard Kesselring, Manager of Human Resources. **E-mail address:** careers@bethsteel.com. **World Wide Web address:** http://www.bethsteel.com. **Description:** Manufactures and sells a wide variety of steel mill products including sheet and tin mill products, plates, bars, rods, and other related products. Operations of Bethlehem Steel also include marine construction and repair, and the mining and sale of raw materials. **Corporate headquarters location:** This location. **Subsidiaries include:** Pennsylvania Steel Technologies, Inc. **Listed on:** New York Stock Exchange. **Stock exchange symbol:** BS. **Annual sales/revenues:** More than $100 million.

BUCK COMPANY, INC.
897 Lancaster Pike, Quarryville PA 17566-9738. 717/284-4114. **Contact:** Mark Broich, Manager of Employee Services. **E-mail address:** bsafe@buckcompany.com. **World Wide Web address:** http://www.buckcompany.com. **Description:** Manufactures malleable aluminum and related products, and brass alloy and gray iron castings.

CABOT PERFORMANCE MATERIALS
County Line Road, Boyertown PA 19512-1608. 610/367-2181. **Contact:** Debby Eschbach, Human Resources. **World Wide Web address:** http://www.cabot-corp.com. **Description:** Manufactures aluminum master alloys and tantalum metal products. **Corporate headquarters location:** Boston MA. **Parent company:** Cabot Corporation.

G.O. CARLSON, INC.
350 Marshallton-Thorndale Road, Downington PA 19335-2063. 610/384-2800. **Toll-free phone:** 800/338-5622. **Fax:** 610/383-6032. **Contact:** Kristin DiFonzo, Human Resources Manager. **E-mail address:** kdifonzo@gocarlson.com. **World Wide Web address:** http://www.gocarlson.com. **Description:** Manufactures stainless steel, nickel alloys, and titanium plate and plate products. **Common positions include:** Computer Programmer; Credit Manager; Customer Service Rep.; Electrical/Electronics Engineer; Human Resources Manager; Mechanical Engineer. **Corporate headquarters location:** This location. **Operations at this facility include:** Administration. **Number of employees at this location:** 150.

COLONIAL METALS COMPANY
217 Linden Street, Columbia PA 17512. 717/684-2311. **Contact:** Robert Shaffer, Personnel Manager. **Description:** Manufactures bronze, brass, and aluminum ingots. **Common positions include:** Administrator; Blue-Collar Worker Supervisor; Buyer; Chemist; Claim Representative; Department Manager; Manufacturer's/Wholesaler's Sales Rep.; Purchasing Agent/Manager; Transportation/Traffic Specialist. **Corporate headquarters location:** This location. **Operations at this facility include:** Administration; Manufacturing; Sales.

CONTAINER RESEARCH CORPORATION
P.O. Box 159, Glen Riddle PA 19037. 610/459-2160. **Contact:** Hank Kalinowsky, Personnel Manager. **World Wide Web address:** http://www.crc-flex.com. **Description:** Engaged in sheet metal fabrication.

DOOLAN INDUSTRIES, INC.
P.O. Box 73, Berlin NJ 08091. 856/791-9250. **Contact:** Tim Stein, President/CEO. **Description:** A holding company. Founded in 1938. **Common positions include:** Environmental Engineer; Sales Representative. **Subsidiaries include:** Doolan Environmental performs remediation and water filtration services. Doolan General Services provides contract facility management for maintenance and repair. Doolan Recovery Technologies recycles fluorescent lamps. Doolan Steel is a steel service center. Psycho Design provides truck lettering, signs, graphics, and striping. **Operations at this facility include:** Administration; Divisional Headquarters; Sales. **Listed on:** Privately held. **Annual sales/revenues:** $5 - $10 million. **Number of employees at this location:** 10. **Number of employees nationwide:** 45.

ENVIROSOURCE
1155 Business Center Drive, Horsham PA 19044. 215/956-5500. **Fax:** 215/956-5588. **Contact:** Michael R. Rochester, Director of Personnel. **E-mail address:** m.rochester@enso.net. **World Wide Web address:** http://www.enso.net. **Description:** A steel slag recovery company. **Corporate headquarters location:** This location. **Parent company:** IMS.

HARSCO CORPORATION
P.O. Box 8888, Camp Hill PA 17001-8888. 717/763-7064. **Physical address:** 350 Poplar Church Road, Camp Hill PA 17001. **Fax:** 717/612-5619. **Contact:** Jerry Vinci, Director of Human Resources Department. **World Wide Web address:** http://www.harsco.com. **Description:** Harsco Corporation is a diversified industrial manufacturing and service company that conducts business through 10 divisions and has 16 classes of products and services. Operations fall into three groups: Metal Reclamation and Mill Services includes scrap management, slab management systems, iron making, materials handling, equipment rental, recycling technology, aggregate marketing, and nonferrous metallurgical industry services; Infrastructure and Construction includes railway maintenance equipment, industrial grating products, and scaffolding, shoring, and concrete forming equipment; and Process Industry Products includes industrial pipe fittings, process equipment, and gas control and containment equipment. **Common positions include:** Accountant/Auditor; Attorney; Buyer; Computer Programmer; Draftsperson; Editor; Environmental Engineer; Financial Analyst; Human Resources Manager; Industrial Production Manager; Mechanical Engineer; Public Relations Specialist; Purchasing Agent/Manager; Quality Control

Supervisor; Structural Engineer; Systems Analyst. **Special programs:** Internships. **Corporate headquarters location:** This location. **Other U.S. locations:** Nationwide. **Listed on:** New York Stock Exchange. **Stock exchange symbol:** HSC. **Number of employees at this location:** 90. **Number of employees worldwide:** 13,000.

HECKETT MULTISERV
612 North Main Street, Box 1071, Butler PA 16001. 724/283-5741. **Contact:** John Cupps, Vice President of Administration. **World Wide Web address:** http://www.heckettmultiserv.com. **Description:** Provides steel mill services.

HIGH INDUSTRIES, INC.
P.O. Box 10008, 1853 William Penn Way, Lancaster PA 17605-0008. 717/293-4486. **Contact:** Vincent Mizeras, Director of Human Resources. **World Wide Web address:** http://www.high.net. **Description:** Operates through several areas of business including design and construction, food services, hotel management, prestress/precast concrete products, real estate development and management, and steel fabrication. **Common positions include:** Accountant/Auditor; Architect; Civil Engineer; Computer Programmer; Customer Service Representative; Draftsperson; Hotel Manager; Human Resources Manager; Services Sales Representative; Systems Analyst. **Corporate headquarters location:** This location. **Operations at this facility include:** Administration; Manufacturing.

HOFMANN INDUSTRIES, INC.
3145 Shillington Road, P.O. Box 2147, Sinking Spring PA 19608. 610/678-8051. **Fax:** 610/678-1091. **Contact:** Human Resources Department. **World Wide Web address:** http://www.hofmann.com. **Description:** Manufactures and markets fabricated, powder-coated, zinc-plated, and electric-welded steel tubing to the houseware, hardware, furniture, lawn and garden, automotive, and recreational markets. **Common positions include:** Accountant/Auditor; Blue-Collar Worker Supervisor; Buyer; Computer Programmer; Credit Manager; Customer Service Representative; Electrician; General Manager; Human Resources Manager; Industrial Engineer; Industrial Production Manager; Manufacturer's/Wholesaler's Sales Representative.; Purchasing Agent/Manager; Systems Analyst; Typist/Word Processor. **Corporate headquarters location:** This location. **Other U.S. locations:** Eau Claire MI. **Listed on:** Privately held. **Annual**

sales/revenues: $21 - $50 million. **Number of employees at this location:** 300. **Number of employees nationwide:** 375.

IMC GROUP
165 Township Line Road, One Pitcairn Place, Suite 1200, Jenkintown PA 19046-3531. 215/517-6090. **Contact:** Human Resources Department. **E-mail address:** hr@imc-group.com. **World Wide Web address:** http://www.imc-group.com. **Description:** A metals refinery that is also engaged in the distribution of metals and chemicals. **Common positions include:** Administrator; Advertising Clerk; Blue-Collar Worker Supervisor; Claim Representative; Credit Manager; Customer Service Representative; Human Resources Manager; Manufacturer's/Wholesaler's Sales Rep.; Marketing Specialist; Metallurgical Engineer; Operations/Production Manager; Purchasing Agent/Manager; Quality Control Supervisor; Transportation/Traffic Specialist. **Corporate headquarters location:** This location. **Operations at this facility include:** Administration; Manufacturing; Regional Headquarters; Sales; Service.

OSRAM SYLVANIA, INC.
1128 Roosevelt Avenue, York PA 17404. 717/848-8080. **Fax:** 717/852-0875. **Contact:** Deb Barshinger, Human Resources. **E-mail address:** deb.barshinger@sylvania.com. **World Wide Web address:** http://www.sylvania.com. **Description:** This location manufactures automotive connectors, deep-drawn metal stampings, lighting components, metal base and stampings, wire drawing and lead wires, formed metal components for the lighting industry, custom metal stampings, and connector products. Overall, the company operates in four divisions: Coated Coil Operation produces tungsten filaments coated with high-performance insulator aluminum oxide for use in television electron guns; Special Refractory Products manufactures products made from refractory metals that are used as furnace hardware; The Ceramics Department produces various types of steatite ceramic electrical insulators used in bases of light bulbs; The Quartz Department produces and finishes quartz crucibles for use by the semiconductor industry. Founded in 1953. **NOTE:** Second and third shifts are offered. **Common positions include:** Accountant; Administrative Assistant; Controller; Design Engineer; Draftsperson; Electrical/Electronics Engineer; Electrician; Environmental Engineer; General Manager; Human Resources Manager; Mechanical Engineer; MIS Specialist; Operations Manager; Production Manager; Purchasing Agent/Manager; Quality Assurance Engineer; Quality Control Supervisor. **Special**

programs: Apprenticeships; Co-ops. **Office hours:** Monday - Friday, 7:30 a.m. - 4:30 p.m. **Corporate headquarters location:** Danvers MA. **Parent company:** OSRAM. **Listed on:** Privately held. **Annual sales/revenues:** $51 - $100 million. **Number of employees at this location:** 310. **Number of employees nationwide:** 16,000.

PENN ENGINEERING & MANUFACTURING CORPORATION
P.O. Box 1000, Danboro PA 18916. 215/766-8853. **Contact:** Human Resources Department. **World Wide Web address:** http://www.pemnet.com. **Description:** Manufactures stainless steel and aluminum fasteners and fastening equipment.

UNICAST COMPANY
241 North Washington Street, Boyertown PA 19512. 610/367-0155. **Contact:** James Mooney, Human Resources. **World Wide Web address:** http://www.unicastco.com. **Description:** A manufacturer of gray iron and aluminum castings. **Common positions include:** Industrial Engineer; Metallurgical Engineer; Operations/Production Manager; Quality Control Supervisor. **Corporate headquarters location:** This location. **Operations at this facility include:** Administration; Manufacturing; Sales. **Number of employees at this location:** 120.

WARD MANUFACTURING INC.
115 Gulick Street, Blossburg PA 16912. 570/638-2131. **Fax:** 570/638-3410. **Contact:** Human Resources Manager. **E-mail address:** hr@wardmfg.com. **World Wide Web address:** http://www.wardmfg.com. **Description:** Manufactures cast iron and malleable iron pipe fittings.

FINANCIAL SERVICES

You can expect to find the following types of companies in this chapter:

Consumer Finance and Credit Agencies • Investment Specialists • Mortgage Bankers and Loan Brokers • Security and Commodity Brokers, Dealers, and Exchanges

ADVANTA CORPORATION
Welsh & McKean Road, P.O. Box 844, Spring House PA 19477. 215/657-4000. **Contact:** Human Resources. **World Wide Web address:** http://www.advanta.com. **Description:** This location is the principal operating office. Overall, Advanta Corporation is a consumer financial services holding company. The company provides origination and management services for credit cards and mortgages; markets deposit products; and engages in credit insurance, life insurance, disability insurance, and unemployment insurance services. **Corporate headquarters location:** This location. **Other U.S. locations:** CA; MD; NJ; NY. **Subsidiaries include:** Advanta Leasing Corporation specializes in small-ticket equipment leasing; Colonial National Bank offers traditional financial services. **Listed on:** NASDAQ. **Stock exchange symbol:** ADVNA; ADVNB. **Number of employees nationwide:** 1,750.

CENDANT MORTGAGE
3000 Leadenhill Road, Mount Laurel NJ 08054. 856/439-6000. **Contact:** Human Resources Department. **E-mail address:** mortgage@cendantjobs.com. **World Wide Web address:** http://www.cendantmortgage.com. **Description:** Provides mortgage financing. **Other U.S. locations:** Hunt Valley MD. **Parent company:** Cendant Corporation.

COLLEGE CREDIT CARD CORPORATION
1500 JFK Boulevard, Suite 800, Philadelphia PA 19102. 215/568-1700. **Fax:** 215/568-1701. **Contact:** Andy Miller, Recruitment Manager. **Description:** Markets credit cards and other financial services to college students on-campus and to the general public at special events and venues. **Special programs:** Internships. **Corporate headquarters location:** This location. **Other U.S. locations:** Monroeville PA. **Parent company:** Campus Dimensions Inc. **Operations at this facility include:** Administration; Sales; Service. **Listed on:** Privately held. **Number of employees at this location:** 60. **Number of employees nationwide:** 115.

DVI, INC.
2500 York Road, Jamison PA 18929. 215/488-5000. **Recorded jobline:** 800/665-4384. **Fax:** 215/488-5401. **Contact:** Human Resources. **E-mail address:** careers@dvi-inc.com. **World Wide Web address:** http://www.dvi-inc.com. **Description:** A specialty finance company. Its core business is financing higher-cost diagnostic imaging, radiation therapy, and other types of sophisticated medical equipment for outpatient health care centers, groups of physicians, and hospitals. The company has extensive expertise in providing large loans to health care providers in markets that are typically undeserved by most banks and finance companies. In addition to equipment financing, a small but growing part of the company's business is providing capital loans to outpatient health care providers secured by their medical receivables and other collateral. **Listed on:** New York Stock Exchange. **Stock exchange symbol:** DVI.

DELAWARE INVESTMENTS
2005 Market Street, Philadelphia PA 19103. 215/255-1200. **Fax:** 215/255-1002. **Contact:** Human Resources Department. **World Wide Web address:** http://www.delawarefunds.com. **Description:** Specializes in mutual funds and investment management.

DUN & BRADSTREET INFORMATIONAL RESOURCES
899 Eaton Avenue, Bethlehem PA 18025. 610/882-7000. **Contact:** Human Resources Department. **World Wide Web address:** http://www.dnb.com. **Description:** Provides business-to-business credit, marketing, and investment management services.

FIRST CLEARFIELD FUNDS INC.
1801 JFK Boulevard, Suite 1109, Philadelphia PA 19103. 215/557-8620. **Contact:** Human Resources. **Description:** Provides homeowner loans.

FISERV
2005 Market Street, Philadelphia PA 19103-3212. 215/636-3000. **Contact:** Anna DiDio, Vice President of Human Resources. **World Wide Web address:** http://www.fiserv.com. **Description:** Provides integrated processing and support services to securities brokerage affiliates of its owner institutions.

GMAC MORTGAGE CORPORATION

100 Witmer Road, P.O. Box 963, Horsham PA 19044-0963. 215/682-1000. **Contact:** Human Resources Department. **World Wide Web address:** http://www.gmacmortgage.com. **Description:** Provides a wide range of mortgage banking and related financial services. Founded in 1908. **Common positions include:** Accountant/Auditor; Attorney; Branch Manager; Computer Programmer; Customer Service Representative; Electrician; Financial Analyst; Human Resources Manager; Management Trainee; Purchasing Agent/Manager; Securities Sales Representative; Systems Analyst; Underwriter/Assistant Underwriter. **Special programs:** Internships. **Office hours:** Monday - Friday, 8:30 a.m. - 5:00 p.m. **Corporate headquarters location:** Bloomington MN. **Other U.S. locations:** Nationwide. **Subsidiaries include:** Residential Funding Corporation. **Parent company:** General Motors Corporation is one of the world's largest full-line vehicle manufacturers with substantial interests in information technology, electronics, and finance. GM conducts business through the following sectors: North American Automotive Operations includes Sales/Service Groups (Buick, Cadillac, Chevrolet, GMC Truck, Oldsmobile, Pontiac, and Saturn) and Vehicle Development Groups (Powertrain, Truck Group, Small Car Group, and Midsize/Luxury Car Group). Delphi Automotive Systems consists of Delphi Chassis Systems, Delphi Packard Electric Systems, Delphi Energy & Engine Management Systems, Delphi Saginaw Steering Systems, Delphi Harrison Thermal Systems, Delphi Interior & Lighting Systems, Delphi Automotive Systems European Region, Delphi Automotive Systems Asia/Pacific Region, and Delphi Automotive Systems South America. International Operations include GM Europe; Asia Pacific Operations; and Latin America, Africa, Middle East Operations. EDS applies information technologies to more than 8,000 customers globally in the communications, energy/chemical, insurance, public sector, travel and transportation, financial services, manufacturing, and retail industries. GM Hughes Electronics Corporation is involved in automotive electronics, telecommunications and space electronics, and defense electronics. **Operations at this facility include:** Administration; Research and Development; Sales; Service. **Number of employees at this location:** 800. **Number of employees nationwide:** 3,300.

INDEPENDENCE FINANCIAL GROUP

150 Monument Road, Suite 310, Bala-Cynwyd PA 19004. 610/771-0800. **Contact:** Human Resources. **Description:**

Offers a variety of financial products including individual and group life and health insurance, individual and group pension policies, annuities, individual stocks and bonds, and professionally managed investment funds. **Common positions include:** Branch Manager; Customer Service Representative; Department Manager; Financial Analyst; Financial Services Sales Representative; General Manager; Insurance Agent/Broker; Management Trainee; Office Manager; Sales Manager; Systems Analyst. **Special programs:** Internships. **Corporate headquarters location:** Horsham PA. **Parent company:** Penn Mutual Life Insurance Company. **Operations at this facility include:** Sales.

JANNEY MONTGOMERY SCOTT INC. (JMS)

1801 Market Street, 9th Floor, Philadelphia PA 19103. 215/665-6000. **Toll-free phone:** 800/JAN-NEYS. **Fax:** 215/587-9623. **Contact:** Human Resources Department. **E-mail address:** careers@jmsonline.com. **World Wide Web address:** http://www.janneys.com. **Description:** A full-service brokerage firm with over 60 branch offices. **Common positions include:** Accountant/Auditor; Financial Services Sales Representative; Securities Sales Representative. **Corporate headquarters location:** This location. **Parent company:** Penn Mutual Life Insurance Company. **Operations at this facility include:** Sales.

PARENTE RANDOLPH, PC

46 Public Square, Suite 400, Wilkes-Barre PA 18701. 570/820-0100. **Fax:** 570/824-9865. **Contact:** Vicky Micheletti, Human Resources Administrator. **E-mail address:** hr@parentenet.com. **World Wide Web address:** http://www.parentenet.com. **Description:** Founded in 1970, Parente Randolph is one of the mid-Atlantic's leading independent accounting and consulting firms. The firm's 400 employees provide accounting, audit, tax, and general business consulting services to corporations and closely held businesses from 10 offices in Pennsylvania, New Jersey, and Delaware. Industry expertise includes healthcare, senior living services, financial services, education, government/nonprofit, manufacturing, construction, real estate, retail, wholesale, and distribution. Specialty services include corporate finance, business reorganization, forensic accounting, and litigation support. Parente Randolph affiliates provide technology consulting, energy consulting, HR consulting, leadership development and training, and executive search services. **Common positions include:** Accountant; Administrative Assistant; Network/Systems Administrator.

PHILADELPHIA STOCK EXCHANGE INC.
1900 Market Street, Philadelphia PA 19103. 215/496-5000. **Fax:** 215/496-1196. **Contact:** Albert Sindoni, Human Resources. **E-mail address:** albert.sindoni@phlx.com. **World Wide Web address:** http://www.phlx.com. **Description:** A stock exchange.

PUBLIC FINANCIAL MANAGEMENT, INC.
2 Logan Square, Suite 1600, Philadelphia PA 19103. 215/567-6100. **Fax:** 215/567-4180. **Contact:** Marie Biggans, Human Resources Associate. **E-mail address:** recruit@publicfm.com. **World Wide Web address:** http://www.pfm.com. **Description:** A leading financial advisory firm serving the public sector. Public Financial Management oversees $7.5 billion in public sector funds. **Common positions include:** Financial Analyst. **Corporate headquarters location:** This location. **Other area locations:** Harrisburg PA. **Other U.S. locations:** Newport Beach CA; San Francisco CA; Washington DC; Miami FL; Fort Myers FL; Orlando FL; Sarasota FL; Atlanta GA; Des Moines IA; Boston MA; Trenton NJ; New York NY; Harrisburg PA; Pittsburgh PA; Memphis TN; Dallas TX; Austin TX; Houston TX. **Parent company:** Marine Midland Bank. **CEO:** F. John White. **Number of employees at this location:** 50.

RITTENHOUSE FINANCIAL SERVICES
2 Radnor Corporate Center, Suite 400, 100 Matsonford Road, Radnor PA 19087-4541. **Toll-free phone:** 800/847-6369. **Contact:** Barbara Fox, Human Resources Department. **E-mail address:** barbara.fox@nuveen.com. **World Wide Web address:** http://www.rittenhousefinancial.com. **Description:** A money management firm.

SEI INVESTMENTS COMPANY
530 East Swedesford Street, Wayne PA 19087. 610/676-1000. **Contact:** Team Leader. **World Wide Web address:** http://www.seic.com. **Description:** SEI Investments operates primarily in two business markets: Trust and Banking and Fund Sponsor/Investment Advisory. The company invests for clients worldwide in both public and private markets. SEI Investments also provides investment and business solutions to those who serve their own investor clients. SEI Investments provides direct investment solutions for $100 billion of investable capital and delivers systems and business solutions to organizations investing nearly $1 trillion. SEI Investments is one of the largest providers of trust systems in the world. **NOTE:** Jobseekers should indicate area of interest when applying. **Common positions include:** Accountant; Financial

Analyst; Fund Manager; Information Systems Consultant; Technician. **Operations at this facility include:** Administration; Research and Development; Sales; Service. **Listed on:** NASDAQ. **Stock exchange symbol:** SEIC. **CEO:** Alfred West. **Annual sales/revenues:** More than $100 million. **Number of employees nationwide:** 1,300. **Number of employees worldwide:** 1,400.

SEI INVESTMENTS COMPANY
One Freedom Valley Drive, Oaks PA 19456. 610/676-1000. **Toll-free phone:** 800/610-1114. **Fax:** 484/676-1490. **Contact:** Human Resources. **E-mail address:** jcrompton@seic.com. **World Wide Web address:** http://www.seic.com. **Description:** SEI operates primarily in two business markets: Trust and Banking, and Fund Sponsor/Investment Advisory. The company invests for clients worldwide in both public and private markets, and also provides investment and business solutions to those in the investment business who in turn serve their own investor clients. SEI provides direct investment solutions for $50 billion of investable capital and delivers systems and business solutions to organizations investing nearly $1 trillion. SEI is one of the largest providers of trust systems in the world. Founded in 1968. **NOTE:** Entry-level positions are offered. **Company slogan:** The art of the people. The science of results. **Common positions include:** Accountant; Applications Engineer; Attorney; Computer Engineer; Computer Programmer; Computer Technician; Content Developer; Database Administrator; Database Manager; Economist; Finance Director; Financial Analyst; Internet Services Manager; Intranet Developer; Marketing Manager; Marketing Specialist; MIS Specialist; Multimedia Designer; Network Engineer; Network/Systems Administrator; Paralegal; Public Relations Specialist; Sales Executive; Sales Representative; Software Engineer; Systems Analyst; Web Advertising Specialist; Webmaster; Website Developer. **Office hours:** Monday - Friday, 8:30 a.m. - 5:30 p.m. **Corporate headquarters location:** This location. **Listed on:** NASDAQ. **Stock exchange symbol:** SEIC. **CEO:** Alfred West. **Annual sales/revenues:** More than $100 million. **Number of employees at this location:** 1,200. **Number of employees nationwide:** 1,300. **Number of employees worldwide:** 1,400.

UBS PAINEWEBBER INC.
2 Logan Square, Suite 2400, Philadelphia PA 19103. 215/972-6800. **Contact:** Human Resources. **World Wide Web address:** http://www.painewebber.com. **Description:** A full-service securities firm with over 300 offices nationwide. Services

include investment banking, asset management, merger and acquisition consulting, municipal securities underwriting, estate planning, retirement programs, and transaction management. UBS PaineWebber offers its services to corporations, governments, institutions, and individuals. Founded in 1879. **Corporate headquarters location:** New York NY. **Other U.S. locations:** Nationwide. **Annual sales/revenues:** More than $100 million.

THE VANGUARD GROUP, INC.

P.O. Box 2600, Valley Forge PA 19482-2600. 610/669-6000. **Contact:** Human Resources. **World Wide Web address:** http://www.vanguard.com. **Description:** A mutual funds company that also offers assistance in educational financing, retirement planning, and trust services. **Corporate headquarters location:** This location.

FOOD AND BEVERAGES/ AGRICULTURE

You can expect to find the following types of companies in this chapter:

Crop Services and Farm Supplies • Dairy Farms • Food Manufacturers/Processors and Agricultural Producers • Tobacco Products

ALL SEASONS SERVICES
4060 Blanche Road, Bensalem PA 19020. 215/638-8800. **Contact:** Human Resources. **World Wide Web address:** http://www.allseasonsservices.com. **Description:** Provides a wide variety coffee, snacks, and vending machines to businesses.

W. ATLEE BURPEE & COMPANY
300 Park Avenue, Warminster PA 18974. 215/674-4900. **Contact:** Stuart Hopkins, Director of Human Resources. **World Wide Web address:** http://www.burpee.com. **Description:** Produces seeds. **Common positions include:** Accountant/Auditor; Blue-Collar Worker Supervisor; Buyer; Computer Programmer; Customer Service Representative; Graphic Artist; Horticulturist; Human Resources Manager; Manufacturer's/Wholesaler's Sales Rep.; Marketing Manager; Operations/Production Manager; Purchasing Agent/Manager; Systems Analyst; Technical Writer/Editor. **Corporate headquarters location:** This location.

CAMPBELL SOUP COMPANY
One Campbell Place, Camden NJ 08103-1799. 856/342-4800. **Contact:** Human Resources Department. **World Wide Web address:** http://www.campbellsoups.com. **Description:** This location houses administrative offices. Overall, Campbell Soup Company is a producer of commercial soups, juices, pickles, frozen foods, canned beans, canned pasta products, spaghetti sauces, and baked goods. The company's products are distributed worldwide. U.S. brand names include Campbell's, Vlasic, V8, Chunky, Home Cookin', Prego, Pepperidge Farm, Inc., LeMenu, Mrs. Paul's, and Swanson. European foods are sold under brand names such as Pleybin, Biscuits Delacre, Freshbake, Groko, Godiva, and Betis. Campbell Soup Company also owns Arnotts Biscuits of Australia. **Corporate headquarters location:** This location. **Listed on:** New York Stock Exchange. **Stock exchange symbol:** CPB.

CONAGRA FOODS, INC.

30 Marr Street, Milton PA 17847. 570/742-7621. **Contact:** Human Resources Department. **World Wide Web address:** http://www.conagra.com. **Description:** Manufactures and markets branded, food service, and store-branded food products. Product names include Bumble Bee, Chef Boyardee, Clover Leaf, Crunch 'n Munch, Louis Kemp, Gulden's, and PAM. **NOTE:** Mail employment correspondence to: ConAgra Foods, Inc., Attn: Resume Processing Center, One ConAgra Drive, Omaha NE 68102-5001.

CUTLER DAIRY PRODUCTS, INC.

612-30 West Sedgley Avenue, Philadelphia PA 19140. 215/229-5400. **Fax:** 215/229-5637. **Contact:** Human Resources Department. **World Wide Web address:** http://www.cutleregg.com. **Description:** Processes and supplies eggs to the food industry. **Common positions include:** Administrative Manager; Biological Scientist; Blue-Collar Worker Supervisor; Food Scientist/Technologist; Heating/AC/Refrigeration Technician; Inspector/Tester/Grader; Production Manager; Truck Driver. **Corporate headquarters location:** This location. **Other U.S. locations:** Abbeyville AL. **Operations at this facility include:** Administration; Manufacturing; Sales; Service. **Number of employees at this location:** 100. **Number of employees nationwide:** 250.

FRISKIES PET CARE COMPANY

2050 Pope Road, Allentown PA 18104-9308. 610/395-3301. **Contact:** Human Resources. **World Wide Web address:** http://www.friskies.com. **Description:** Produces and sells the Alpo brand of premium canned dog foods and the Friskies brand of premium canned cat foods. Friskies Pet Care Company is one of the largest dog and cat food manufacturers and distributors in the United States. **Corporate headquarters location:** St. Louis MO. **Parent company:** Nestle Purina Pet Care Company.

HATFIELD QUALITY MEATS INC.

2700 Funks Road, P.O. Box 902, Hatfield PA 19440-0902. 215/368-2500. **Toll-free phone:** 800/523-5291. **Fax:** 215/368-3018. **Contact:** Recruiter. **World Wide Web address:** http://www.hqm.com. **Description:** Manufactures meat products.

J&J SNACK FOODS CORPORATION

6000 Central Highway, Pennsauken NJ 08109. 856/665-9533. **Contact:** Human Resources. **World Wide Web address:**

http://www.jjsnack.com. **Description:** Manufactures a line of nutritional snack foods. Its principal products include frozen soft pretzels under Superpretzel and other brand names; Icee and Arctic Blast frozen carbonated beverages; frozen juice bars and desserts under Shapeups and other brand names; Luigi's Real Italian Ice; Mama Tish's Premium Italian Ices; Tio Pepe's churros; The Funnel Cake Factory funnel cakes; and Pride O' The Farm healthy baked goods.

LEHIGH VALLEY DAIRIES, L.P.

880 Allentown Road, Lansdale PA 19446. 215/855-8205. **Toll-free phone:** 800/937-3233. **Fax:** 215/393-3363. **Contact:** Diane Kett, Human Resources Manager. **Description:** A dairy products company. **Common positions include:** Accountant/Auditor; Branch Manager; Clerical Supervisor; Computer Programmer; Credit Manager; Electrician; Environmental Engineer; Financial Analyst; General Manager; Human Resources Manager; Industrial Production Manager; Manufacturer's/Wholesaler's Sales Representative; Operations/Production Manager; Purchasing Agent/Manager; Quality Control Supervisor; Systems Analyst. **Corporate headquarters location:** This location. **Other U.S. locations:** Schuylkill Haven PA. **Operations at this facility include:** Administration; Manufacturing; Sales. **President/CEO:** Robert Allen. **Number of employees at this location:** 350. **Number of employees nationwide:** 560.

NABISCO BISCUIT COMPANY

12000 East Roosevelt Boulevard, Philadelphia PA 19116. 215/673-4800. **Contact:** Human Resources. **World Wide Web address:** http://www.nabisco.com. **Description:** This location is a bakery and distribution center. Overall, Nabisco is one of the largest consumer food operations in the country. The company markets a broad line of cookie and cracker products including brand names such as Oreo, Ritz, Premium, Teddy Grahams, Chips Ahoy!, and Wheat Thins. **Common positions include:** Accountant/Auditor; Blue-Collar Worker Supervisor; Department Manager; Electrical/Electronics Engineer; Food Scientist/Technologist; Human Resources Manager; Industrial Production Manager; Operations/Production Manager; Quality Control Supervisor. **Special programs:** Internships. **Corporate headquarters location:** East Hanover NJ. **International locations:** Asia; Canada; Europe. **Parent company:** Kraft Foods, Inc. **Operations at this facility include:** Manufacturing. **Listed on:** New York Stock Exchange. **Stock exchange symbol:** KFT.

NEW WORLD PASTA

P.O. Box 126457, Harrisburg PA 17112-6457. 717/526-2200. **Contact:** Human Resources. **World Wide Web address:** http://www.nwpasta.com. **Description:** Produces a variety of pasta products including macaroni, spaghetti, and egg noodles. **Common positions include:** Accountant/Auditor; Blue-Collar Worker Supervisor; Computer Programmer; Customer Service Representative; Department Manager; Human Resources Manager; Industrial Engineer; Quality Control Supervisor. **Parent company:** Hershey Foods Corporation (Hershey PA). **Operations at this facility include:** Manufacturing; Service. **Listed on:** New York Stock Exchange. **Stock exchange symbol:** HSY.

OAK VALLEY FARMS

P.O. Box 778, Voorhees NJ 08043. 856/435-0900. **Contact:** Julia O'Connor, Director of Human Resources. **World Wide Web address:** http://www.oakvalleyfarms.com. **Description:** Processes turkey products for correctional facilities, distributors, food service companies, government agencies, and schools. **Parent company:** El Jay Corporation.

R.M. PALMER COMPANY

P.O. Box 1723, Reading PA 19603. 610/372-8971. **Contact:** Human Resources Manager. **World Wide Web address:** http://www.rmpalmer.com. **Description:** Manufactures chocolates and other confections for Halloween, Christmas, Easter, and Valentine's Day. **Common positions include:** Accountant/Auditor; Blue-Collar Worker Supervisor; Buyer; Commercial Artist; Computer Programmer; Credit Manager; Customer Service Rep.; Human Resources Manager; Industrial Engineer; Operations/Production Manager; Purchasing Agent/Manager. **Operations at this facility include:** Administration; Manufacturing; Sales.

PEPPERIDGE FARM, INC.

421 Boot Road, Downingtown PA 19335. 610/873-4400. **Contact:** Human Resources Department. **World Wide Web address:** http://www.pfgoldfish.com. **Description:** This location is a frozen food plant. Overall, Pepperidge Farm, Inc. manufactures and distributes a range of fresh and frozen baked goods and confections including bread, cookies, cakes, pastries, and Goldfish brand crackers. **Parent company:** Campbell Soup Company.

PEPSI-COLA COMPANY

11701 Roosevelt Boulevard, Philadelphia PA 19154. 215/676-6400. **Contact:** Human Resources Department. **World Wide Web address:** http://www.pepsico.com. **Description:** This location is a sales office and a warehousing facility. Overall, Pepsi-Cola Company produces and distributes a wide variety of beverages including the brand names Pepsi-Cola, Mountain Dew, Mug Root Beer, and Slice. **Parent company:** PepsiCo, Inc. (Purchase NY) consists of Frito-Lay Company, Pepsi-Cola Company, and Tropicana Products, Inc. **Operations at this facility include:** Warehouse/Distribution.

PEPSI-COLA
NATIONAL BRAND BEVERAGES LTD.

8275 U.S. Route 130, Pennsauken NJ 08110. 856/665-6200. **Contact:** Human Resources Department. **World Wide Web address:** http://www.pepsi.com. **Description:** This location bottles Canada Dry products. Overall, Pepsi-Cola Company produces and distributes a variety of beverages including the brand names Pepsi-Cola, Mountain Dew, Mug Root Beer, and Slice.

SNOWBALL FOODS, INC.

1051 Sykes Lane, Williamstown NJ 08094. 856/629-4081. **Contact:** Robert Thompson, Human Resources Manager. **Description:** Engaged in poultry processing. **Common positions include:** Accountant/Auditor; Blue-Collar Worker Supervisor; Buyer; Customer Service Representative; Food Scientist/Technologist; Human Resources Manager; Manufacturer's/Wholesaler's Sales Representative; Operations Manager; Quality Control Supervisor; Transportation/Traffic Specialist. **Special programs:** Internships. **Corporate headquarters location:** This location. **Operations at this facility include:** Administration; Manufacturing; Research and Development; Sales; Service. **Number of employees at this location:** 250.

TASTY BAKING COMPANY

2801 Hunting Park Avenue, Philadelphia PA 19129. 215/221-8500. **Contact:** Debbie Clarke, Manager of Human Resources. **World Wide Web address:** http://www.tastykake.com. **Description:** Engaged in the manufacture and sale of a variety of small, single-portion cakes, pies, and cookies under the brand name Tastykake. The company offers approximately 45 different products. **Corporate headquarters location:** This location. **Listed on:** American Stock Exchange. **Stock exchange symbol:** TBC.

TAYLOR PACKING COMPANY INC.

P.O. Box 188, Wyalusing PA 18853. 570/746-3000. **Fax:** 570/746-3888. **Contact:** Human Resources. **World Wide Web address:** http://www.taylorpacking.com. **Description:** This location is a beef processing plant. Overall, Taylor Packing Company is a multimillion-dollar operation capable of processing 1,800 cattle daily. Taylor Packing produces a complete line of vacuum-packaged, boxed beef cuts; custom-blended coarse ground beef; and fresh, vacuum-packed, and frozen variety meats for sale to supermarket chains, wholesalers, food-service distributors, institutions, and processed beef manufacturers. **NOTE:** Entry-level positions, part-time jobs and second and third shifts are offered. **Common positions include:** Accountant/Auditor; Biological Scientist; Blue-Collar Worker Supervisor; Claim Representative; Computer Programmer; Credit Manager; Draftsperson; Electrical/Electronics Engineer; Electrician; Financial Analyst; General Manager; Industrial Engineer; Industrial Production Manager; Licensed Practical Nurse; Management Trainee; Operations/Production Manager; Purchasing Agent/Manager; Quality Control Supervisor; Registered Nurse. **Special programs:** Internships; Apprenticeships; Training; Summer Jobs. **Corporate headquarters location:** This location. **Subsidiaries include:** Taylor By-Products, Inc. (also at this location) operates a modern rendering plant that produces tallow and protein meals for sale to feed companies, pet food manufacturers, and chemical processors. This location also hires seasonally. **Listed on:** Privately held. **Number of employees at this location:** 1,050.

U.S. FOODSERVICE

2255 High Hill Road, Bridgeport NJ 08014. 856/467-4900. **Fax:** 856/467-7819. **Contact:** Human Resources Department. **World Wide Web address:** http://www.usfoodservice.com. **Description:** An institutional food production and distribution company with clients in the restaurant and health care industries. **Corporate headquarters location:** Columbia MD. **Number of employees worldwide:** 12,000.

U.S. FOODSERVICE

300 Berkeley Drive, Swedesboro NJ 08085. 856/241-4000. **Contact:** Human Resources Department. **World Wide Web address:** http://www.usfoodservice.com. **Description:** Processes and distributes a wide variety of frozen and cultured dairy products. **Office hours:** Monday - Friday, 8:00 a.m. - 5:00 p.m. **Corporate headquarters location:** Columbia MD. **Number of employees worldwide:** 12,000.

U.S. FOODSERVICE

1200 Hoover Avenue, Allentown PA 18109. 610/821-9000. **Toll-free phone:** 800/441-0998. **Fax:** 610/776-2179. **Contact:** Human Resources Department. **World Wide Web address:** http://www.usfoodservice.com. **Description:** An institutional food production and distribution company with clients in the restaurant and health care industries. **Corporate headquarters location:** Columbia MD. **Number of employees nationwide:** 12,000. **Number of employees worldwide:** 14,000.

U.S. FOODSERVICE

13 Rutledge Drive, Pittston PA 18640. 570/654-3374. **Fax:** 570/654-2510. **Contact:** Human Resources. **World Wide Web address:** http://www.usfoodservice.com. **Description:** An institutional food production and distribution company with clients in the restaurant and health care industries. **Corporate headquarters location:** Columbia MD. **Number of employees nationwide:** 12,000. **Number of employees worldwide:** 14,000.

VENICEMAID FOODS, INC.

P.O. Box 1505, Vineland NJ 08362-1505. 856/691-2100. **Physical address:** 270 North Mill Road, Vineland NJ 08360. **Fax:** 856/696-1295. **Contact:** Patricia Haas, Personnel. **World Wide Web address:** http://www.venicemaid.com. **Description:** One of the nation's largest food manufacturers for private brands. The company produces over 375 institutional and retail products. Founded in 1927. **NOTE:** Entry-level positions and second and third shifts are offered. **Common positions include:** Accountant/Auditor; Administrative Assistant; Controller; Credit Manager; Customer Service Representative; Electrician; Food Scientist/Technologist; Food Service Manager; Purchasing Agent/Manager; Quality Control Supervisor; Sales Manager; Sales Rep.; Secretary. **Operations at this facility include:** Administration; Manufacturing; Research and Development; Sales. **Listed on:** Privately held. **Number of employees at this location:** 190.

WAMPLER FOODS, INC.

471 Harleysville Pike, P.O. Box 8, Franconia PA 18924. 215/721-5671. **Fax:** 215/723-8938. **Contact:** Alan Landis, Human Resources Manager. **World Wide Web address:** http://www.wampler.com. **Description:** Produces poultry products. **Common positions include:** Accountant/Auditor; Clerical Supervisor; Computer Programmer; Cost Estimator; Customer Service Representative; Electrician; Food Scientist/Technologist; Industrial Production Manager;

Manufacturer's/Wholesaler's Sales Representative; Purchasing Agent/Manager; Services Sales Representative. **Corporate headquarters location:** Broadway VA. **Parent company:** WLR Foods, Inc. **Listed on:** NASDAQ. **Stock exchange symbol:** WLRF. **Number of employees at this location:** 700. **Number of employees nationwide:** 8,000.

GOVERNMENT

You can expect to find the following types of agencies in this chapter:

Courts • Executive, Legislative, and General Government • Public Agencies (Firefighters, Military, Police) • United States Postal Service

INTERNAL REVENUE SERVICE
P.O. Box 21145, Philadelphia PA 19114. 215/516-JOBS. **Contact:** Delegated Examining Unit. **World Wide Web address:** http://www.irs.gov. **Description:** This location is a submission processing and customer service center. Overall, the IRS provides American taxpayers service by helping them to understand and meet their tax responsibilities and by applying tax laws. **Number of employees nationwide:** 85,000.

PENNSYLVANIA STATE CIVIL SERVICE COMMISSION
Strawberry Square Complex, 2nd Floor, P.O. Box 569, Harrisburg PA 17108-0569. 717/783-3085. **Contact:** Recruiter. **World Wide Web address:** http://www.scsc.state.pa.us. **Description:** Engaged in government administration and management at the state level. **Common positions include:** Medical Records Technician; Occupational Therapist; Physical Therapist; Physician; Registered Nurse. **Corporate headquarters location:** This location. **Number of employees at this location:** 60,000.

U.S. DEPARTMENT OF DEFENSE
DEFENSE SUPPLY CENTER PHILADELPHIA
700 Robbins Avenue, Philadelphia PA 19111-5092. 215/737-2333. **Fax:** 215/737-8364. **Contact:** Elizabeth Warden, Human Resources Department. **World Wide Web address:** http://www.dscp.dla.mil. **Description:** Provides federal logistical services and distributes food, clothing, and medical supplies to members of the U.S. armed forces and their families. **Common positions include:** Biomedical Engineer; Buyer; Chemist; Civil Engineer; Electrical/Electronics Engineer; Food Scientist/Technologist; Pharmacist; Purchasing Agent/Manager. **Operations at this facility include:** Administration.

U.S. DEPARTMENT OF HEALTH AND HUMAN SERVICES
150 South Independence Mall West, Public Ledger Building, Suite 436, Philadelphia PA 19106. 215/861-4633. **Toll-free phone:** 800/368-1019. **Contact:** Office of Human Resources.

World Wide Web address: http://www.hhs.gov. **Description:** Protects and provides necessary health care and human services, especially to those who cannot provide for themselves.

U.S. DEPARTMENT OF THE AIR FORCE
913TH SPTG/DPC
1051 Fairchild Street, Willow Grove ARS PA 19090-5203. 215/443-1034. **Contact:** Personnel. **World Wide Web address:** http://www.usajobs.opm.gov. **Description:** Trains Air Force reservists to perform aerial resupply missions including the task of delivering people, equipment, and supplies to the battlefield. **NOTE:** Jobseekers interested in becoming Air Reserve Technicians must have an active reserve membership. **Common positions include:** Administrative Assistant; Budget Analyst; Civil Engineer; Computer Support Technician; Computer Technician; Electrical/Electronics Engineer; Electrician; Environmental Engineer; Medical Assistant; Pilot; Public Relations Specialist; Secretary; Transportation/Traffic Specialist.

U.S. ENVIRONMENTAL PROTECTION AGENCY (EPA)
1650 Arch Street, Philadelphia PA 19103-2029. 215/814-5240. **Contact:** Human Resources-3PM40. **World Wide Web address:** http://www.epa.gov. **Description:** The EPA is dedicated to improving and preserving the quality of the environment, both nationally and globally, and protecting human health and the productivity of natural resources. The agency is committed to ensuring that federal environmental laws are implemented and enforced effectively; U.S. policy, both foreign and domestic, encourages the integration of economic development and environmental protection so that economic growth can be sustained over the long term; and public and private decisions affecting energy, transportation, agriculture, industry, international trade, and natural resources fully integrate considerations of environmental quality. **Special programs:** Internships. **Corporate headquarters location:** Washington DC. **Other U.S. locations:** San Francisco CA; Denver CO; Atlanta GA; Chicago IL; Kansas City KS; Boston MA; New York NY; Dallas TX; Seattle WA. **Number of employees nationwide:** 19,000.

U.S. FEDERAL BUREAU OF INVESTIGATION (FBI)
8th Floor, William J. Green Jr. FOB, 600 Arch Street, Pittsburgh PA 19106. 215/418-4000. **Contact:** Personnel. **World Wide Web address:** http://www.fbi.gov. **Description:** The Federal Bureau of Investigation (FBI) is a federal law

enforcement agency. The agents carry out the responsibilities of the FBI by enforcing more than 260 federal statutes. This involves conducting investigations in organized crime, white-collar crime, civil rights violations, bank robbery, kidnapping, terrorism, foreign counterintelligence, fugitive and drug trafficking matters, and many other violations against federal statutes. **Special programs:** Internships. **Corporate headquarters location:** Washington DC.

U.S. GENERAL SERVICES ADMINISTRATION
100 Penn Square East, Room 826, Philadelphia PA 19107-3396. 215/656-5621. **Fax:** 215/656-6440. **Contact:** Audrey Peel, Regional Personnel Officer. **E-mail address:** audrey.peel@gsa.gov. **World Wide Web address:** http://www.gsa.gov. **Description:** A diversified, government-wide operation engaged in building management, supply, real and personal property sales, telecommunication services, data processing, and motor vehicle operations. It is the job of the GSA to ensure that governmental entities are receiving the highest quality products and services at the best prices. **Common positions include:** Civil Engineer; Mechanical Engineer; Property and Real Estate Manager; Purchasing Agent/Manager; Systems Analyst; Transportation/Traffic Specialist. **Special programs:** Internships. **Corporate headquarters location:** Washington DC. **Other U.S. locations:** San Francisco CA; Denver CO; Atlanta GA; Auburn GA; Chicago IL; Boston MA; Kansas City MO; New York NY; Fort Worth TX. **Operations at this facility include:** Regional Headquarters. **Number of employees at this location:** 1,500. **Number of employees nationwide:** 14,000.

HEALTH CARE: SERVICES, EQUIPMENT, AND PRODUCTS

You can expect to find the following types of companies in this chapter:

Dental Labs and Equipment • Home Health Care Agencies •
Hospitals and Medical Centers • Medical Equipment
Manufacturers and Wholesalers • Offices and Clinics of Health
Practitioners • Residential Treatment Centers/Nursing Homes •
Veterinary Services

ALBERT EINSTEIN MEDICAL CENTER
5501 Old York Road, Philadelphia PA 19141. 215/456-7890.
Contact: Human Resources. **World Wide Web address:**
http://www.einstein.edu. **Description:** A teaching hospital
specializing in behavioral health; coronary care; geriatrics;
liver, kidney, and pancreas transplants; orthopedics; and
women's and children's health. **NOTE:** For additional job
information contact: Albert Einstein Healthcare Network
Recruiting and Placement Center, One Penn Boulevard, 1st
Floor Main Building, Philadelphia PA 19144.

APRIA HEALTHCARE GROUP INC.
16 Creek Parkway, Boothwyn PA 19061. 610/364-2000. **Fax:**
724/873-7849. **Contact:** Regional Human Resources. **World
Wide Web address:** http://www.apria.com. **Description:** One
of the largest national providers of home health care products
and services, providing a broad range of respiratory therapy
services, home medical equipment, and infusion therapy
services. Apria has over 400 branches throughout the United
States and two respiratory therapy branches in the United
Kingdom. Apria's home health care services are provided to
patients who have been discharged from hospitals, skilled
nursing facilities, or convalescent homes and are being treated
at home. In conjunction with medical professionals, Apria
personnel deliver, install, and service medical equipment, as
well as provide appropriate therapies and coordinate plans of
care for their patients. Apria personnel also instruct patients
and caregivers in the correct use of equipment and monitor the
equipment's effectiveness. Patients and their families receive
training from registered nurses and respiratory therapy
professionals concerning the therapy administered, including
instruction in proper infusion technique and the care and use
of equipment and supplies. **NOTE:** Mail job correspondence
to: Regional Human Resources, 250 Technology Drive,

Canonsburg PA 15317. **Corporate headquarters location:** Costa Mesa CA.

ARROW INTERNATIONAL INC.
P.O. Box 12888, Reading PA 19612-2888. 610/378-0131. **Physical address:** 2400 Burnville Road, Reading PA 19605. **Fax:** 610/478-3194. **Contact:** Staffing Manager. **E-mail address:** staffing.manager@arrowintl.com. **World Wide Web address:** http://www.arrowintl.com. **Description:** Develops, markets, and manufactures clinically advanced, disposable central vascular access catheterization products. Arrow International's products are also used for patient monitoring, diagnosis, pain management, and treating patients with heart and vascular disease. **Common positions include:** Mechanical Engineer. **Corporate headquarters location:** This location. **Other U.S. locations:** NJ; NC. **Operations at this facility include:** Administration; Manufacturing; Research and Development. **Listed on:** NASDAQ. **Stock exchange symbol:** ARRO. **Number of employees nationwide:** 1,540.

BARNES-KASSON COUNTY HOSPITAL S.N.F.
400 Turnpike Street, Susquehanna PA 18847. 570/853-3135. **Fax:** 570/853-2075. **Contact:** Human Resources Department. **World Wide Web address:** http://www.barnes-kasson.org. **Description:** A 50-bed community hospital with an attached 58-bed skilled nursing facility. The hospital also offers home health services and outpatient therapy. **NOTE:** Second and third shifts are offered. **Common positions include:** Accountant; Administrative Assistant; Advertising Executive; Certified Nurses Aide; Chief Financial Officer; Clinical Lab Technician; Computer Operator; Controller; Dietician/Nutritionist; EKG Technician; Emergency Medical Technician; Human Resources Manager; Licensed Practical Nurse; Marketing Manager; Medical Records Technician; Nuclear Medicine Technologist; Occupational Therapist; Pharmacist; Physical Therapist; Physician; Purchasing Agent/Manager; Quality Control Supervisor; Radiological Technologist; Registered Nurse; Respiratory Therapist; Secretary; Social Worker; Speech-Language Pathologist; Surgical Technician; Typist/Word Processor. **Special programs:** Internships; Summer Jobs. **CEO:** Sara Iveson. **Annual sales/revenues:** $11 - $20 million. **Number of employees at this location:** 350.

BELMONT CENTER FOR COMPREHENSIVE TREATMENT
4200 Monument Road, Philadelphia PA 19131. 215/877-2000. **Contact:** Human Resources Department. **World Wide Web**

address: http://www.einstein.edu. **Description:** Offers inpatient and outpatient treatment to adolescents, adults, and families for a range of problems including addictions and eating disorders. **Parent company:** Albert Einstein Healthcare Network.

BENCO DENTAL COMPANY

11 Bear Creek Boulevard, Wilkes-Barre PA 18702. 570/825-7781. **Contact:** Human Resources Department. **World Wide Web address:** http://www.benco.com. **Description:** Distributes and rents dental equipment to hospitals, schools, and governmental agencies.

BIOCHEM IMMUNOSYSTEMS

754 Roble Road, Suite 70, Allentown PA 18109. 610/264-0885. **Contact:** Linda Kurtz, Manager of Human Resources. **World Wide Web address:** http://www.biochem.com. **Description:** A manufacturer and distributor of diagnostic medical instrument systems. **Common positions include:** Accountant/Auditor; Buyer; Electrical/Electronics Engineer; Financial Analyst; Manufacturer's/Wholesaler's Sales Rep.; Marketing Specialist; Mechanical Engineer; Purchasing Agent/Manager. **Special programs:** Internships. **Corporate headquarters location:** Boston MA. **Operations at this facility include:** Manufacturing; Sales.

B. BRAUN MEDICAL, INC.

901 Marcon Boulevard, Allentown PA 18109. 610/266-0500. **Fax:** 610/266-5702. **Contact:** Human Resources Department. **E-mail address:** hr.allentown@bbraunusa.com. **World Wide Web address:** http://www.bbraunusa.com. **Description:** Manufactures intravenous systems and solutions. The company also offers IV accessories, critical care products, epidural anesthesia, and pharmaceutical devices. **Common positions include:** Customer Service Representative; Industrial Engineer; Materials Engineer; Packaging Engineer; Quality Control Supervisor. **Other area locations:** Bethlehem, PA. **Parent company:** B. Braun of America.

B. BRAUN/McGAW, INC.

824 12th Avenue, Bethlehem PA 18018. 610/691-5400. **Fax:** 610/861-5991. **Contact:** Human Resources. **E-mail address:** hr.bethlehem@bbraunusa.com. **World Wide Web address:** http://www.bbraunusa.com. **Description:** Manufactures intravenous systems and solutions. The company also offers IV accessories, critical care products, epidural anesthesia, and

pharmaceutical devices. **Other area locations:** Allentown PA. **Parent company:** B. Braun of America.

BRYN MAWR HOSPITAL
130 South Bryn Mawr Avenue, Bryn Mawr PA 19010. 610/526-3026. **Fax:** 610/526-3068. **Contact:** Human Resources Department. **World Wide Web address:** http://www.mainlinehealth.org/bmh. **Description:** A teaching hospital that provides medical, psychiatric, and surgical services, and offers the surrounding community the following specialized programs: Primary Care Services, the Arthritis and Orthopaedic Center, Comprehensive Cancer Care Center, Cardiovascular Center, and Women and Children's Health Resources. In addition, the hospital provides a wide array of other community programs including support groups, educational programs, physician referral services, health screenings, and a speakers bureau. **Common positions include:** Accountant/Auditor; EEG Technologist; Emergency Medical Technician; Occupational Therapist; Pharmacist; Physical Therapist; Registered Nurse; Respiratory Therapist; Social Worker; Speech-Language Pathologist. **Corporate headquarters location:** Radnor PA. **Parent company:** Mainline Health System.

CATHOLIC HEALTH EAST
14 Campus Boulevard, Suite 300, Newtown Square PA 19073. 610/355-2000. **Fax:** 610/355-2050. **Contact:** Human Resources. **World Wide Web address:** http://www.che.org. **Description:** This location houses administrative offices. Overall, Catholic Health East is a health care system operation 28 regional systems in 10 Eastern states. The health care system includes three behavioral health facilities, 32 hospitals, and 28 skilled nursing centers. **Common positions include:** Accountant/Auditor; Financial Analyst; Human Resources Manager; Insurance Agent/Broker; Public Relations Specialist; Purchasing Agent/Manager. **Number of employees at this location:** 35.

CHESTER COUNTY HOSPITAL
701 East Marshall Street, West Chester PA 19380. 610/431-5000. **Recorded jobline:** 610/430-2903. **Fax:** 610/430-2956. **Contact:** Human Resources. **World Wide Web address:** http://www.cchosp.com. **Description:** A hospital. **Number of employees at this location:** 1,400.

COOPER HEALTH

3 Cooper Plaza, Suite 500, Camden NJ 08103. 856/342-2000. **Fax:** 856/968-8319. **Contact:** Human Resources. **World Wide Web address:** http://www.cooperhealth.org. **Description:** A 554-bed, nonprofit, academic medical center. Cooper Health specializes in the care of seriously-ill and critically-injured patients.

CROZER-CHESTER MEDICAL CENTER

One Medical Center Boulevard, Upland PA 19013-3995. 610/447-2000. **Contact:** Human Resources. **World Wide Web address:** http://www.crozer.org. **Description:** This location is a 675-bed teaching hospital. The medical center also offers the Antepartum Assessment Center, Comprehensive Breast Health Program, Crozer Home, Crozer Regional Cancer Center, Heart Surgery/Cardiac Center, John E. DuPont Trauma Center, Maternity Center, and Nathan Speare Burn Center. **Parent company:** Crozer-Keystone Health System.

DAVITA, INC.

1180 West Swedesford Road, Suite 300, Berwyn PA 19312. 610/644-4796. **Toll-free phone:** 800/633-9757. **Contact:** Recruiting. **World Wide Web address:** http://www.davita.com. **Description:** One of the largest providers of dialysis services to patients suffering from End Stage Renal Disease (ESRD). Davita's services have come to include clinical laboratory and pharmacy services, and both pre- and postsurgery management. Founded in 1988. **Common positions include:** Accountant; Administrative Assistant; Billing Clerk; Budget Analyst; Certified Nurses Aide; Chief Financial Officer; Claim Representative; Clinical Lab Technician; Collections Agent; Controller; Customer Service Rep.; Dietician/Nutritionist; Financial Analyst; Human Resources Manager; Licensed Practical Nurse; Paralegal; Registered Nurse; Secretary; Social Worker; Systems Analyst. **Special programs:** Internships. **Office hours:** Monday - Friday, 9:00 a.m. - 5:00 p.m. **Corporate headquarters location:** Torrance CA. **Other U.S. locations:** Nationwide. **International locations:** Argentina. **Subsidiaries include:** Renal Diagnostic Laboratory (Las Vegas NV). **Operations at this facility include:** Divisional Headquarters. **Listed on:** New York Stock Exchange. **Stock exchange symbol:** RXT. **CEO:** Robert Mayer. **Annual sales/revenues:** More than $100 million. **Number of employees at this location:** 250. **Number of employees nationwide:** 3,400.

DENTSPLY INTERNATIONAL INC.
570 West College Avenue, P.O. Box 872, York PA 17405-0872. 717/845-7511. **Fax:** 717/849-4376. **Contact:** Human Resources. **E-mail address:** corpjobs@dentsply.com. **World Wide Web address:** http://www.dentsply.com. **Description:** A leading manufacturer of X-ray equipment and other products for the dental field including artificial teeth, prophylaxis paste, ultrasonic sealers, and bone substitute/grafting materials. **Corporate headquarters location:** This location. **Other U.S. locations:** Carlsbad CA; Encino CA; Los Angeles CA; Lakewood CO; Milford DE; Des Plaines IL; Elgin IL; Burlington NJ; Maumee OH; Tulsa OK; Johnson City TN. **International locations:** Argentina; Australia; Brazil; Canada; China; England; France; Germany; Hong Kong; India; Italy; Japan; Mexico; Philippines; Puerto Rico; Russia; Switzerland; Thailand; Vietnam. **Listed on:** NASDAQ. **Stock exchange symbol:** XRAY.

DOYLESTOWN HOSPITAL
595 West State Street, Doylestown PA 18901. 215/345-2276. **Fax:** 215/345-2827. **Recorded jobline:** 215/345-2538. **Contact:** Human Resources Department. **World Wide Web address:** http://www.dh.org. **Description:** A hospital. **Common positions include:** Food Service Manager; Health Care Administrator; Occupational Therapist; Pharmacist; Physical Therapist; Preschool Worker; Recreational Therapist; Registered Nurse; Respiratory Therapist; Social Worker; Speech-Language Pathologist. **Number of employees at this location:** 1,400.

EAST COAST TECHNOLOGIES
301 Pinedge Drive, Pinedge Industrial Park, West Berlin NJ 08091. 856/753-7778. **Contact:** Human Resources. **World Wide Web address:** http://www.eastcoasttech.com. **Description:** Wholesales and repairs medical equipment, primarily laser and medical imaging systems.

EASTON HOSPITAL
250 South 21st Street, Easton PA 18042. 610/250-4120. **Fax:** 610/250-4876. **Contact:** Human Resources. **World Wide Web address:** http://www.easton-hospital.com. **Description:** A hospital.

ELWYN INC.
111 Elwyn Road, Elwyn PA 19063. 610/891-2000. **Fax:** 610/891-2900. **Contact:** Sharon E. Hill, Human Resources. **E-mail address:** sharon_hill@elwyn.org. **World Wide Web**

address: http://www.elwyn.org. **Description:** A long-term care rehabilitation center for people with physical and mental disabilities.

FLOWERS MILL VETERINARY HOSPITAL P.C.
10 South Flowers Mill Road, Langhorne PA 19047. 215/752-1010. **Contact:** Human Resources Department. **Description:** Offers boarding services and general medical and surgical care to small and exotic animals.

FOX CHASE CANCER CENTER
7701 Burholme Avenue, Philadelphia PA 19111. 215/728-6900. **Contact:** Human Resources. **World Wide Web address:** http://www.fccc.edu. **Description:** A comprehensive cancer center that serves as a national resource for converting research findings into medical applications. Applications are designed to improve cancer detection, treatment, and prevention. **Corporate headquarters location:** This location. **Number of employees at this location:** 1,700.

FRANKFORD HOSPITAL
Knights and Red Lion Roads, Philadelphia PA 19114. 215/612-4000. **Contact:** Human Resources Department. **World Wide Web address:** http://www.frankfordhospitals.org. **Description:** A full-service hospital providing a cancer center, inpatient medicine, a Level II neonatal care, a Level II trauma center, obstetrics, and surgery.

GEISINGER MEDICAL CENTER
100 North Academy Avenue, Danville PA 17822. 570/271-6211. **Contact:** Human Resources. **World Wide Web address:** http://www.geisinger.org. **Description:** A tertiary care teaching hospital with 45 regional clinics in central and northeastern Pennsylvania. Geisinger Medical Center is a Level I trauma center. **Common positions include:** Accountant/Auditor; Attorney; Biological Scientist; Chemist; Computer Programmer; Dental Assistant/Dental Hygienist; Dental Lab Technician; Dietician/Nutritionist; EEG Technologist; EKG Technician; Medical Records Technician; Nuclear Medicine Technologist; Occupational Therapist; Pharmacist; Physical Therapist; Psychologist; Registered Nurse; Respiratory Therapist; Social Worker; Speech-Language Pathologist; Surgical Technician; Systems Analyst. **Operations at this facility include:** Administration; Divisional Headquarters; Research and Development. **Number of employees at this location:** 3,500.

GENESIS HEALTH VENTURES, INC.
101 East State Street, Kennett Square PA 19348. 610/444-6350. **Fax:** 610/925-4352. **Contact:** Recruitment Manager. **World Wide Web address:** http://www.ghv.com. **Description:** Provides services, centers, and programs for the elderly. Genesis Health Ventures operates its skilled nursing and assisted living centers under the Genesis ElderCare name. Founded in 1985. **Common positions include:** Accountant; Administrative Assistant; Auditor; Certified Nurses Aide; Computer Operator; Computer Programmer; Database Manager; Licensed Practical Nurse; MIS Specialist; Secretary; Systems Analyst. **Corporate headquarters location:** This location. **Listed on:** New York Stock Exchange. **Stock exchange symbol:** GHVI. **Number of employees at this location:** 270. **Number of employees nationwide:** 30,000.

GRADUATE HOSPITAL
1800 Lombard Street, Philadelphia PA 19146. 215/893-2000. **Recorded jobline:** 215/893-4111. **Fax:** 215/893-7521. **Contact:** Sharita Barnett, Human Resources Department. **E-mail address:** sharita.barnett@tenethealth.com. **World Wide Web address:** http://www.graduatehospital.com. **Description:** A full-service hospital consisting of 303 inpatient beds, four intensive care units, an emergency department, and a variety of inpatient and outpatient diagnostic and treatment facilities. **Parent company:** Tenet Healthcare.

HCR MANOR CARE HEALTH SERVICES
1412 Marlton Pike, Cherry Hill NJ 08034. 856/428-6100. **Contact:** Human Resources Department. **E-mail address:** jobline@hcr.manorcare.com. **World Wide Web address:** http://www.manorcare.com. **Description:** An inpatient and outpatient rehabilitation center providing physical, occupational, and speech therapies. **Special programs:** Training. **Corporate headquarters location:** Toledo OH. **Other U.S. locations:** Nationwide. **Subsidiaries include:** Milestone Healthcare. **Listed on:** New York Stock Exchange. **Stock exchange symbol:** HCR. **Number of employees nationwide:** 50,000.

HCR MANORCARE HEALTH SERVICES
800 King Russ Road, Harrisburg PA 17109. 717/657-1520. **Contact:** Human Resources. **E-mail address:** jobline@hcr-manorcare.com. **World Wide Web address:** http://www.hcr-manorcare.com. **Description:** An inpatient and outpatient rehabilitation center providing physical, occupational, and speech therapies. **Common positions include:** Certified Nurses

Aide; Human Resources Manager; Licensed Practical Nurse; Occupational Therapist; Physical Therapist; Registered Nurse; Speech-Language Pathologist. **Corporate headquarters location:** Toledo OH. **Listed on:** New York Stock Exchange. **Stock exchange symbol:** HCR.

HCR MANORCARE HEALTH SERVICES
3000 Windmill Road, Sinking Spring PA 19608. 610/670-2100. **Contact:** Human Resources Department. **E-mail address:** jobline@hcr-manorcare.com. **World Wide Web address:** http://www.hcr-manorcare.com. **Description:** An inpatient and outpatient rehabilitation center providing physical, occupational, and speech therapies. **Common positions include:** Certified Nurses Aide; Human Resources Manager; Licensed Practical Nurse; Occupational Therapist; Physical Therapist; Registered Nurse; Speech-Language Pathologist. **Corporate headquarters location:** Toledo OH. **Listed on:** New York Stock Exchange. **Stock exchange symbol:** HCR.

HCR MANORCARE HEALTH SERVICES
600 West Valley Forge Road, King of Prussia PA 19406. 610/337-1775. **Contact:** Human Resources Department. **E-mail address:** jobline@hcr-manorcare.com. **World Wide Web address:** http://www.hcr-manorcare.com. **Description:** An inpatient and outpatient rehabilitation center providing physical, occupational, and speech therapies. **Common positions include:** Certified Nurses Aide; Human Resources Manager; Licensed Practical Nurse; Occupational Therapist; Physical Therapist; Registered Nurse; Speech-Language Pathologist. **Corporate headquarters location:** Toledo OH. **Listed on:** New York Stock Exchange. **Stock exchange symbol:** HCR.

HCR MANORCARE HEALTH SERVICES
200 Second Avenue, Kingston PA 18704. 570/288-9315. **Contact:** Human Resources. **E-mail address:** jobline@hcr-manorcare.com. **World Wide Web address:** http://www.hcr-manorcare.com. **Description:** An inpatient and outpatient rehabilitation center providing physical, occupational, and speech therapies. **Common positions include:** Certified Nurses Aide; Human Resources Manager; Licensed Practical Nurse; Occupational Therapist; Physical Therapist; Registered Nurse; Speech-Language Pathologist. **Corporate headquarters location:** Toledo OH. **Listed on:** New York Stock Exchange. **Stock exchange symbol:** HCR.

HCR MANORCARE HEALTH SERVICES
100 West Queen Street, Dallastown PA 17313. 717/246-1671. **Contact:** Human Resources. **E-mail address:** jobline@hcr-manorcare.com. **World Wide Web address:** http://www.hcr-manorcare.com. **Description:** An inpatient and outpatient rehabilitation center providing physical, occupational, and speech therapies. **Common positions include:** Certified Nurses Aide; Human Resources Manager; Licensed Practical Nurse; Occupational Therapist; Physical Therapist; Registered Nurse; Speech-Language Pathologist. **Corporate headquarters location:** Toledo OH. **Listed on:** New York Stock Exchange. **Stock exchange symbol:** HCR.

HCR MANORCARE HEALTH SERVICES
940 Walnut Bottom Road, Carlisle PA 17013. 717/249-0085. **Contact:** Human Resources. **E-mail address:** jobline@hcr-manorcare.com. **World Wide Web address:** http://www.hcr-manorcare.com. **Description:** An inpatient and outpatient rehabilitation center providing physical, occupational, and speech therapies. **Common positions include:** Certified Nurses Aide; Human Resources Manager; Licensed Practical Nurse; Occupational Therapist; Physical Therapist; Registered Nurse; Speech-Language Pathologist. **Corporate headquarters location:** Toledo OH. **Listed on:** New York Stock Exchange. **Stock exchange symbol:** HCR.

HCR MANORCARE HEALTH SERVICES
425 Buttonwood Street, West Reading PA 19611. 610/373-5166. **Contact:** Human Resources Department. **E-mail address:** jobline@hcr-manorcare.com. **World Wide Web address:** http://www.hcr-manorcare.com. **Description:** An inpatient and outpatient rehabilitation center providing physical, occupational, and speech therapies. **Common positions include:** Certified Nurses Aide; Human Resources Manager; Licensed Practical Nurse; Occupational Therapist; Physical Therapist; Registered Nurse; Speech-Language Pathologist. **Corporate headquarters location:** Toledo OH. **Listed on:** New York Stock Exchange. **Stock exchange symbol:** HCR.

HCR MANORCARE HEALTH SERVICES
800 Court Street, Sunbury PA 17801. 570/286-7121. **Contact:** Human Resources. **World E-mail address:** jobline@hcr-manorcare.com. **Wide Web address:** http://www.hcr-manorcare.com. **Description:** An inpatient and outpatient rehabilitation center providing physical, occupational, and speech therapies. **NOTE:** Part-time jobs and second and third shifts are offered. **Common positions include:** Certified Nurses

Aide; Human Resources Manager; Licensed Practical Nurse; Medical Records Technician; Occupational Therapist; Physical Therapist; Physical Therapy Assistant; Registered Nurse; Social Worker; Speech-Language Pathologist. **Office hours:** Monday - Friday, 7:30 a.m. - 5:30 p.m. **Corporate headquarters location:** Toledo OH. **Operations at this facility include:** Administration; Sales; Service. **Listed on:** New York Stock Exchange. **Stock exchange symbol:** HCR. **Number of employees at this location:** 130.

HCR MANORCARE HEALTH SERVICES
2600 Northampton Street, Easton PA 18045. 610/250-0150. **Contact:** Human Resources. **E-mail address:** jobline@hcr-manorcare.com. **World Wide Web address:** http://www.hcr-manorcare.com. **Description:** An inpatient and outpatient rehabilitation center providing physical, occupational, and speech therapies. **NOTE:** Second and third shifts are offered. **Common positions include:** Certified Nurses Aide; Human Resources Manager; Licensed Practical Nurse; Occupational Therapist; Physical Therapist; Registered Nurse; Speech-Language Pathologist. **Special programs:** Training. **Corporate headquarters location:** Toledo OH. **Listed on:** New York Stock Exchange. **Stock exchange symbol:** HCR.

HCR MANORCARE HEALTH SERVICES
101 Leader Drive, Williamsport PA 17701. 570/323-3758. **Contact:** Human Resources Director. **E-mail address:** jobline@hcr-manorcare.com. **World Wide Web address:** http://www.hcr-manorcare.com. **Description:** An inpatient and outpatient rehabilitation center providing physical, occupational, and speech therapies. **Common positions include:** Licensed Practical Nurse; Occupational Therapist; Physical Therapist; Recreational Therapist; Registered Nurse; Social Worker. **Corporate headquarters location:** Toledo OH. **Operations at this facility include:** Administration. **Listed on:** New York Stock Exchange. **Stock exchange symbol:** HCR.

HCR MANORCARE HEALTH SERVICES
420 Pulaski Drive, Pottsville PA 17901-3698. 570/622-9582. **Contact:** Human Resources. **E-mail address:** jobline@hcr-manorcare.com. **World Wide Web address:** http://www.hcr-manorcare.com. **Description:** An inpatient and outpatient rehabilitation center providing physical, occupational, and speech therapies. **Common positions include:** Certified Nurses Aide; Human Resources Manager; Licensed Practical Nurse; Occupational Therapist; Physical Therapist; Registered Nurse; Speech-Language Pathologist. **Corporate headquarters**

location: Toledo OH. **Listed on:** New York Stock Exchange. **Stock exchange symbol:** HCR.

HCR MANORCARE HEALTH SERVICES
1070 Stouffer Avenue, Chambersburg PA 17201. 717/263-0436. **Contact:** Human Resources Department. **E-mail address:** jobline@hcr-manorcare.com. **World Wide Web address:** http://www.hcr-manorcare.com. **Description:** An inpatient and outpatient rehabilitation center providing physical, occupational, and speech therapies. **Common positions include:** Certified Nurses Aide; Human Resources Manager; Licensed Practical Nurse; Occupational Therapist; Physical Therapist; Registered Nurse; Speech-Language Pathologist. **Corporate headquarters location:** Toledo OH. **Listed on:** New York Stock Exchange. **Stock exchange symbol:** HCR.

HCR MANORCARE HEALTH SERVICES
1265 South Cedar Crest Boulevard, Allentown PA 18103. 610/776-7522. **Contact:** Human Resources Department. **E-mail address:** jobline@hcr-manorcare.com. **World Wide Web address:** http://www.hcr-manorcare.com. **Description:** An inpatient and outpatient rehabilitation center providing physical, occupational, and speech therapies. **Common positions include:** Certified Nurses Aide; Human Resources Manager; Licensed Practical Nurse; Occupational Therapist; Physical Therapist; Registered Nurse; Speech-Language Pathologist. **Corporate headquarters location:** Toledo OH. **Listed on:** New York Stock Exchange. **Stock exchange symbol:** HCR.

HCR MANORCARE HEALTH SERVICES
640 Bethlehem Pike, Montgomeryville PA 18936. 215/368-4350. **Contact:** Human Resources Department. **E-mail address:** jobline@hcr-manorcare.com. **World Wide Web address:** http://www.hcr-manorcare.com. **Description:** An inpatient and outpatient rehabilitation center providing physical, occupational, and speech therapies. **NOTE:** Part-time jobs and second and third shifts are offered. **Common positions include:** Certified Nurses Aide; Human Resources Manager; Licensed Practical Nurse; Occupational Therapist; Physical Therapist; Registered Nurse; Speech-Language Pathologist. **Special programs:** Training. **Corporate headquarters location:** Toledo OH. **Listed on:** New York Stock Exchange. **Stock exchange symbol:** HCR.

HANOVER HOSPITAL

300 Highland Avenue, Hanover PA 17331. 717/633-2143. **Toll-free phone:** 800/673-2426. **Fax:** 717/633-2217. **Contact:** Jen Walton, Human Resources. **World Wide Web address:** http://www.hanoverhospital.org. **Description:** A 174-bed, acute care hospital. **Common positions include:** Licensed Practical Nurse; Nuclear Medicine Technologist; Occupational Therapist; Pharmacist; Physical Therapist; Radiological Technologist; Registered Nurse; Respiratory Therapist; Speech-Language Pathologist; Surgical Technician. **Special programs:** Internships. **Parent company:** Hanover HealthCare Plus Network. **Number of employees at this location:** 800.

HOLY REDEEMER HOSPITAL

1648 Huntingdon Pike, Meadowbrook PA 19046. 215/947-3000. **Recorded jobline:** 877/499-4473. **Fax:** 215/938-3121. **Contact:** Linda Bivenour, Human Resources Department. **E-mail address:** hrhmc@ttd-mail.net. **World Wide Web address:** http://www.holyredeemer.com. **Description:** A 299-bed community hospital offering a variety of inpatient, outpatient, and emergency services.

HOLY SPIRIT HEALTH SYSTEM

503 North 21st Street, Camp Hill PA 17011. 717/763-2100. **Fax:** 717/763-2351. **Recorded jobline:** 717/972-4121. **Contact:** Employment Manager. **E-mail address:** resume@hsh.org. **World Wide Web address:** http://www.hsh.org. **Description:** A nonprofit health system that operates a 349-bed hospital as well as several home health, hospice, and family care centers. Holy Spirit Health System also provides ambulance and emergency care services. Founded in 1963. **NOTE:** Entry-level positions, part-time jobs, and second and third shifts are offered. **Common positions include:** Administrative Assistant; Certified Nurses Aide; Claim Representative; EEG Technologist; EKG Technician; Emergency Medical Technician; Help-Desk Technician; Home Health Aide; Licensed Practical Nurse; Medical Assistant; Medical Records Technician; Medical Secretary; Network/Systems Administrator; Nuclear Medicine Technologist; Occupational Therapist; Pharmacist; Physical Therapist; Radiological Technologist; Registered Nurse; Respiratory Therapist; Secretary; Social Worker; Speech-Language Pathologist; Surgical Technician. **Special programs:** Internships. **Office hours:** Monday - Friday, 7:30 a.m. - 4:00 p.m. **Corporate headquarters location:** This location. **Parent company:** Holy Spirit Health System. **Listed on:** Privately held. **Number of employees at this location:** 2,000.

INTEGRATED HEALTH SERVICES/BROOMALL
50 North Malin Road, Business Office, Broomall PA 19008. 610/356-0800. **Fax:** 610/325-9499. **Contact:** Human Resources Department. **Description:** A subacute care nursing facility with an oncology specialty unit. **NOTE:** For information on employment throughout Pennsylvania, contact the Division Recruitment office: 866/212-0510. **Common positions include:** Dietician/Nutritionist; Housekeeper; Registered Nurse. **Corporate headquarters location:** Owings Mills MD. **Other U.S. locations:** Nationwide. **Operations at this facility include:** Administration; Service. **Number of employees at this location:** 310.

INTEGRATED HEALTH SERVICES/WHITEMARSH
9209 Ridge Pike, Whitemarsh PA 19128. 610/825-6560. **Fax:** 610/825-9478. **Contact:** Employment. **Description:** A subacute care nursing home. **NOTE:** For information on employment throughout Pennsylvania, contact the Division Recruitment office: 866/212-0510. **Corporate headquarters location:** Owings Mills MD. **Other U.S. locations:** Nationwide.

JENNERSVILLE REGIONAL HOSPITAL
1015 West Baltimore Pike, West Grove PA 19390. 610/869-1345. **Fax:** 610/869-1246. **Recorded jobline:** 610/869-1200. **Contact:** Employment Coordinator. **World Wide Web address:** http://www.sccmc.com. **Description:** A 75-bed, nonprofit acute care medical center that offers a surgery/ER center, an intensive care unit, and maternity and outpatient services. The hospital also operates Jenner's Pond, an independent and assisted living retirement community. Founded in 1920. **NOTE:** Entry-level positions, part-time jobs, and second and third shifts are offered. **Common positions include:** Certified Nurses Aide; Dietician/Nutritionist; EKG Technician; Emergency Medical Technician; Home Health Aide; Human Resources Manager; Medical Records Technician; Occupational Therapist; Pharmacist; Physical Therapist; Physical Therapy Assistant; Physician; Psychologist; Radiological Technologist; Registered Nurse; Respiratory Therapist; Social Worker; Surgical Technician. **Special programs:** Summer Jobs. **Number of employees at this location:** 600.

LANKENAU HOSPITAL
100 Lancaster Avenue, Wynnewood PA 19096. 610/645-2000. **Fax:** 610/645-8492. **Contact:** Personnel. **World Wide Web address:** http://www.jeffersonhealth.org/lh. **Description:** A hospital. **Parent company:** Jefferson Health System.

LUZERNE OPTICAL LABORATORIES, INC.
180 North Wilkes-Barre Boulevard, P.O. Box 998, Wilkes-Barre PA 18703. 570/822-3183. **Toll-free phone:** 800/233-9637. **Fax:** 800/525-5597. **Contact:** Lorraine Dougherty, Human Resources Representative. **World Wide Web address:** http://www.luzerneoptical.com. **Description:** Manufactures optical products including eyeglasses and contact lenses. Founded in 1973. **NOTE:** Entry-level positions and second and third shifts are offered. **Company slogan:** With an eye on service and quality. **Common positions include:** Clerical Supervisor; Computer Operator; Computer Programmer; Controller; Credit Manager; Customer Service Representative; Database Manager; General Manager; Marketing Manager; Production Manager; Purchasing Agent/Manager; Quality Control Supervisor; Sales Executive; Sales Manager; Sales Representative. **Office hours:** Monday - Friday, 7:00 a.m. - 6:30 p.m. **Corporate headquarters location:** This location. **Listed on:** Privately held. **President:** John Dougherty. **Annual sales/revenues:** $11 - $20 million. **Number of employees at this location:** 110.

MEDIQ/PRN
One Mediq Plaza, Pennsauken NJ 08110. 856/665-9300. **Toll-free phone:** 800/257-7477. **Fax:** 856/661-0223. **Contact:** Personnel. **E-mail address:** resumes@mediq.net. **World Wide Web address:** http://www.mediqprn.net. **Description:** Rents moveable life-support equipment such as ventilators, monitors, and incubators to hospitals, nursing homes, and home-care companies. **Corporate headquarters location:** This location.

MEMORIAL HOSPITAL
P.O. Box 15118, York PA 17405. 717/849-5479. **Physical address:** 325 South Belmont Street, York PA 17403. **Fax:** 717/849-5495. **Contact:** Human Resources Department. **E-mail address:** hrinfo@mhyork.org. **World Wide Web address:** http://www.mhyork.org. **Description:** An acute care, community-based, teaching hospital serving York County. **Common positions include:** Accountant/Auditor; Biomedical Engineer; Buyer; Claim Representative; Clerical Supervisor; Counselor; Credit Manager; Customer Service Representative; Dietician/Nutritionist; EEG Technologist; EKG Technician; Electrical/Electronics Engineer; Emergency Medical Technician; Health Services Manager; Human Resources Manager; Human Service Worker; Licensed Practical Nurse; Medical Records Technician; Nuclear Medicine Technologist; Occupational Therapist; Pharmacist; Physical Therapist; Physician; Psychologist; Public Relations Specialist;

Radiological Technologist; Registered Nurse; Respiratory Therapist; Restaurant/Food Service Manager; Services Sales Representative; Social Worker; Speech-Language Pathologist. **Parent company:** Memorial Healthcare System. **Operations at this facility include:** Administration; Service. **Annual sales/revenues:** $21 - $50 million. **Number of employees at this location:** 900.

MERCY FITZGERALD HOSPITAL
1500 Lansdowne Avenue, Darby PA 19023. 610/237-4000. **Fax:** 610/853-7030. **Contact:** Central Employment Office. **E-mail address:** mercyjobs@mercyhealth.org. **World Wide Web address:** http://www.mercyhealth.org. **Description:** A 441-bed, acute-care, community hospital that serves southwest Pennsylvania. **NOTE:** For employment opportunities contact: Central Employment Office, 2000 Old West Chester Pike, Havertown PA 19083. 610/853-7333. **Parent company:** Mercy Health System.

MERCY HOSPITAL OF PHILADELPHIA
501 South 54th Street, Philadelphia PA 19143. 215/748-9000. **Fax:** 610/853-7030. **Contact:** Central Employment Office. **E-mail address:** mercyjobs@mercyhealth.org. **World Wide Web address:** http://www.mercyhealth.org. **Description:** A 200-bed medical center. **NOTE:** For employment opportunities contact: Central Employment Office, 2000 Old West Chester Pike, Havertown PA 19083. 610/853-7333.

METHODIST HOSPITAL
Thomas Jefferson University Hospital, 2301 South Broad Street, Philadelphia PA 19148. 215/952-9000. **Fax:** 215/952-9588. **Contact:** Human Resources. **World Wide Web address:** http://www.jeffersonhospital.org. **Description:** A hospital licensed for 165 beds. Methodist Hospital is affiliated with Thomas Jefferson University Hospital.

NAZARETH HOSPITAL
2601 Holme Avenue, Philadelphia PA 19152. 215/335-6000. **Fax:** 610/853-7030. **Contact:** Human Resources Department. **E-mail address:** mercyjobs@mercyhealth.org. **World Wide Web address:** http://www.mercyhealth.org/nazareth. **Description:** An acute care hospital serving the northeast Philadelphia community. **NOTE:** Mail resumes to: Central Employment Office, 2000 Old West Chester Pike, Havertown PA 19083. 610/853-7333. **Common positions include:** Accountant/Auditor; Dietician/Nutritionist. **Special programs:**

Internships. **Parent company:** Mercy Health System. **Number of employees at this location:** 1,400.

NEIGHBORCARE

9 Creek Parkway, Boothwyn PA 19061. 610/364-2700. **Contact:** Human Resources Department. **World Wide Web address:** http://www.neighborcare.com. **Description:** Distributes medical equipment including wheelchairs, diabetic equipment, and home medical supplies. **Corporate headquarters location:** Baltimore MD.

NOVACARE REHABILITATION

680 American Avenue, Suite 200, King of Prussia PA 19406. 610/992-7200. **Toll-free phone:** 800/331-8840. **Contact:** Human Resources Department. **World Wide Web address:** http://www.novacare.com. **Description:** Novacare provides comprehensive medical rehabilitation services to patients with physical disabilities. NovaCare's services include speech-language pathology, occupational therapy, and physical therapy. Services are provided on a contract basis primarily to long-term health care institutions, through inpatient rehabilitation hospitals and community-integrated programs, and through a national network of patient care centers providing orthotic and prosthetic rehabilitation services. **Corporate headquarters location:** This location. **Other U.S. locations:** Nationwide. **Listed on:** New York Stock Exchange. **Stock exchange symbol:** NOV.

NUTRI/SYSTEM L.P.

202 Welsh Road, Horsham PA 19044. 215/706-5300. **Fax:** 215/706-5388. **Contact:** Human Resources Department. **World Wide Web address:** http://www.nutrisystem.com. **Description:** A chain of weight loss/weight maintenance centers providing professionally supervised services through a network of 700 company-owned and franchised centers. **Common positions include:** Accountant/Auditor; Advertising Clerk; Attorney; Computer Programmer; Customer Service Representative; Dietician/Nutritionist; Financial Analyst; Food Scientist/Technologist; Health Services Manager; Marketing Specialist; Operations/Production Manager; Public Relations Specialist; Purchasing Agent/Manager; Quality Control Supervisor; Systems Analyst; Technical Writer/Editor. **Corporate headquarters location:** This location. **Other U.S. locations:** Nationwide. **International locations:** Canada; Saudi Arabia. **Operations at this facility include:** Administration; Research and Development. **Listed on:** NASDAQ. **Stock**

exchange symbol: THIN. **Number of employees at this location:** 75. **Number of employees nationwide:** 600.

PARKVIEW HOSPITAL
1331 East Wyoming Avenue, Philadelphia PA 19124. 215/537-7601. **Contact:** Employment Manager. **E-mail address:** parkviewjobs@tenethealth.com. **World Wide Web address:** http://www.parkviewhosp.com. **Description:** A hospital. **Common positions include:** Accountant/Auditor; Counselor; EEG Technologist; EKG Technician; Human Resources Manager; Licensed Practical Nurse; Medical Records Technician; MIS Specialist; Pharmacist; Physician; Psychologist; Public Relations Specialist; Quality Control Supervisor; Radiological Technologist; Recreational Therapist; Registered Nurse; Respiratory Therapist; Social Worker; Stationary Engineer; Surgical Technician. **Special programs:** Internships. **Other U.S. locations:** Reading PA. **Parent company:** Tenet Health Care Group. **Annual sales/revenues:** $21 - $50 million. **Number of employees at this location:** 800.

PENNSYLVANIA HOSPITAL
800 Spruce Street, Philadelphia PA 19107. 215/829-3000. **Contact:** Human Resources/Employment. **World Wide Web address:** http://www.pahosp.com. **Description:** A 513-bed hospital. Founded in 1751.

PERFECSEAL
9800 Bustleton Avenue, Philadelphia PA 19115. 215/673-4500. **Fax:** 215/856-6393. **Contact:** Mr. Reno Bianco, Human Resources Manager. **E-mail address:** perfecseal@bemis.com. **World Wide Web address:** http://www.perfecseal.com. **Description:** Manufactures sterilizable medical packaging for the medical device industry. The company is a world leader in thermoplastic flexible packaging, heat-sealed coated Tyvek, and paper. Products include Perfecseal adhesive coating on Tyvek and paper, film and foil lamination; Breather Bag and linear tear packaging; easy-open and chevron peel pouches; oriented films; custom thermoformed trays and die-cut lids; pharmaceutical labels, cold seal technology, extrusion and saran coating, flexographic and rotogravure printing; and vacuum metallizing. Founded in 1905. **NOTE:** Entry-level positions and second and third shifts are offered. **Common positions include:** Accountant; Administrative Assistant; Blue-Collar Worker Supervisor; Buyer; Chemical Engineer; Chemist; Computer Programmer; Controller; Customer Service Representative; Electrician; Graphic Designer; Human Resources Manager; Marketing Manager; Mechanical Engineer;

Operations Manager; Production Manager; Purchasing Agent/Manager; Quality Control Supervisor; Sales Executive; Sales Manager; Sales Representative; Secretary; Systems Manager. **Special programs:** Internships. **Corporate headquarters location:** This location. **Other U.S. locations:** Mankato MN; New London WI; Oshkosh WI. **International locations:** Carolina, Puerto Rico; Londonderry, Northern Ireland. **Parent company:** Bemis, Inc. **Operations at this facility include:** Administration; Manufacturing; Research and Development; Sales; Service. **Annual sales/revenues:** More than $100 million. **Number of employees at this location:** 200. **Number of employees worldwide:** 700.

PHILADELPHIA CENTER FOR AQUATIC REHABILITATION
3600 Grant Avenue, Philadelphia PA 19114. 215/677-0400. **Contact:** Human Resources. **Description:** Provides aquatic physical therapy, land therapy, and work conditioning for people recovering from back and neck injuries, industrial injuries, sports-related orthopedic injuries, post-operative arthroscopic surgeries, joint replacement, postfracture recovery and postoperative knee/shoulder recovery.

PHILHAVEN BEHAVIORAL HEALTH SERVICES
283 South Butler Road, P.O. Box 550, Mount Gretna PA 17064. 717/270-2451. **Fax:** 717/270-2455. **Contact:** Human Resources. **E-mail address:** hr@philhaven.com. **World Wide Web address:** http://www.philhaven.com. **Description:** A psychiatric treatment center offering inpatient, outpatient, residential, and community-based services. **NOTE:** Entry-level positions and second and third shifts are offered. **Common positions include:** Account Representative; Licensed Practical Nurse; Medical Records Technician; Physician; Psychologist; Registered Nurse; Secretary; Social Worker. **Corporate headquarters location:** This location. **Operations at this facility include:** Administration; Service. **CEO:** LaVern J. Yutzy. **Annual sales/revenues:** $21 - $50 million. **Number of employees at this location:** 600.

POTTSTOWN MEMORIAL MEDICAL CENTER
1600 East High Street, Pottstown PA 19464. 610/327-7057. **Fax:** 610/327-7690. **Contact:** Human Resources Department. **E-mail address:** hr@pmmctr.com. **World Wide Web address:** http://www.pmmctr.org. **Description:** A full-service hospital. **NOTE:** Entry-level positions and second and third shifts are offered. **Common positions include:** Accountant; Administrative Assistant; Certified Nurses Aide; Clerical Supervisor; Computer Operator; Controller; Credit Manager;

Dietician/Nutritionist; EEG Technologist; EKG Technician; Financial Analyst; Human Resources Manager; Librarian; Licensed Practical Nurse; Medical Records Technician; MIS Specialist; Nuclear Medicine Technologist; Occupational Therapist; Pharmacist; Physical Therapist; Physician; Radiological Technologist; Registered Nurse; Respiratory Therapist; Secretary; Social Worker; Speech-Language Pathologist; Surgical Technician; Telecommunications Manager; Typist/Word Processor; Vice President. **Corporate headquarters location:** This location. **Facilities Manager:** Scott Adams. **Number of employees at this location:** 1,100.

THE POTTSVILLE HOSPITAL AND WARNE CLINIC
420 South Jackson Street, Pottsville PA 17901. 570/621-5097. **Contact:** Human Resources. **World Wide Web address:** http://www.pottsville.com/hospital. **Description:** An acute care facility providing a full range of medical services including the Inpatient Rehabilitation Unit, the Institute for Behavioral Health (an inpatient psychiatric unit), and the Schuylkill Rehabilitation Center (a comprehensive outpatient rehabilitation facility). **Common positions include:** Accountant/Auditor; Dietician/Nutritionist; EEG Technologist; EKG Technician; Human Resources Manager; Human Service Worker; Librarian; Licensed Practical Nurse; Medical Records Technician; Medical Technologist; Nuclear Medicine Technologist; Occupational Therapist; Pharmacist; Physical Therapist; Physician; Radiological Technologist; Recreational Therapist; Registered Nurse; Respiratory Therapist; Social Worker; Speech-Language Pathologist; Surgical Technician. **Operations at this facility include:** Administration; Service. **Number of employees at this location:** 800.

PREMIER MEDICAL PRODUCTS
1710 Romano Street, Plymouth Meeting PA 19462. 610/239-6000. **Contact:** Human Resources. **World Wide Web address:** http://www.premusa.com. **Description:** Manufactures and distributes tracheal and laryngectomy tubes, as well as medical instruments used in gynecology and podiatry.

PRESBYTERIAN MEDICAL CENTER
39th & Market Streets, Philadelphia PA 19104. 215/662-8000. **Fax:** 215/662-8936. **Recorded jobline:** 215/662-8222. **Contact:** Human Resources. **Description:** A teaching hospital specializing in oncology, cardiology, general medicine, and surgery. **Common positions include:** Accountant/Auditor; Actuary; Adjuster; Administrative Manager; Cashier; Chemist; Chiropractor; Claim Representative; Clerical Supervisor;

Clinical Lab Technician; Computer Operator; Computer Programmer; Cost Estimator; Counselor; Credit Clerk and Authorizer; Credit Manager; Customer Service Representative; Dental Assistant/Dental Hygienist; Dentist; Education Administrator; EEG Technologist; EKG Technician; Emergency Medical Technician; Employment Interviewer; Financial Analyst; Health Services Manager; Human Resources Manager; Human Service Worker; Librarian; Library Technician; Licensed Practical Nurse; Line Installer/Cable Splicer; Medical Records Technician; New Accounts Clerk; Occupational Therapist; Operations Research Analyst; Optician; Order Clerk; Payroll Clerk; Pharmacist; Physical Therapist; Physician; Physician Assistant; Podiatrist; Postal Clerk/Mail Carrier; Printing Press Operator; Psychologist; Public Relations Specialist; Purchasing Agent/Manager; Quality Control Supervisor; Radiological Technologist; Receptionist; Recreation Worker; Registered Nurse; Respiratory Therapist; Secretary; Social Worker; Surgical Technician; Systems Analyst. **Special programs:** Internships. **Operations at this facility include:** Administration; Research and Development; Service. **Number of employees at this location:** 1,500.

REGINA NURSING CENTER
550 East Fornance Street, Norristown PA 19401-3561. 610/272-5600. **Fax:** 610/279-0529. **Contact:** Bonnie A. Dudley, RN, Director of Nursing. **World Wide Web address:** http://www.reginanursingcenter.org. **Description:** A 121-bed nursing care center.

REGINA NURSING CENTER
230 North 65th Street, Philadelphia PA 19139. 215/472-0541. **Contact:** Human Resources. **World Wide Web address:** http://www.reginanursingcenter.org. **Description:** A 44-bed nursing care center.

RIDDLE MEMORIAL HOSPITAL
1068 West Baltimore Pike, Media PA 19063. 610/566-9400. **Fax:** 610/891-3644. **Contact:** Human Resources. **E-mail address:** wzaloga@riddlehospital.org. **World Wide Web address:** http://www.riddlehospital.org. **Description:** A short-term, acute care, community hospital and outpatient medical facility. **Common positions include:** Accountant/Auditor; Buyer; Cashier; Chef; Claim Representative; Clerical Supervisor; Computer Operator; Computer Programmer; Credit Clerk and Authorizer; Department Manager; Dietician/Nutritionist; EEG Technologist; EKG Technician; Emergency Medical Technician; Employment Interviewer;

Financial Manager; Food and Beverage Service Worker; Licensed Practical Nurse; Marketing Manager; Medical Records Technician; Nuclear Medicine Technologist; Pharmacist; Physician; Physician Assistant; Purchasing Agent/Manager; Radiological Technologist; Receptionist; Social Worker; Speech-Language Pathologist; Stock Clerk; Surgical Technician; Typist/Word Processor. **Number of employees at this location:** 1,300.

SAINT LUKE'S MINERS MEMORIAL MEDICAL CENTER
360 West Ruddle Street, Coaldale PA 18218-0067. 570/645-8113. **Fax:** 570/645-8149. **Contact:** Human Resources. **Description:** A 108-bed, acute care facility with a 48-bed geriatric center. **NOTE:** Entry-level positions and second and third shifts are offered. **Common positions include:** Accountant/Auditor; Architect; Biomedical Engineer; Blue-Collar Worker Supervisor; Certified Nurses Aide; Clinical Lab Technician; Construction Contractor; Draftsperson; EEG Technologist; EKG Technician; Food Scientist/Technologist; Health Services Manager; Human Resources Manager; Licensed Practical Nurse; Medical Records Technician; Nuclear Medicine Technologist; Occupational Therapist; Pharmacist; Physical Therapist; Physician; Public Relations Specialist; Purchasing Agent/Manager; Radiological Technologist; Registered Nurse; Respiratory Therapist; Social Worker; Speech-Language Pathologist; Typist/Word Processor. **Special programs:** Internships. **Operations at this facility include:** Administration; Service. **Listed on:** Privately held. **Number of employees at this location:** 400.

SHAMOKIN AREA COMMUNITY HOSPITAL
4200 Hospital Road, Coal Township PA 17866. 570/644-4200. **Fax:** 570/644-4356. **Contact:** Human Resources. **World Wide Web address:** http://www.shamokinhospital.org. **Description:** A 61-bed nonprofit, community hospital offering acute care, general surgery, subacute and outpatient rehabilitation, inpatient and partial hospitalization care for geriatric-psychiatric patients, 24-hour emergency services, occupational health, specialty clinics and community health programs. Founded in 1912. **NOTE:** Entry-level positions, part-time jobs, and second and third shifts are offered. **Company slogan:** Quality care close to home. **Common positions include:** Accountant; Certified Nurses Aide; Certified Occupational Therapy Assistant; Chief Financial Officer; Clinical Lab Technician; Dietician/Nutritionist; Education Administrator; Emergency Medical Technician; Licensed Practical Nurse; Medical Assistant; Medical Records Technician; Nuclear

Medicine Technologist; Pharmacist; Physical Therapist; Physical Therapy Assistant; Physician; Physician Assistant; Radiological Technologist; Registered Nurse; Respiratory Therapist; Secretary; Social Worker; Surgical Technician; Systems Manager. **Special programs:** Summer Jobs. **Office hours:** Monday - Friday, 8:00 a.m. - 5:00 p.m. **Corporate headquarters location:** This location. **Other U.S. locations:** Elysburg PA. **Subsidiaries include:** Northumberland Health Services. **President/CEO:** John P. Wiercinski. **Annual sales/revenues:** $21 - $50 million. **Number of employees at this location:** 285.

SMITHS INDUSTRIES
101 Lindenwood Drive, Suite 125, Malvern PA 19355. 610/578-9600. **Contact:** Vice President of Human Resources. **World Wide Web address:** http://www.smiths-group.com. **Description:** Engaged in a variety of businesses through three business groups: Smiths Industries Aerospace Group manufactures instrumentation and systems for civil and military aircraft; Smiths Industries Medical Systems Group (SIMS) manufactures surgical, dental, veterinary, and home health care supplies; Smiths Industries Industrial Group operates in four divisions. Flex-Tek produces flexible ducting and conduits. Vent-Axia produces ventilation fans. Engineering produces specialized engineering products. Hypertac Interconnect manufactures electrical connectors. **NOTE:** Entry-level positions are offered. **Common positions include:** Accountant; Budget Analyst; Computer Programmer; Electrical/Electronics Engineer; Financial Analyst; Human Resources Manager; Marketing Manager; Marketing Specialist; Sales Engineer; Sales Representative; Software Engineer; Systems Analyst; Technical Writer/Editor. **Corporate headquarters location:** London, England. **Other U.S. locations:** Irvine CA; Sunnyvale CA; Clearwater FL; Fort Myers FL; Hudson MA; Rockland MA; Grand Rapids MI; St. Paul MN; Keene NH; Florham Park NJ; Abbeville SC; Cookeville TN. **Parent company:** Smiths Industries plc. **Annual sales/revenues:** More than $100 million. **Number of employees nationwide:** 6,000. **Number of employees worldwide:** 13,000.

SOUTH JERSEY HEALTH SYSTEM
SOUTH JERSEY HOSPITAL
333 Irving Avenue, Bridgeton NJ 08302-2123. 856/451-6600. **Fax:** 856/575-4500. **Contact:** Personnel. **World Wide Web address:** http://www.sjhs.com. **Description:** Provides extensive medical services throughout southern New Jersey. **NOTE:** Mail employment correspondence to: 65 South State Street,

Vineland NJ 08360. **Subsidiaries include:** Elmer Community Hospital has 91 beds. Millville Hospital has 109 beds. Newcomb Medical Center has 235 beds. South Jersey Hospital (also at this location) has 224 beds.

SURGICAL LASER TECHNOLOGIES, INC.
147 Keystone Drive, Montgomeryville PA 18936. 215/619-3600. **Contact:** Colleen Hamilton, Personnel Director. **World Wide Web address:** http://www.slti.com. **Description:** Develops, manufactures, and sells proprietary laser systems for contact surgery. The company's Contact Laser System allows the surgeon to use a laser in direct contact with the tissue being treated, thereby making laser surgery both more precise and easier to perform. Surgical Laser Technologies also provides free-beam, noncontact laser delivery systems. Its product line includes six portable Contact Laser units of various power levels; a family of disposable optical fibers and handpieces; and more than 80 probes, scalpels, fibers, and hand pieces that provide different wavelength conversion effect properties, power densities, and configurations appropriate for cutting, coagulation, or vaporization. As a result of the system's design, a single contact laser system can be used within most surgical specialties to perform a broad range of minimally-invasive and open surgical procedures. **Corporate headquarters location:** This location. **Number of employees at this location:** 160.

TEMPLE CONTINUING CARE CENTER
5301 Old York Road, Philadelphia PA 19141. 215/456-2900. **Fax:** 215/456-2048. **Recorded jobline:** 215/456-2929. **Contact:** Human Resources Department. **World Wide Web address:** http://www.health.temple.edu. **Description:** A nonprofit nursing home. **NOTE:** Entry-level positions and second and third shifts are offered. **Common positions include:** Accountant/Auditor; Administrative Assistant; Administrative Manager; Certified Nurses Aide; Construction Contractor; Counselor; Dietician/Nutritionist; Electrician; General Manager; Licensed Practical Nurse; Medical Records Technician; Occupational Therapist; Physical Therapist; Physician; Psychologist; Public Relations Specialist; Quality Control Supervisor; Recreational Therapist; Registered Nurse; Respiratory Therapist; Secretary; Social Worker; Speech-Language Pathologist; Systems Analyst; Typist/Word Processor. **Special programs:** Internships. **Listed on:** Privately held. **Number of employees at this location:** 1,000.

TEMPLE UNIVERSITY HOSPITAL
3333 North Broad Street, GSB Room 107, Philadelphia PA 19140. 215/707-2000. **Contact:** Human Resources. **World Wide Web address:** http://www.temple.edu/tuhs. **Description:** A hospital that also operates a physicians' information bureau.

TENDER LOVING CARE/STAFF BUILDERS
25 Bala Avenue, Suite 100, Bala-Cynwyd PA 19004. 610/668-2800. **Fax:** 610/668-9990. **Contact:** Ann May, Manager. **World Wide Web address:** http://www.tlcathome.com. **Description:** A home health care agency. **Common positions include:** Certified Nurses Aide; Licensed Practical Nurse; Occupational Therapist; Physical Therapist; Registered Nurse; Respiratory Therapist; Social Worker; Speech-Language Pathologist. **Corporate headquarters location:** Lake Success NY. **Other U.S. locations:** Nationwide. **Number of employees nationwide:** 20,000.

THERAKOS, INC.
437 Creamery Way, Exton PA 19341. 610/280-1000. **Contact:** Human Resources Department. **World Wide Web address:** http://www.jnj.com. **Description:** Develops and manufactures the UVAR Photopheresis System. The system is used in phototherapy treatment for certain types of cancers. **Parent company:** Johnson & Johnson (New Brunswick NJ).

TRI-COUNTY MOUNT TREXLER MANOR
15201 St. Joseph's Road, P.O. Box 1001, Limeport PA 18060. 610/965-9021. **Contact:** William Mains, Administrator. **Description:** A residential psychiatric treatment facility. Tri-County Mount Trexler Manor also runs a nonresident day program for people with mental illnesses. **Common positions include:** Counselor; Human Service Worker; Licensed Practical Nurse; Recreational Therapist; Social Worker; Teacher/Professor. **Special programs:** Internships. **Corporate headquarters location:** Doylestown PA. **Other U.S. locations:** Quakertown PA. **Parent company:** Tri-County Respite operates another subsidiary, Quakertown House. **Operations at this facility include:** Administration; Divisional Headquarters; Service. **Number of employees nationwide:** 60.

UNDERWOOD MEMORIAL HOSPITAL
509 North Broad Street, Woodbury NJ 08096. 856/845-0100. **Recorded jobline:** 856/853-2050. **Contact:** Personnel. **E-mail address:** humanresources@umhospital.org. **World Wide Web address:** http://www.umhospital.org. **Description:** A hospital.

U.S. DEPARTMENT OF VETERANS AFFAIRS
VETERANS ADMINISTRATION MEDICAL CENTER

1111 East End Boulevard, Wilkes-Barre PA 18711. 570/824-3521x7209. **Contact:** Reese Thomas III, Chief of Human Resources Management Service. **Description:** A medical center operated by the U.S. Department of Veterans Affairs. From 54 hospitals in 1930, the VA health care system has grown to include 171 medical centers; more than 364 outpatient, community, and outreach clinics; 130 nursing home care units; and 37 domiciliary residences. The VA operates at least one medical center in each of the 48 contiguous states, Puerto Rico, and the District of Columbia. With approximately 76,000 medical center beds, the VA treats nearly 1 million patients in VA hospitals, 75,000 in nursing home care units, and 25,000 in domiciliary residences. The VA's outpatient clinics register approximately 24 million visits per year. **Common positions include:** Accountant/Auditor; Clinical Lab Technician; Computer Programmer; Counselor; Dental Assistant/Dental Hygienist; Dentist; Dietician/Nutritionist; EEG Technologist; EKG Technician; Electrician; Human Resources Manager; Librarian; Library Technician; Licensed Practical Nurse; Medical Records Technician; Nuclear Medicine Technologist; Occupational Therapist; Pharmacist; Physical Therapist; Physician; Psychologist; Recreational Therapist; Registered Nurse; Respiratory Therapist; Social Worker. **Special programs:** Internships. **Corporate headquarters location:** Washington DC. **Other U.S. locations:** Nationwide. **Operations at this facility include:** Administration. **Number of employees at this location:** 1,300.

UNIVERSAL HEALTH SERVICES, INC.

367 South Gulph Road, P.O. Box 61558, King of Prussia PA 19406. **Toll-free phone:** 800/347-7750. **Fax:** 610/768-3466. **Contact:** Coleen Johns, Human Resources Department. **E-mail address:** cjohns@uhsinc.com. **World Wide Web address:** http://www.uhsinc.com. **Description:** Owns and operates acute care hospitals, behavioral health centers, ambulatory surgery centers, and radiation/oncology centers. The company operates 29 hospitals with approximately 3,600 licensed beds. Of these facilities, 15 are general acute care hospitals and 14 are psychiatric care facilities (two of which are substance abuse facilities). The company, as a part of its Ambulatory Treatment Centers Division, owns, operates, or manages surgery and radiation therapy centers located in various states. Universal Health Services has also entered into other specialized medical service arrangements including laboratory services, mobile computerized tomography and magnetic

imaging services, preferred provider organization agreements, health maintenance organization contracts, medical office building leasing, construction management services, and real estate management and administrative services. **Common positions include:** Accountant/Auditor; Computer Programmer; Paralegal; Systems Analyst. **Corporate headquarters location:** This location. **Operations at this facility include:** Administration. **Listed on:** New York Stock Exchange. **Stock exchange symbol:** UHS. **Number of employees at this location:** 145. **Number of employees nationwide:** 81,000.

UNIVERSITY OF PENNSYLVANIA HEALTH SYSTEM
3930 Chestnut Street, Philadelphia PA 19104. 215/615-2606. **Recorded jobline:** 215/615-2688. **Contact:** Staffing. **World Wide Web address:** http://www.med.upenn.edu/php/jobs. **Description:** A 722-bed, academic, teaching hospital involved in patient care, education, and research. **Number of employees at this location:** 5,000.

UNIVERSITY OF PENNSYLVANIA VETERINARY HOSPITAL
3900 Delancey Street, Philadelphia PA 19104. 215/898-8666. **Contact:** Human Resources. **World Wide Web address:** http://www.vet.upenn.edu. **Description:** A full-service animal hospital whose many departments include oncology, radiology, dermatology, internal medicine, and emergency.

VILLA TERESA
1051 Avila Road, Harrisburg PA 17109. 717/652-5900. **Fax:** 717/652-5941. **Contact:** Human Resources Director. **Description:** Provides skilled nursing care for the elderly. Founded in 1973. **Common positions include:** Accountant; Administrative Assistant; Certified Nurses Aide; Controller; Dietician/Nutritionist; Human Resources Manager; Licensed Practical Nurse; Medical Records Technician; Occupational Therapist; Physical Therapist; Purchasing Agent/Manager; Quality Control Supervisor; Registered Nurse; Secretary; Social Worker; Speech-Language Pathologist; Typist/Word Processor. **Office hours:** Monday - Friday, 8:00 a.m. - 4:00 p.m. **Corporate headquarters location:** This location. **Number of employees at this location:** 230.

VINELAND DEVELOPMENTAL CENTER
1676 East Landis Avenue, P.O. Box 1513, Vineland NJ 08362-1513. 856/696-6000. **Contact:** Human Resources Department. **Description:** A residential treatment facility for females who have mental retardation.

VISITING NURSE SERVICE SYSTEM, INC.
150 East 9th Avenue, P.O. Box 250, Runnemede NJ 08078. 856/939-9000. **Contact:** Human Resources. **World Wide Web address:** http://www.vnss.com. **Description:** Provides home-based health care services including nursing, physical therapy, occupational therapy, speech pathology, nutritional therapy, mental health and enterostomal therapy, medical social services, and hospice care. **Other U.S. locations:** Nationwide.

HOTELS AND RESTAURANTS

You can expect to find the following types of companies in this chapter:

Casinos • Dinner Theaters • Hotel/Motel Operators • Resorts • Restaurants

ARAMARK BUSINESS SERVICES GROUP

ARAMARK Tower, 1101 Market Street, Philadelphia PA 19107. 215/238-3590. **Contact:** Human Resources. **E-mail address:** resumes@aramark.com. **World Wide Web address:** http://www.aramark.com. **Description:** ARAMARK Business Services consists of Business Dining Services and Conference Center Management. Business Dining Services serves over 3 million people every business day at over 7,000 locations and offers a wide range of operations, marketing, and merchandising programs for executive dining rooms, plant cafeterias, and fully catered functions. Business Dining Services offers Cafe Connection service that brings food management to small and mid-sized facilities with limited production capabilities. ARAMARK's Conference Center Management provides comprehensive specialized services, ranging from food and beverage to total hospitality and property management. Services are provided in both residential and nonresidential centers such as executive retreats, corporate training complexes, resorts, and continuing education centers. **Parent company:** ARAMARK is one of the world's leading providers of managed services. The company operates in all 50 states and 10 foreign countries, offering a broad range of services to businesses of all sizes including many *Fortune* 500 companies and thousands of universities; hospitals; and municipal, state, and federal government facilities. ARAMARK is employee-owned. The company is among the market leaders in all of its businesses, which are: Food, Leisure and Support Services, including Campus Dining Services, School Nutrition Services, Leisure Services, Business Dining Services, International Services, Healthcare Support Services, Conference Center Management, and Refreshment Services; Facility Services; Correctional Services; Industrial Services; Uniform Services, which includes Wearguard, a direct marketer of work clothing; Health and Education Services including Spectrum Healthcare Services and Children's World Learning Centers; and Book and Magazine Services. **Listed on:** New York Stock Exchange. **Stock exchange symbol:** RMK. **Annual sales/revenues:** More than $100 million. **Number of employees nationwide:** 150,000.

ARAMARK CAMPUS DINING SERVICES

ARAMARK Tower, 1101 Market Street, Philadelphia PA 19106. 215/238-3085. **Contact:** Human Resources. **World Wide Web address:** http://www.aramark.com. **Description:** ARAMARK's Campus Dining Services serve more than 200 million meals a year at over 300 college and university campuses. Campus Dining Services provides an integrated program of national brand franchises as well as ARAMARK's own signature brands such as Itza Pizza and Deli Corner. **Parent company:** ARAMARK is one of the world's leading providers of managed services. The company operates in all 50 states and 10 foreign countries, offering a broad range of services to businesses of all sizes including many *Fortune* 500 companies and thousands of universities; hospitals; and municipal, state, and federal government facilities. ARAMARK is employee-owned. The company is among the market leaders in all of its businesses, which are: Food, Leisure and Support Services including Campus Dining Services, School Nutrition Services, Leisure Services, Business Dining Services, International Services, Healthcare Support Services, Conference Center Management, and Refreshment Services; Facility Services; Correctional Services; Industrial Services; Uniform Services, which includes Wearguard, a direct marketer of work clothing; Health and Education Services including Spectrum Healthcare Services and Children's World Learning Centers; and Book and Magazine Services. **Listed on:** New York Stock Exchange. **Stock exchange symbol:** RMK. **Annual sales/revenues:** More than $100 million. **Number of employees nationwide:** 150,000.

ARAMARK HEALTHCARE SUPPORT SERVICES

ARAMARK Tower, 1101 Market Street, Philadelphia PA 19107. 215/238-3541. **Contact:** Human Resources. **World Wide Web address:** http://www.aramark.com. **Description:** ARAMARK Healthcare Support Services serves 115 million meals annually for over 300 health care customers nationwide and also provides food service, clinical nutrition management, facility services, and engineering support to assist health care administrators. ARAMARK Healthcare Support provides value-added services related to resource management, revenue generation, and business planning. **Parent company:** ARAMARK is one of the world's leading providers of managed services. The company operates in all 50 states and 10 foreign countries, offering a broad range of services to businesses of all sizes including many *Fortune* 500 companies and thousands of universities; hospitals; and municipal, state, and federal government facilities. ARAMARK is employee-owned. The company is among the market leaders in all of its businesses, which are: Food, Leisure and Support Services including Campus Dining Services, School Nutrition Services, Leisure Services, Business Dining Services, International Services, Healthcare Support Services, Conference Center Management, and Refreshment Services; Facility Services; Correctional Services; Industrial Services; Uniform Services, which includes Wearguard, a direct marketer of work clothing; Health and Education Services including Spectrum Healthcare Services and Children's World Learning Centers; and Book and Magazine Services. **Listed on:** New York Stock Exchange. **Stock exchange symbol:** RMK. **Annual sales/revenues:** More than $100 million. **Number of employees nationwide:** 150,000.

ARAMARK INTERNATIONAL SERVICES

ARAMARK Tower, 1101 Market Street, Philadelphia PA 19107. 215/238-3077. **Contact:** Human Resources. **World Wide Web address:** http://www.aramark.com. **Description:** ARAMARK International Services provides a broad range of food and related services for customers worldwide. **Parent company:** ARAMARK is one of the world's leading providers of managed services. The company operates in all 50 states and 10 foreign countries, offering a broad range of services to businesses of all sizes including many *Fortune* 500 companies and thousands of universities; hospitals; and municipal, state, and federal government facilities. ARAMARK is employee-owned. The company is among the market leaders in all of its businesses, which are: Food, Leisure and Support Services including Campus Dining Services, School Nutrition Services, Leisure Services, Business Dining Services, International Services, Healthcare Support Services, Conference Center Management, and Refreshment Services; Facility Services; Correctional Services; Industrial Services; Uniform Services, which includes Wearguard, a direct marketer of work clothing; Health and Education Services including Spectrum Healthcare Services and Children's World Learning Centers; and Book and Magazine Services. **Listed on:** New York Stock Exchange. **Stock exchange symbol:** RMK. **Annual sales/revenues:** More than $100 million. **Number of employees nationwide:** 150,000.

ARAMARK REFRESHMENT SERVICES

ARAMARK Tower, 1101 Market Street, Philadelphia PA 19107. 215/238-3525. **Contact:** Human Resources. **World Wide Web address:** http://www.aramark.com. **Description:** ARAMARK Refreshment Services serves more than 1 billion cups of coffee, 400 million cans and cups of soda, and 200 million snacks annually. Over 70 market centers across the country provide service to customers. ARAMARK Refreshment Services operates more than 900 joint accounts with other ARAMARK lines of business including health care, education, leisure, and business dining. **Parent company:** ARAMARK is one of the world's leading providers of managed services. The company operates in all 50 states and 10 foreign countries, offering a broad range of services to businesses of all sizes including many *Fortune* 500 companies and thousands of universities; hospitals; and municipal, state, and federal government facilities. ARAMARK is employee-owned. The company is among the market leaders in all of its businesses, which are: Food, Leisure and Support Services including Campus Dining Services, School Nutrition Services, Leisure Services, Business Dining Services, International Services, Healthcare Support Services, Conference Center Management, and Refreshment Services; Facility Services; Correctional Services; Industrial Services; Uniform Services, which includes Wearguard, a direct marketer of work clothing; Health and Education Services including Spectrum Healthcare Services and Children's World Learning Centers; and Book and Magazine Services. **Listed on:** New York Stock Exchange. **Stock exchange symbol:** RMK. **Annual sales/revenues:** More than $100 million. **Number of employees nationwide:** 150,000.

ARAMARK SCHOOL SUPPORT SERVICES

ARAMARK Tower, 1101 Market Street, Philadelphia PA 19107. 215/238-3526. **Contact:** Human Resources. **World Wide Web address:** http://www.aramark.com. **Description:** ARAMARK School Support Services provides professional food service management for more than 1 million students in over 280 school districts. The company offers comprehensive services including menu management to food-handling safety, marketing, merchandising, nutrition education, and recycling programs. **Parent company:** ARAMARK is one of the world's leading providers of managed services. The company operates in all 50 states and 10 foreign countries, offering a broad range of services to businesses of all sizes including many *Fortune* 500 companies and thousands of universities; hospitals; and municipal, state, and federal government facilities. ARAMARK is employee-owned. The company is among the market leaders in all of its businesses, which are: Food, Leisure and Support Services including Campus Dining Services, School Nutrition Services, Leisure Services, Business Dining Services, International Services, Healthcare Support Services,

Conference Center Management, and Refreshment Services; Facility Services; Correctional Services; Industrial Services; Uniform Services, which includes Wearguard, a direct marketer of work clothing; Health and Education Services including Spectrum Healthcare Services and Children's World Learning Centers; and Book and Magazine Services. **Listed on:** New York Stock Exchange. **Stock exchange symbol:** RMK. **Annual sales/revenues:** More than $100 million. **Number of employees nationwide:** 150,000.

BROCK AND COMPANY, INC.

77 Great Valley Parkway, Malvern PA 19355. 610/647-5656. **Fax:** 610/647-0867. **Contact:** Mark Snyder, Human Resources Manager. **E-mail address:** hr@brockco.com. **World Wide Web address:** http://www.brockco.com. **Description:** A contract food service company offering corporate dining, vending, and office coffee services. **Common positions include:** Account Representative; Accountant; Administrative Assistant; Computer Operator; Computer Technician; General Manager; Graphic Designer; Human Resources Manager; Marketing Manager; MIS Specialist; Operations Manager; Purchasing Agent/Manager; Secretary. **Special programs:** Apprenticeships; Co-ops. **Corporate headquarters location:** This location. **Annual sales/revenues:** $11 - $20 million. **Number of employees at this location:** 300.

HIGH INDUSTRIES, INC.

P.O. Box 10008, 1853 William Penn Way, Lancaster PA 17605-0008. 717/293-4486. **Contact:** Vincent Mizeras, Director of Human Resources. **World Wide Web address:** http://www.high.net. **Description:** Operates through several areas of business including design and construction, food services, hotel management, prestress/precast concrete products, real estate development and management, and steel fabrication. **Common positions include:** Accountant/Auditor; Architect; Civil Engineer; Computer Programmer; Customer Service Representative; Draftsperson; Hotel Manager; Human Resources Manager; Services Sales Representative; Systems Analyst. **Corporate headquarters location:** This location. **Operations at this facility include:** Administration; Manufacturing.

NUTRITION MANAGEMENT SERVICES COMPANY

P.O. Box 725, 2071 Kimberton Road, Kimberton PA 19442. 610/935-2050. **Fax:** 610/935-8287. **Contact:** Human Resources. **World Wide Web address:** http://www.nmsc.com. **Description:** A food service management company specializing in food service programs for health care, retirement, and acute care facilities. **Common positions include:** Dietician/Nutritionist; Food Production Worker; Food Scientist/Technologist; Food Service Manager. **Corporate headquarters location:** This location.

RADISSON VALLEY FORGE HOTEL & CONVENTION CENTER

1160 First Avenue, King of Prussia PA 19406. 610/337-2000. **Fax:** 610/354-8214. **Contact:** Lisa McLean, Human Resources. **Description:** A 488-room hotel and tri-level convention center featuring three full-service restaurants, and Lily Langtry's, a Las Vegas-style dinner theater facility. **NOTE:** Entry-level positions are offered. **Common positions include:** Accountant/Auditor; Administrative Assistant; Assistant Manager; Controller; Customer Service Representative; Electrician; General Manager; Human Resources Manager; Marketing Manager; Mechanical Engineer; Operations Manager; Project Manager; Purchasing Agent/Manager; Sales Executive; Sales Manager; Secretary. **Special programs:** Internships. **Parent company:** GF Management. **Number of employees at this location:** 600.

INSURANCE

You can expect to find the following types of companies in this chapter:
Commercial and Industrial Property/Casualty Insurers • Health Maintenance Organizations (HMOs) • Medical/Life Insurance Companies

AETNA U.S. HEALTHCARE
980 Jolly Road, Blue Bell PA 19422-1904. 215/775-4800. **Contact:** Human Resources Department. **World Wide Web address:** http://www.aetna.com. **Description:** Operates health maintenance organizations. **NOTE:** All resumes should be sent to Aetna U.S. Healthcare, National Scanning Center, 151 Farmington Avenue, Hartford CT 06156. **Common positions include:** Accountant/Auditor; Claim Representative; Computer Programmer; Customer Service Representative; Services Sales Representative. **Corporate headquarters location:** Hartford CT. **Operations at this facility include:** Administration; Sales; Service.

ADMIRAL INSURANCE COMPANY
1255 Caldwell Road, Cherry Hill NJ 08034. 856/429-9200. **Contact:** Human Resources Department. **World Wide Web address:** http://www.admiralins.com. **Description:** Underwrites casualty and property insurance.

ALLSTATE INSURANCE COMPANY
71 Valley Forge Commons A, Valley Forge PA 19481. 610/240-3000. **Contact:** Human Resources. **World Wide Web address:** http://www.allstate.com. **Description:** One of the nation's largest insurance companies, Allstate provides a full spectrum of property, liability, life, reinsurance, and commercial lines of insurance. **Corporate headquarters location:** Northbrook IL. **Listed on:** New York Stock Exchange. **Stock exchange symbol:** ALL.

AON RISK SERVICES
One Liberty Place, 1650 Market Street, Suite 1000, Philadelphia PA 19103. 215/255-2000. **Fax:** 215/255-1893. **Contact:** Human Resources Department. **World Wide Web address:** http://www.aon.com. **Description:** An insurance brokerage firm. Overall, Aon Risk Services is primarily involved with property and casualty, marine, and public entities specialties. **Corporate headquarters location:** Chicago IL. **Other U.S. locations:** Nationwide. **International locations:**

Worldwide. **Listed on:** New York Stock Exchange. **Stock exchange symbol:** AOC.

CHUBB GROUP OF INSURANCE COMPANIES
Liberty One Building, 1650 Market Street, Philadelphia PA 19103. 215/569-9660. **Contact:** Ms. Latrell Johnson, Human Resources. **World Wide Web address:** http://www.chubb.com. **Description:** A property and casualty insurer with more than 115 offices in 30 countries worldwide. The Chubb Group of Insurance Companies offers a broad range of specialty insurance products and services designed for individuals and businesses including high technology, financial institutions, and general manufacturers. **Corporate headquarters location:** Warren NJ. **Listed on:** New York Stock Exchange. **Stock exchange symbol:** CB. **Number of employees nationwide:** 8,500.

COLONIAL PENN
399 Market Street, Philadelphia PA 19181. 215/928-8000. **Contact:** Gay Woltemate, Personnel Manager. **World Wide Web address:** http://www.colonialpenn.com. **Description:** Provides life insurance, specializing in graded-benefit policies. Founded in 1957.

FIDELITY MUTUAL LIFE INSURANCE COMPANY
250 King of Prussia Road, Radnor PA 19087. 610/964-7000. **Contact:** Mary Culbreath, Human Resources. **Description:** A life insurance company. **Corporate headquarters location:** This location.

HARLEYSVILLE INSURANCE COMPANIES
355 Maple Avenue, Harleysville PA 19438-2297. 215/256-3300. **Toll-free phone:** 800/523-6344. **Fax:** 215/256-5602. **Contact:** Human Resources Department. **E-mail address:** resumes@harleysvillegroup.com. **World Wide Web address:** http://www.harleysvillegroup.com. **Description:** A multiline property/casualty and life insurance carrier with offices located throughout the Mid-Atlantic states. Products are marketed through an independent agency system. **Common positions include:** Accountant/Auditor; Actuary; Attorney; Branch Manager; Claim Representative; Commercial Artist; Computer Programmer; Customer Service Representative; Financial Analyst; Financial Services Sales Rep.; Human Resources Manager; Technical Writer/Editor; Underwriter/Assistant Underwriter. **Corporate headquarters location:** This location. **Other U.S. locations:** East, Midwest, Southeast.

INDEPENDENCE BLUE CROSS OF GREATER PHILADELPHIA
1901 Market Street, 25th Floor, Philadelphia PA 19103.
215/241-2400. **Fax:** 215/241-3237. **Contact:** Human
Resources Department. **E-mail address:** recruiter@ibx.com.
World Wide Web address: http://www.ibx.com. **Description:**
Provides individual and group subscribers with health benefits
that complement their lifestyle and their medical and financial
needs. **Common positions include:** Accountant/Auditor;
Actuary; Attorney; Claim Representative; Human Resources
Manager; Public Relations Specialist; Services Sales Rep.;
Statistician; Systems Analyst; Underwriter/Assistant
Underwriter.

LIBERTY MUTUAL INSURANCE GROUP
15 Kings Grant Drive, Bala-Cynwyd PA 19004. 610/664-6380.
Fax: 603/422-9670. **Contact:** Human Resources. **World Wide
Web address:** http://www.libertymutual.com. **Description:** A
diversified financial services company with $8.9 billion in
consolidated revenue and more than $37 billion in
consolidated assets. Liberty Mutual Insurance Group has been
a leading provider of workers' compensation insurance,
programs, and services for 60 years, and is one of the largest
multiline insurers in the property/casualty field. The company
provides a wide array of products and services including
commercial insurance, personal insurance, international
services, individual life products, and group products. **NOTE:**
Jobseekers should send resumes to: Liberty Mutual Insurance
Group, Employment 01-D, 175 Berkeley Street, Boston MA
02116. **Common positions include:** Administrator; Attorney;
Claim Representative; Customer Service Representative;
Insurance Agent/Broker; Sales Manager; Services Sales
Representative; Underwriter/Assistant Underwriter. **Corporate
headquarters location:** Boston MA. **Operations at this facility
include:** Divisional Headquarters.

LINCOLN NATIONAL CORPORATION (LNC)
dba LINCOLN FINANCIAL GROUP
Center Square, West Tower, 1500 Market Street, Suite 3900,
Philadelphia PA 19102. 215/448-1400. **Contact:** Human
Resources. **World Wide Web address:** http://www.lfg.com.
Description: An insurance holding company with businesses
that sell insurance and investment products. **Corporate
headquarters location:** This location. **Subsidiaries include:**
Delaware Investments (investment management services); First
Penn-Pacific Life Insurance Company (life insurance); Lincoln
National Life Insurance Company (individual life, annuities,
and pensions); Lincoln Re (life and health reinsurance);

Vantage Investment Advisors (investment management services).

ONEBEACON INSURANCE
100 Corporate Center Drive, Camp Hill PA 17001-8851. 717/763-7331. **Contact:** Deb Singer, Human Resources. **World Wide Web address:** http://www.onebeacon.com. **Description:** A carrier of property, casualty, and life insurance. **Corporate headquarters location:** Boston MA. **Other U.S. locations:** Nationwide.

THE PMA INSURANCE GROUP
380 Sentry Parkway, Blue Bell PA 19422. 610/397-5000. **Contact:** Andrea Clark, Human Resources Department. **World Wide Web address:** http://www.pmagroup.com. **Description:** Provides workers' compensation insurance. **Common positions include:** Actuary; Claim Representative; Customer Service Representative; Underwriter/Assistant Underwriter. **Special programs:** Internships. **Corporate headquarters location:** This location. **Other area locations:** Allentown PA; Harrisburg PA; Pittsburgh PA; Ridgeway PA; Valley Forge PA; Williamsport PA. **Other U.S. locations:** Hunt Valley MD; Charlotte NC; Raleigh NC; Mount Laurel NJ; Richmond VA; Roanoke VA. **Listed on:** Privately held. **Number of employees at this location:** 1,050.

PENN MUTUAL LIFE INSURANCE COMPANY
600 Dresher Road, Horsham PA 19044. 215/956-8000. **Contact:** Human Resources Department. **World Wide Web address:** http://www.pennmutual.com. **Description:** Offers life insurance and annuities. **Corporate headquarters location:** This location. **Subsidiaries include:** Independence Financial Group.

PENN TREATY AMERICAN CORPORATION
3440 Lehigh Street, Allentown PA 18103. 610/965-2222. **Fax:** 610/967-4616. **Contact:** Human Resources Department. **World Wide Web address:** http://www.penntreaty.com. **Description:** A long-term care insurance company. Through its wholly-owned subsidiaries, the company underwrites, markets, and sells individual supplemental accident and health insurance policies designed to cover the costs of long-term care. The company also offers life insurance policies, supplemental accident and health insurance policies, and policies providing benefits to supplement Medicare payments.

PRUDENTIAL INSURANCE COMPANY OF AMERICA

1100 Horizon Circle, Chalfont PA 18914. 215/996-0803. **Contact:** Human Resources Department. **World Wide Web address:** http://www.prudential.com. **Description:** One of the largest diversified financial services organizations in the world and one of the largest insurance companies in North America. The company's primary business is to offer a full range of products and services in three areas: insurance, investment, and home ownership for individuals and families; health care management and other benefit programs for employees of companies and members of groups; and asset management for institutional clients and their associates. The company insures or provides other financial services to more than 50 million people worldwide. **Corporate headquarters location:** Newark NJ. **Number of employees worldwide:** 100,000.

RADIAN GUARANTY INC.

1601 Market Street, Philadelphia PA 19103. 215/564-6600. **Contact:** Human Resources Department. **World Wide Web address:** http://www.radianmi.com. **Description:** A national insurance company providing private mortgage insurance and risk management services to mortgage lending institutions. **Corporate headquarters location:** This location. **Other U.S. locations:** Nationwide. **Parent company:** Radian Group Inc. (also at this location).

UNION FIDELITY LIFE INSURANCE COMPANY

500 Virginia Drive, Fort Washington PA 19034. 267/468-3000. **Contact:** Human Resources Department. **World Wide Web address:** http://www.gefn.com. **Description:** An insurance company specializing in accident policies and life insurance. **Parent company:** GE Financial Network.

LEGAL SERVICES

You can expect to find the following types of companies in this chapter:

Law Firms • Legal Service Agencies

BLANK ROME COMISKY AND McCAULEY LLP
One Logan Square, Philadelphia PA 19103. 215/569-5500.
Fax: 215/569-5555. **Contact:** Marilyn Mason, Personnel
Director. **World Wide Web address:** http://www.brcm.com.
Description: A law firm.

DRINKER BIDDLE AND REATH LLP
One Logan Square, 18th & Cherry Streets, Philadelphia PA
19103. 215/988-2700. **Contact:** Joeanne DelSignore,
Recruiter. **World Wide Web address:** http://www.dbr.com.
Description: A law firm. Founded in 1849.

DUANE, MORRIS & HECKSCHER LLP
One Liberty Place, 42nd Floor, 1650 Market Street,
Philadelphia PA 19103-7396. 215/979-1000. **Contact:** Mary
Robinson, Human Resources Manager. **World Wide Web
address:** http://www.duanemorris.com. **Description:** A law
firm practicing in over 50 disciplines including administrative
and regulatory law, employment, energy, medical malpractice,
real estate, and taxation. Founded in 1904. **Common positions
include:** Attorney; Paralegal. **Operations at this facility
include:** Service.

PEPPER HAMILTON LLP
3000 Two Logan Square, 18th & Arch Streets, Philadelphia PA
19103-2799. 215/981-4000. **Fax:** 215/981-4750. **Contact:** Ms.
Meg Urbanski, Director of Recruitment. **E-mail address:**
urbanskim@pepperlaw.com. **World Wide Web address:**
http://www.pepperlaw.com. **Description:** An international law
firm. **NOTE:** Part-time jobs are offered. **Common positions
include:** Attorney; Clerk; Computer Operator; Legal Secretary;
Paralegal. **Corporate headquarters location:** This location.
Operations at this facility include: Administration. **Number of
employees at this location:** 560. **Number of employees
nationwide:** 910.

REED SMITH SHAW & McCLAY LLP
2500 One Liberty Place, Philadelphia PA 19103. 215/851-
8100. **Fax:** 215/851-1420. **Contact:** Denise Papanier, Human
Resources Manager. **World Wide Web address:**

http://www.rssm.com. **Description:** A business-oriented law firm specializing in financial and corporate law. **Other U.S. locations:** Washington DC; Princeton NJ; Harrisburg PA; Pittsburgh PA; McLean VA.

SCHNADER HARRISON SEGAL & LEWIS LLP
1600 Market Street, Suite 3600, Philadelphia PA 19103. 215/751-2000. **Contact:** Wanda Whitted, Human Resources Manager. **World Wide Web address:** http://www.shsl.com. **Description:** A law firm.

WILLIG WILLIAMS & DAVIDSON
1845 Walnut Street, 24th Floor, Philadelphia PA 19103-4708. 215/656-3600. **Contact:** Human Resources. **World Wide Web address:** http://www.willigwilliamsdavidson.com. **Description:** A law firm.

MANUFACTURING: MISCELLANEOUS CONSUMER

You can expect to find the following types of companies in this chapter:
Art Supplies • Batteries • Cosmetics and Related Products • Household Appliances and Audio/Video Equipment • Jewelry, Silverware, and Plated Ware • Miscellaneous Household Furniture and Fixtures • Musical Instruments • Tools • Toys and Sporting Goods

ALL-LUMINUM PRODUCTS, INC.
10981 Decatur Road, Philadelphia PA 19154. 215/632-2800. **Contact:** Human Resources. **World Wide Web address:** http://www.all-luminum.com. **Description:** A manufacturer of casual outdoor and indoor furniture. **Common positions include:** Accountant/Auditor; Blue-Collar Worker Supervisor; Customer Service Representative; Purchasing Agent/Manager; Quality Control Supervisor. **Corporate headquarters location:** This location. **Operations at this facility include:** Administration; Manufacturing; Research and Development; Sales; Service.

ALLEN ORGAN COMPANY
150 Locust Street, P.O. Box 36, Macungie PA 18062-0036. 610/966-2200. **Fax:** 610/965-3098. **Contact:** T. O'Malley, Personnel. **E-mail address:** tomalley@allenorgan.com. **World Wide Web address:** http://www.allenorgan.com. **Description:** A manufacturer of electronic keyboard musical instruments including digital computer organs and related accessories. **Corporate headquarters location:** This location.

BACOU-DALLOZ
1150 First Avenue, Park View Tower, Suite 400, King of Prussia 19406. 610/728-1900. **Contact:** Rodney M. Fogelman, Director of Human Resources. **E-mail address:** resumes@dallozsafety.com. **World Wide Web address:** http://www.bacou-dalloz.com. **Description:** Manufactures respiratory protection and personal safety protection products for the head, ears, and eyes. **Corporate headquarters location:** This location. **Parent company:** Christian Dalloz (also at this location).

BALDWIN HARDWARE CORPORATION

P.O. Box 15048, Reading PA 19612-5048. 610/777-7811. **Contact:** Carl Salmon, VP of Human Resources. **World Wide Web address:** http://www.baldwinbrass.com. **Description:** Manufacturer of decorative hardware including handle sets, doorknobs, and hinges. The company also manufactures a variety of home decor products including bath accessories, candlesticks, sconces, and both interior and exterior lighting products. **NOTE:** Entry-level positions and second and third shifts are offered. **Common positions include:** Account Manager; Accountant; AS400 Programmer Analyst; Blue-Collar Worker Supervisor; Buyer; Chief Financial Officer; Computer Operator; Computer Support Technician; Customer Service Representative; Design Engineer; Financial Analyst; General Manager; Industrial Engineer; Internet Services Manager; Manufacturing Engineer; Marketing Manager; Marketing Specialist; Mechanical Engineer; Network/Systems Administrator; Operations Manager; Production Manager; Purchasing Agent/Manager; Sales Manager; Sales Rep.; Vice President. **Special programs:** Training; Summer Jobs. **Corporate headquarters location:** This location. **Parent company:** MASCO Corporation. **Operations at this facility include:** Administration; Divisional Headquarters; Manufacturing; Research and Development; Service.

BINNEY & SMITH, INC.

P.O. Box 431, Easton PA 18044-0431. 610/253-6271. **Physical address:** 1100 Church Lane, Easton PA 18040. **Contact:** Martha Collins, Human Resources. **World Wide Web address:** http://www.binney-smith.com. **Description:** Produces a line of crayons, markers, writing instruments, chalk, clay, artist kits, oils, acrylics, watercolors, and brushes. Brand names include Crayola, Magic Marker, Liquitex, and Artista. **Common positions include:** Accountant/Auditor; Administrative Manager; Blue-Collar Worker Supervisor; Clerical Supervisor; Computer Programmer; Credit Manager; Customer Service Representative; Financial Analyst; General Manager; Human Resources Manager; Management Analyst/Consultant; Management Trainee; Mechanical Engineer; Public Relations Specialist; Systems Analyst; Technical Writer/Editor; Travel Agent. **Special programs:** Internships. **Corporate headquarters location:** This location. **Other U.S. locations:** Winfield KS. **Parent company:** Hallmark Corporation. **Operations at this facility include:** Administration; Divisional Headquarters; Manufacturing; Marketing; Regional Headquarters; Research and Development; Sales; Service. **Number of employees at this location:** 900. **Number of employees nationwide:** 1,200.

BRITE STAR MANUFACTURING COMPANY

2900 South 20th Street, Philadelphia PA 19145. 215/271-7600. **Contact:** Mr. Sandy Kinderman, Vice President. **E-mail address:** dje@britestar.com. **World Wide Web address:** http://www.britestar.com. **Description:** Manufactures and imports a wide variety of Christmas decorations, trees, and other holiday items. **Common positions include:** Industrial Engineer; Purchasing Agent/Manager. **Corporate headquarters location:** This location. **Operations at this facility include:** Manufacturing.

FLEXSTEEL INDUSTRIES, INC.

P.O. Box 10908, Lancaster PA 17605. 717/392-4161. **Fax:** 717/291-1748. **Contact:** Deborah Frey, Human Resources. **World Wide Web address:** http://www.flexsteel.com. **Description:** This location manufactures upholstered living room furniture. Overall, Flexsteel Industries manufactures and markets upholstered furniture for the retail furniture market and the recreational vehicle field. Products of Flexsteel Industries include a variety of wood and upholstered chairs, rockers, sofas, sofabeds, loveseats, bucket seats, and convertible bedding units for use in offices, homes, vans, and recreational vehicles. **Common positions include:** Blue-Collar Worker Supervisor; Customer Service Representative; Purchasing Agent/Manager; Transportation/Traffic Specialist. **Office hours:** Monday - Friday, 8:00 a.m. - 5:00 p.m. **Corporate headquarters location:** Dubuque IA. **Operations at this facility include:** Divisional Headquarters; Manufacturing; Sales; Service.

FOX POOL CORPORATION

P.O. Box 549, York PA 17405. 717/764-8581. **Physical address:** 3490 Board Road, York PA 17402. **Contact:** Department of Human Resources. **World Wide Web address:** http://www.foxpool.com. **Description:** Manufactures and sells in- and above-ground swimming pools.

FRANKLIN MINT

M/D 405 M, Franklin Center PA 19091. 610/459-6000. **Fax:** 610/459-6750. **Contact:** Human Resources. **E-mail address:** jobs@web.franklinmint.com. **World Wide Web address:** http://www.franklinmint.com. **Description:** Manufactures jewelry, precious metals, and collectibles.

GRAPHIC CONTROLS CORPORATION

One Carnegie Plaza, Cherry Hill NJ 08003. 856/424-2200. **Contact:** Human Resources Department. **World Wide Web**

address: http://www.graphiccontrols.com. **Description:** Manufactures and wholesales disposable writing instruments.

HUNT CORPORATION
One Commerce Square, 2005 Market Street, 7th Floor, Philadelphia PA 19103. 215/656-0300. **Contact:** Human Resources. **World Wide Web address:** http://www.hunt-corp.com. **Description:** Manufactures art supplies, office supplies, and office furniture. **Common positions include:** Accountant/Auditor; Budget Analyst; Computer Operator; Computer Programmer; Credit Manager; Department Manager; General Manager; Graphic Artist; Human Resources Manager; Manufacturer's/Wholesaler's Sales Rep.; Market Research Analyst; Marketing Manager; Public Relations Specialist; Receptionist; Secretary; Systems Analyst. **Corporate headquarters location:** This location. **Other U.S. locations:** AL; CT; KY; NC; TX; WI. **Operations at this facility include:** Administration. **Listed on:** New York Stock Exchange. **Stock exchange symbol:** HUN. **Number of employees at this location:** 1,000.

KOEHLER-BRIGHT STAR, INC.
380 Stewart Road, Wilkes-Barre PA 18706. 570/825-1900. **Contact:** Patti Leonard, Human Resources Manager. **World Wide Web address:** http://www.flashlight.com. **Description:** Manufactures and distributes industrial batteries, dry cell batteries, and other related lighting products. **Corporate headquarters location:** This location. **Other U.S. locations:** Passaic NJ; Paterson NJ.

LASKO PRODUCTS, INC.
820 Lincoln Avenue, West Chester PA 19380. 610/692-7400. **Contact:** Human Resources Department. **E-mail address:** hr@laskoproducts.com. **World Wide Web address:** http://www.laskoproducts.com. **Description:** Manufactures consumer and industrial fans as well as other home comfort appliances.

MAKITA USA, INC.
364 Wilmington-West Chester Pike, Glen Mills PA 19342. 610/459-4122. **Contact:** Human Resources. **World Wide Web address:** http://www.makita.com. **Description:** A manufacturer of power-driven hand tools.

C.F. MARTIN & COMPANY, INC.
510 Sycamore Street, Nazareth PA 18064. 610/759-2837. **Contact:** Debbie Karlowitch, Personnel Manager. **World Wide**

Web address: http://www.mguitar.com. **Description:** Produces a line of acoustic guitars and guitar strings and is engaged in the processing of selected hardwoods.

MATTEL INC.
6000 Midlantic Drive, Mount Laurel NJ 08054. 856/234-7400. **Contact:** Human Resources Manager. **E-mail address:** mattel@rpc.webhire.com. **World Wide Web address:** http://www.mattel.com. **Description:** This location performs marketing activities for the toy manufacturer. Overall, Mattel manufactures and distributes toys, electronic products, games, books, hobby products, and family entertainment products. **Corporate headquarters location:** El Segundo CA.

PENNSYLVANIA HOUSE
137 North 10th Street, Lewisburg PA 17837. 570/523-1285. **Contact:** Human Resources Department. **World Wide Web address:** http://www.pennsylvaniahouse.com. **Description:** Manufactures upholstered furniture under the Pennsylvania House brand name.

THE PFALTZGRAFF COMPANY
140 East Market Street, York PA 17401. 717/848-5500. **Contact:** William Scott, VP of Corporate Human Resources. **World Wide Web address:** http://www.pfaltzgraff.com. **Description:** A stoneware and dinnerware manufacturer. The Pfaltzgraff Company also produces a line of tabletop accessories. **Corporate headquarters location:** This location.

SHOP VAC CORPORATION
2323 Reach Road, P.O. Box 3307, Williamsport PA 17701. 570/326-0502. **Fax:** 570/321-7089. **Contact:** Employment Coordinator. **E-mail address:** hr@shopvac.com. **World Wide Web address:** http://www.shopvac.com. **Description:** Manufactures and wholesales vacuum cleaners. **Corporate headquarters location:** This location. **Listed on:** Privately held.

SPRINGS WINDOW FASHIONS
8601, Route 405 Highway South, Montgomery PA 17752. 570/547-6671. **Contact:** Human Resources. **World Wide Web address:** http://www.springs.com. **Description:** A manufacturer of window dressings. The company specializes in horizontal, vertical, and pleated blinds as well as vinyl shades.

WILTON ARMETALE
Plumb & Square Streets, P.O. Box 600, Mount Joy PA 17552. 717/653-4444. **Contact:** Kathleen Adams, Director of Human

Resources Department. **World Wide Web address:** http://www.armetale.com. **Description:** Produces Armetale (10-metal composite) giftware products. **Corporate headquarters location:** This location. **Operations at this facility include:** Administration; Manufacturing. **Listed on:** Privately held. **Number of employees at this location:** 180.

MANUFACTURING: MISCELLANEOUS INDUSTRIAL

You can expect to find the following types of companies in this chapter:

Ball and Roller Bearings • Commercial Furniture and Fixtures • Fans, Blowers, and Purification Equipment • Industrial Machinery and Equipment • Motors and Generators/Compressors and Engine Parts • Vending Machines

ACCO CHAIN & LIFTING PRODUCTS

P.O. Box 792, York PA 17405. 717/741-4863. **Physical address:** 76 ACCO Drive, York PA 17402. **Contact:** Mr. Terry Staley, Human Resources Manager. **World Wide Web address:** http://www.accochain.com. **Description:** Manufactures welded and weldless chains, hooks, slings, tire chains, load binders, hoists, and other lifting equipment. **Common positions include:** Accountant/Auditor; Blue-Collar Worker Supervisor; Buyer; Computer Programmer; Credit Manager; Customer Service Representative; Draftsperson; Electrical/Electronics Engineer; General Manager; Human Resources Manager; Industrial Designer; Industrial Engineer; Manufacturer's/Wholesaler's Sales Rep.; Mechanical Engineer; Metallurgical Engineer; Operations/Production Manager; Purchasing Agent/Manager; Quality Control Supervisor; Systems Analyst. **Corporate headquarters location:** Fairfield CT. **Operations at this facility include:** Administration; Design; Divisional Headquarters; Manufacturing; Sales; Service.

ALFA LAVAL SEPARATION INC.

955 Mearns Road, Warminster PA 18974. 215/443-4262. **Fax:** 215/443-4253. **Contact:** Human Resources Department. **E-mail address:** humanresources.usa@alfalaval.com. **World Wide Web address:** http://www.alfalaval.com. **Description:** Alfa Laval Separation is divided into five market sectors: Industrial Separation supplies separation equipment for the chemical, pharmaceutical, and other process industries; Marine and Power specializes in cleaning and conditioning systems for fuel oils and lubricant oils in marine and power station diesel engines, as well as fuel cleaning and forwarding systems for gas-turbine power stations; Desalination supplies desalination plants for producing freshwater for ships, power stations, and offshore platforms; Pulp and Paper's products include equipment for pulp cleaning, filters and presses for dewatering,

and new technology for processing recycled fibers; and Oil Field products include high-capacity separation systems for use in onshore and offshore oil and gas production, and in the storage and refining of crude oil. **Common positions include:** Accountant/Auditor; Administrative Manager; Blue-Collar Worker Supervisor; Buyer; Chemical Engineer; Credit Manager; Customer Service Representative; Draftsperson; Electrical/Electronics Engineer; Financial Analyst; General Manager; Human Resources Manager; Industrial Engineer; Industrial Production Manager; Management Trainee; Manufacturer's/Wholesaler's Sales Representative; Materials Engineer; Mechanical Engineer; Metallurgical Engineer; Operations/Production Manager; Purchasing Agent/Manager; Software Engineer; Systems Analyst; Technical Writer/Editor. **Special programs:** Internships. **Corporate headquarters location:** This location. **Parent company:** Alfa Laval, one of Sweden's oldest companies, was formed in 1883 to market the continuous separator. Operations include environmental protection, optimal utilization of energy, and food supply. The group develops and markets products such as separators, heat exchangers, flow equipment, and computerized control systems. Alfa Laval has production facilities, marketing companies, and representatives throughout the world. **Operations at this facility include:** Administration; Manufacturing; Research and Development; Sales; Service. **Listed on:** Privately held. **Number of employees at this location:** 450. **Number of employees nationwide:** 600.

AMERICAN METER COMPANY

300 Welsh Road, Building One, Horsham PA 19044-2224. 215/830-1800. **Contact:** Department WE&E. **E-mail address:** hra@americanmeter.com. **World Wide Web address:** http://www.americanmeter.com. **Description:** Manufactures vapor gas measurement products. **Corporate headquarters location:** This location.

AMETEK, INC.

900 Clymer Avenue, Sellersville PA 18960. 215/257-6531. **Contact:** Human Resources Department. **World Wide Web address:** http://www.ametek.com. **Description:** This location manufactures various types of gauges. Overall, AMETEK is a global manufacturing company that serves a variety of industrial and commercial markets through its Electromechanical, Precision Instruments, and Industrial Materials Groups. The Electromechanical Group has a leading market share in the production of electric motors for vacuum cleaners and floor care products, with a growing business in

technical motor products for computer, medical, and other markets. The company operates more than 30 manufacturing facilities in 12 states. **Corporate headquarters location:** Paoli PA. **International locations:** Denmark; England; Italy; Mexico. **Listed on:** New York Stock Exchange. **Stock exchange symbol:** AME. **Number of employees worldwide:** 6,200.

AMETEK, INC.

37 North Valley Road, Building 4, P.O. Box 1764, Paoli PA 19301. 610/647-2121. **Toll-free phone:** 800/473-1286. **Fax:** 610/296-3412. **Contact:** Human Resources. **World Wide Web address:** http://www.ametek.com. **Description:** A global manufacturing company that serves a variety of industrial and commercial markets through its Electromechanical, Precision Instruments, and Industrial Materials Groups. **Common positions include:** Accountant/Auditor; Financial Analyst; Human Resources Manager; Management Trainee; Public Relations Specialist; Purchasing Agent/Manager; Travel Agent. **Corporate headquarters location:** This location. **Other U.S. locations:** Nationwide. **International locations:** Denmark; England; Italy; Mexico. **Listed on:** New York Stock Exchange. **Stock exchange symbol:** AME. **Number of employees at this location:** 90. **Number of employees worldwide:** 6,200.

ANDRITZ, INC.

35 Sherman Street, Muncy PA 17756. 570/546-8211. **Fax:** 570/546-1667. **Contact:** Dennis M. Shulick, Director of Human Resources Department. **World Wide Web address:** http://www.andritz.com. **Description:** Engineers and manufactures capital equipment for the pulp, paper, feed, and grain industries. Founded in 1866. **Common positions include:** Accountant; Accountant/Auditor; Administrative Assistant; Agricultural Engineer; Applications Engineer; Attorney; Blue-Collar Worker Supervisor; Buyer; Chemical Engineer; Chief Financial Officer; Computer Engineer; Computer Programmer; Computer Technician; Controller; Credit Manager; Customer Service Representative; Design Engineer; Designer; Draftsperson; Electrical/Electronics Engineer; Electrician; Environmental Engineer; Financial Analyst; Help-Desk Technician; Human Resources Manager; Industrial Engineer; Manufacturing Engineer; Materials Engineer; Mechanical Engineer; Metallurgical Engineer; Network Engineer; Production Manager; Project Manager; Purchasing Agent/Manager; Quality Assurance Engineer; Secretary; Systems Analyst; Systems Manager. **Special programs:** Co-ops. **Office hours:** Monday - Friday, 8:00 a.m. - 5:00 p.m. **Corporate headquarters location:** This location. **Other U.S.**

locations: Atlanta GA; Springfield OH. **Parent company:** Andritz A.G. **Operations at this facility include:** Administration; Manufacturing. **Listed on:** Privately held. **Annual sales/revenues:** More than $100 million. **Number of employees at this location:** 450. **Number of employees nationwide:** 500. **Number of employees worldwide:** 3,000.

ARMSTRONG WORLD INDUSTRIES, INC.
P.O. Box 3001, Lancaster PA 17604-3001. 717/397-0611. **Physical address:** 2500 Columbia Avenue, Lancaster PA 17603. **Contact:** Human Resources Department. **World Wide Web address:** http://www.armstrong.com. **Description:** Manufactures flooring, ceiling systems, furniture, and industrial specialty products through approximately 85 plants worldwide. **Common positions include:** Accountant/Auditor; Chemical Engineer; Chemist; Electrical/Electronics Engineer; Industrial Engineer; Manufacturer's/Wholesaler's Sales Rep.; Mechanical Engineer; Systems Analyst. **Corporate headquarters location:** This location. **Operations at this facility include:** Administration; Manufacturing; Research and Development; Sales; Service. **Listed on:** New York Stock Exchange. **Stock exchange symbol:** ACK. **Number of employees nationwide:** 20,000.

AVERY DENNISON CORPORATION
7722 Dungan Road, Philadelphia PA 19111. 215/725-4700. **Contact:** Human Resources. **World Wide Web address:** http://www.averydennison.com. **Description:** This location manufactures industrial marking machines, tickets, tags, tapes, and related products. Overall, Avery Dennison Corporation is a worldwide manufacturer of self-adhesive products, pressure sensitive base materials, label components, labeling systems, office products, and related products. **Corporate headquarters location:** Pasadena CA. **Other U.S. locations:** Nationwide. **International locations:** Worldwide. **Listed on:** New York Stock Exchange. **Stock exchange symbol:** AVY.

BEMIS COMPANY INC.
Valmont Industrial Park, 20 Jaycee Drive, West Hazleton PA 18202-1142. 570/455-7741. **Contact:** John Meier, Human Resources Manager. **World Wide Web address:** http://www.bemis.com. **Description:** Bemis is a diversified producer of consumer and industrial packaging materials, film products, and business products. Packaging products include tapes, paper bags, and packaging for pharmaceuticals, candy, toilet paper, and detergents. The company also produces roll labels, laminates, and adhesive products. **Corporate**

headquarters location: Minneapolis MN. **Listed on:** New York Stock Exchange. **Stock exchange symbol:** BMS.

THE BETHLEHEM CORPORATION
25th & Lennox Streets, Easton PA 18045. 610/258-7111. **Contact:** Human Resources Department. **World Wide Web address:** http://www.bethcorp.com. **Description:** Engaged in the development, manufacture, and sale of equipment for environmental, energy, and continuous processing applications. The Bethlehem Corporation also provides subcontracting services for industrial products made to customers' specifications. Typical products include multiple-hearth furnaces, filter presses, industrial dryers, flow tubes, and transfer cars. **Common positions include:** Accountant/Auditor; Blue-Collar Worker Supervisor; Buyer; Computer Programmer; Purchasing Agent/Manager; Quality Control Supervisor. **Operations at this facility include:** Administration; Manufacturing; Research and Development; Sales.

BRADFORD WHITE CORPORATION
725 Talamore Drive, Ambler PA 19002-2755. 215/641-9400. **Contact:** Michael Marcellino, Manager of Human Resources. **World Wide Web address:** http://www.bradfordwhite.com. **Description:** Manufactures and markets water heaters. **Common positions include:** Accountant/Auditor; Administrator; Computer Programmer; Credit Manager; Customer Service Representative. **Operations at this facility include:** Regional Headquarters.

BURNHAM CORPORATION
1135 Dillerville Road, P.O. Box 3079, Lancaster PA 17604. 717/397-4701. **Fax:** 717/390-7808. **Contact:** Robert Beecher, Human Resources Director. **World Wide Web address:** http://www.burnham.com. **Description:** Manufactures boilers and related heating equipment for residential, commercial, and industrial applications. The company operates through two groups: The Distributor Products Group offers a broad range of residential boilers, radiators, and light commercial boilers to plumbing and heating wholesale distributors through America's Boiler Company, New Yorker Boiler, and Governale, Inc. The Commercial Group provides boilers, burners, and boiler room accessories for large commercial and industrial applications through Burnham Commercial Boilers and Kewanee Boiler. The company's operations are supported by the Burnham Foundry Division, which produces castings for commercial sales. **NOTE:** Entry-level positions and second and third shifts are offered. **Common positions include:** Account

Manager; Accountant; Administrative Assistant; Advertising Clerk; Applications Engineer; Assistant Manager; Auditor; Blue-Collar Worker Supervisor; Buyer; Chief Financial Officer; Computer Operator; Computer Programmer; Controller; Cost Estimator; Draftsperson; Electrician; Finance Director; Human Resources Manager; Industrial Engineer; Marketing Manager; Marketing Specialist; Public Relations Specialist; Purchasing Agent/Manager; Quality Control Supervisor; Sales Manager; Sales Representative; Secretary. **Corporate headquarters location:** This location. **Annual sales/revenues:** More than $100 million. **Number of employees at this location:** 460. **Number of employees nationwide:** 1,000.

C&D TECHNOLOGIES
1400 Union Meeting Road, P.O. Box 3053, Blue Bell PA 19422. 215/619-2700. **Fax:** 215/619-7837. **Contact:** Human Resources. **E-mail address:** cdjobs@cdtechno.com. **World Wide Web address:** http://www.cdtechno.com. **Description:** Manufactures and supplies industrial and reserve power systems and batteries for the telecommunications and utility switchgear markets. **Corporate headquarters location:** This location. **Listed on:** New York Stock Exchange. **Stock exchange symbol:** CHP.

CSS INDUSTRIES, INC.
1845 Walnut Street, Suite 800, Philadelphia PA 19119. 215/569-9900. **Contact:** Jacqueline Tully, Manager of Administration. **Description:** Manufactures and distributes business forms and supplies, and specialty metal containers. **Parent company:** Philadelphia Industries, Inc. **Number of employees nationwide:** 11,650.

CERTAINTEED CORPORATION
P.O. Box CN-E, Williams Junction NJ 07009. 856/767-7200. **Contact:** Human Resources Department. **E-mail address:** ctrecruitment@saint-gobain.com. **World Wide Web address:** http://www.certainteed.com. **Description:** This location is a distribution center. Overall, Certainteed Corporation operates in two business segments: Building Materials includes roofing products, vinyl siding, and door and sash products; Fiberglass Products includes thermal and acoustical insulation, a wide range of other fiberglass products, and piping products for the industrial, irrigation, sewer, mining, construction, and manufacturing markets. **NOTE:** Interested jobseekers should address inquiries to Certainteed Corporation, Human Resources, P.O. Box 860, Valley Forge PA 19482. **Corporate headquarters location:** Valley Forge PA. **Parent company:**

Compagnie de Saint-Gobain (Paris, France) operates through four branches: Abrasives, Construction Materials, Industrial Ceramics, and Insulation and Reinforcements. The Saint-Gobain companies based in North America are organized under the umbrella of the Saint-Gobain Corporation, which includes the Certainteed Corporation, the Norton Company, and all of their subsidiaries. **Number of employees nationwide:** 8,000.

CROWN CORK & SEAL COMPANY, INC.

One Crown Way, Philadelphia PA 19154. 215/698-5100. **Fax:** 215/676-7245. **Contact:** Personnel. **World Wide Web address:** http://www.crowncork.com. **Description:** Founded in 1892. Crown Cork & Seal manufactures cans, plastic bottles, and metal and plastic closures, as well as machinery for the packaging industry and disposable medical devices and closures. **NOTE:** Entry-level positions are offered. **Common positions include:** Accountant; Administrative Assistant; Applications Engineer; Chemical Engineer; Chief Financial Officer; Clerical Supervisor; Database Manager; Graphic Artist; Graphic Designer; Human Resources Manager; Industrial Engineer; Manufacturing Engineer; Metallurgical Engineer; MIS Specialist; Secretary; Systems Analyst; Systems Manager; Typist/Word Processor. **Special programs:** Internships; Co-ops; Summer Jobs. **Corporate headquarters location:** This location. **International locations:** Worldwide. **Operations at this facility include:** Administration; Divisional Headquarters; Manufacturing. **Listed on:** New York Stock Exchange. **Stock exchange symbol:** CCK. **Annual sales/revenues:** More than $100 million. **Number of employees at this location:** 600. **Number of employees nationwide:** 22,000. **Number of employees worldwide:** 50,000.

DANAHER MOTION INC.

110 Westtown Road, West Chester PA 19382. 610/692-2700. **Fax:** 610/696-4598. **Contact:** Human Resources Department. **World Wide Web address:** http://www.danahermotion.com. **Description:** Manufactures resolvers, brushless DC motors, and geared assemblies. **Common positions include:** Accountant/Auditor; Administrative Assistant; Blue-Collar Worker Supervisor; Buyer; Computer Programmer; Controller; Customer Service Representative; Design Engineer; Draftsperson; Electrical/Electronics Engineer; General Manager; Human Service Worker; Industrial Production Manager; Manufacturing Engineer; Mechanical Engineer; MIS Specialist; Operations/Production Manager; Purchasing Agent/Manager; Quality Assurance Engineer; Quality Control Supervisor;

Typist/Word Processor. **Corporate headquarters location:** Amherst NY. **Parent company:** Danaher Corporation. **Listed on:** New York Stock Exchange. **Stock exchange symbol:** DHR. **President:** Patrick J. Dulin. **Number of employees at this location:** 105. **Number of employees nationwide:** 1,500.

EAST PENN MANUFACTURING COMPANY INC.
P.O. Box 147, Deka Road, Lyon Station PA 19536. 610/682-6361. **Contact:** Human Resources Department. **World Wide Web address:** http://www.eastpenndeka.com. **Description:** Produces automotive and industrial batteries. Founded in 1946. **Common positions include:** Accountant/Auditor; Administrator; Advertising Clerk; Blue-Collar Worker Supervisor; Buyer; Chemical Engineer; Chemist; Computer Programmer; Draftsperson; Electrical/Electronics Engineer; Industrial Designer; Industrial Engineer; Marketing Specialist; Mechanical Engineer; Operations/Production Manager; Purchasing Agent/Manager; Quality Control Supervisor; Sales Executive; Transportation/Traffic Specialist. **Corporate headquarters location:** This location. **Operations at this facility include:** Administration; Manufacturing; Research and Development; Sales; Service.

ENVIRONMENTAL TECTONICS COMPANY (ETC)
125 James Way, Southampton PA 18966. 215/355-9100. **Fax:** 215/357-4000. **Contact:** Human Resources. **World Wide Web address:** http://www.etcusa.com. **Description:** Designs and manufactures sterilization systems, hyperbaric systems, air crew training systems, and environmental testing equipment. **Common positions include:** Aerospace Engineer; Agricultural Engineer; Electrical/Electronics Engineer; Electrician; Mechanical Engineer; Software Engineer; Structural Engineer. **Corporate headquarters location:** This location. **Other U.S. locations:** Orlando FL.

F.L. SMIDTH
2040 Avenue C, Bethlehem PA 18017-2188. 610/264-6011. **Fax:** 610/264-6230. **Contact:** Human Resources Department. **World Wide Web address:** http://www.flsmidth.com. **Description:** An international producer of equipment for the cement and minerals processing industry. F.L. Smidth designs, engineers, manufactures, and installs these products for customers worldwide. **Common positions include:** Accountant/Auditor; Buyer; Ceramics Engineer; Chemical Engineer; Civil Engineer; Computer Programmer; Customer Service Representative; Designer; Draftsperson; Electrical/Electronics Engineer; Materials Engineer; Mechanical

Engineer; Metallurgical Engineer; Mining Engineer; Purchasing Agent/Manager; Quality Control Supervisor; Structural Engineer; Systems Analyst. **Corporate headquarters location:** This location. **Parent company:** FLS Industries. **Operations at this facility include:** Administration; Sales; Service. **Number of employees at this location:** 800. **Number of employees nationwide:** 1,200.

FEDERAL-MOGUL SYSTEMS PROTECTION GROUP
241 Welsh Pool Road, Exton PA 19341. 610/363-2600. **Fax:** 610/363-4851. **Contact:** Human Resources Department. **World Wide Web address:** http://www.federal-mogul.com. **Description:** A manufacturer of protective sleeving, heat shields, oven-seal gaskets, and advanced composites. **Common positions include:** Accountant/Auditor; Buyer; Chemical Engineer; Chemist; Computer Programmer; Customer Service Representative; Designer; Electrical/Electronics Engineer; Financial Analyst; General Manager; Human Resources Manager; Industrial Engineer; Industrial Production Manager; Mechanical Engineer; Operations/Production Manager; Quality Control Supervisor; Systems Analyst. **Special programs:** Internships. **Parent company:** T&N, plc. **Listed on:** New York Stock Exchange. **Stock exchange symbol:** FMO. **Annual sales/revenues:** More than $100 million. **Number of employees at this location:** 200.

FIBRE METAL PRODUCTS COMPANY
P.O. Box 248, Concordville PA 19331. 610/459-5300. **Physical address:** Route 1, Brinton Lake Road, Concordville PA 19331. **Contact:** Personnel Director. **World Wide Web address:** http://www.fibre-metal.com. **Description:** Produces welding and head safety products.

FRANCE COMPRESSOR PRODUCTS
104 Pheasant Run, Newtown PA 18940. 215/968-5959. **Contact:** Human Resources Department. **World Wide Web address:** http://www.francecomp.com. **Description:** Manufactures compressor rings and other sealing components.

GARLAND U.S. RANGE
185 South Street, Freeland PA 18224-1916. 570/636-1000. **Contact:** Human Resources. **World Wide Web address:** http://www.garland-group.com. **Description:** A manufacturer of commercial cooking equipment. The company's products include ovens, ranges, pizza ovens, and deep fryers.

GASBOY INTERNATIONAL, INC.

P.O. Box 309, Lansdale PA 19446-0309. 215/855-4631. **Physical address:** 707 North Valley Forge Road, Lansdale PA 19446. **Fax:** 215/361-5404. **Contact:** Human Resources. **E-mail address:** hr@gasboy.com. **World Wide Web address:** http://www.gasboy.com. **Description:** Develops, manufactures, and markets petroleum dispensing pumps, computer-controlled management systems, and related components. Founded in 1819. **NOTE:** Entry-level positions and part-time jobs are offered. **Common positions include:** Accountant; Administrative Assistant; AS400 Programmer Analyst; Computer Support Technician; Computer Technician; Customer Service Representative; Help-Desk Technician; Network Engineer; Purchasing Agent/Manager; Software Engineer; Systems Analyst. **Special programs:** Training; Co-ops; Summer Jobs. **Corporate headquarters location:** This location. **Parent company:** Tokheim Company. **Listed on:** New York Stock Exchange. **Stock exchange symbol:** TOK. **Annual sales/revenues:** $51 - $100 million. **Number of employees at this location:** 310.

GROVE WORLDWIDE

P.O. Box 21, Shady Grove PA 17256. 717/597-8121. **Physical address:** 1565 Buchanan Trail East, Shady Grove PA 17256. **Contact:** Human Resources Department. **E-mail address:** careers@groveworldwide.com. **World Wide Web address:** http://www.groveworldwide.com. **Description:** A manufacturer of mobile lifting and access equipment. **Common positions include:** Accountant/Auditor; Buyer; Ceramics Engineer; Civil Engineer; Computer Programmer; Designer; Electrical Engineer; Financial Analyst; Industrial Engineer; Industrial Production Manager; Materials Engineer; Mechanical Engineer; Metallurgical Engineer; Operations/Production Manager; Quality Control Supervisor; Structural Engineer; Systems Analyst. **Corporate headquarters location:** This location. **Parent company:** Hanson Industries. **Operations at this facility include:** Administration; Manufacturing; Research and Development; Sales. **Number of employees at this location:** 2,000.

HMG INTERMARK WORLDWIDE MANUFACTURING, INC.

234 South Eighth Street, P.O. Box 1217, Reading PA 19602. 610/376-5701. **Contact:** Human Resources. **Description:** Produces a wide range of plastic displays, safety lenses, precision glasswork, and industrial products. **Common positions include:** Accountant/Auditor; Credit Manager; Design Engineer; Human Resources Manager; Industrial Engineer;

Operations/Production Manager; Purchasing Agent/Manager; Typist/Word Processor. **Parent company:** HMG Worldwide Inc. (New York NY). **Operations at this facility include:** Divisional Headquarters; Manufacturing. **Annual sales/revenues:** $51 - $100 million. **Number of employees at this location:** 70. **Number of employees nationwide:** 250.

HAZLETON PUMPS, INC.
225 North Cedar Street, Hazleton PA 18201. 570/455-7711. **Contact:** Ernest Stauffer, Personnel Manager. **World Wide Web address:** http://www.hazletonpumps.com. **Description:** Manufactures a wide range of centrifugal pumps. **Common positions include:** Draftsperson; Mechanical Engineer. **Corporate headquarters location:** This location. **Parent company:** Warman International Group (Australia). **Operations at this facility include:** Administration; Manufacturing; Research and Development; Sales; Service. **Number of employees at this location:** 200.

ITT INDUSTRIES ENGINEERED VALVES
P.O. Box 6164, 33 Centerville Road, Lancaster PA 17603-2064. 717/291-1901. **Fax:** 717/509-2214. **Contact:** Patricia Lyons, Human Resources Representative. **E-mail address:** engvalves_hr@fluids.ittind.com. **World Wide Web address:** http://www.engvalves.com. **Description:** Manufactures industrial valves. **Corporate headquarters location:** New York NY. **Parent company:** ITT Corporation.

INGERSOLL-RAND COMPANY
312 Ingersoll Drive, Shippensburg PA 17257-9125. 717/532-9181. **Contact:** Human Resources. **World Wide Web address:** http://www.ingersoll-rand.com. **Description:** Ingersoll-Rand Company is a manufacturer of road machinery and forklifts.

JLG INDUSTRIES, INC.
One JLG Drive, McConnellsburg PA 17233. 717/485-5161. **Fax:** 717/485-6466. **Recorded jobline:** 717/485-6684. **Contact:** Corporate Employment Manager. **World Wide Web address:** http://www.jlg.com. **Description:** A leading manufacturer, distributor, and international marketer of mobile work platforms. Founded in 1969. **NOTE:** Entry-level positions are offered. **Common positions include:** Design Engineer; Electrical/Electronics Engineer; Industrial Engineer; Manufacturing Engineer; Mechanical Engineer. **Special programs:** Internships; Apprenticeships; Co-ops. **Office hours:** Monday - Friday, 8:00 a.m. - 4:45 p.m. **Corporate headquarters location:** This location. **Other U.S. locations:**

Bedford PA. **International locations:** Australia; Scotland. **Listed on:** New York Stock Exchange. **Stock exchange symbol:** JLG. **Number of employees at this location:** 1,840. **Number of employees worldwide:** 2,760.

K-TRON INTERNATIONAL INC.
P.O. Box 888, Routes 55 and 553, Pitman NJ 08071. 856/589-0500. **Contact:** Human Resources. **World Wide Web address:** http://www.ktron.com. **Description:** Produces industrial feeders and blenders.

KBA-MOTTER CORPORATION
P.O. Box 12015, York PA 17402-0615. 717/755-1071. **Contact:** Gerrit Zwergel, Personnel Administrator. **Description:** Produces high-speed, web-fed rotogravure presses and related equipment. **Common positions include:** Accountant/Auditor; Buyer; Computer Programmer; Draftsperson; Electrical/Electronics Engineer; Human Resources Manager; Machinist; Mechanical Engineer; Operations/Production Manager; Quality Control Supervisor. **Corporate headquarters location:** This location. **Parent company:** Koening & Bauer-Albert. **Operations at this facility include:** Administration; Manufacturing; Research and Development; Sales; Service. **Number of employees at this location:** 135.

KERR GROUP, INC.
500 New Holland Avenue, Lancaster PA 17602. 717/299-6511. **Contact:** Human Resources. **World Wide Web address:** http://www.kerrgroup.com. **Description:** Manufactures plastic containers, closures, and vials for the pharmaceutical and food and beverage industries.

LAFRANCE CORPORATION
One LaFrance Way, Concordville PA 19331. 610/361-4300. **Fax:** 610/361-4301. **Contact:** Personnel. **World Wide Web address:** http://www.lafrancecorp.com. **Description:** A manufacturer of three-dimensional nameplates for product identification.

LYON METAL PRODUCTS
524 B Imperial Court, Bensalem PA 19020. 215/244-7930. **Contact:** Human Resources. **World Wide Web address:** http://www.lyonmetal.com. **Description:** Manufactures and sells steel products for industrial, commercial, office, and institutional use. Products include shelving, lockers, desktops, workbenches, office furniture, and custom products. Products are distributed nationally through dealers and direct sales.

MARKEL CORPORATION
P.O. Box 752, School Lane, Plymouth Meeting PA 19462. 610/272-8960. **Contact:** Human Resources. **World Wide Web address:** http://www.markelcorporation.com. **Description:** Produces sleevings and wire and cable products.

MARSULEX ENVIRONMENTAL TECHNOLOGIES
200 North Seventh Street, Lebanon PA 17046-5000. 717/274-7000. **Contact:** Human Resources Department. **World Wide Web address:** http://www.marsulex.com. **Description:** Manufactures industrial air pollution control equipment for the utilities industry.

MET-PRO CORPORATION
160 Cassell Road, P.O. Box 144, Harleysville PA 19438. 215/723-6751. **Contact:** Human Resources. **World Wide Web address:** http://www.met-pro.com. **Description:** Through its divisions and subsidiaries, Met-Pro manufactures a wide range of products for industrial, commercial, and residential markets. These products include pollution control systems and allied equipment for purification of air and liquids, and fluid handling equipment for corrosive, abrasive, and high-temperature liquids. **Listed on:** New York Stock Exchange. **Stock exchange symbol:** MPR.

NEW HOLLAND, INC.
P.O. Box 1895, New Holland PA 17557-0903. 717/355-1121. **Fax:** 717/363-6556. **Contact:** Linda Tajnai, Human Resources. **World Wide Web address:** http://www.newholland.com. **Description:** A manufacturer of agricultural equipment including tractors and balers. **Common positions include:** Accountant/Auditor; Agricultural Engineer; Budget Analyst; Buyer; Computer Programmer; Customer Service Representative; Financial Analyst; Human Resources Manager; Industrial Engineer; Mechanical Engineer; Systems Analyst. **Special programs:** Internships. **Corporate headquarters location:** London, England. **Parent company:** Fiat. **Operations at this facility include:** Administration; Divisional Headquarters; Manufacturing; Research and Development; Sales; Service. **Number of employees at this location:** 2,000. **Number of employees nationwide:** 4,000.

PEERLESS HEATER COMPANY
231 North Walnut Street, Boyertown PA 19512-0121. 610/367-2153. **Contact:** Human Resources Department. **World Wide Web address:** http://www.peerlessheater.com.

Description: Manufactures cast iron boilers for commercial and residential customers.

PENCO PRODUCTS, INC.
P.O. Box 378, 99 Brower Avenue, Oaks PA 19456. 610/666-0500. **Contact:** Howard Easton, Manager of Human Resources. **World Wide Web address:** http://www.pencoproducts.com. **Description:** Manufactures steel storage products including lockers, shelves, and cabinets.

PHILADELPHIA GEAR CORPORATION
One Montgomery Plaza, Suite 700, Norristown PA 19401. 610/265-3000. **Fax:** 610/337-5637. **Contact:** Kurt Keseric, Human Resources Department. **World Wide Web address:** http://www.philagear.com. **Description:** Produces a wide variety of gears and gear drives for various industrial uses. Founded in 1892. **Common positions include:** Account Manager; Accountant; Applications Engineer; Blue-Collar Worker Supervisor; Buyer; Chief Financial Officer; Computer Programmer; Credit Manager; Customer Service Representative; Design Engineer; Electrician; Human Resources Manager; Industrial Engineer; Industrial Production Manager; Manufacturing Engineer; Mechanical Engineer; MIS Specialist; Quality Control Supervisor; Sales Engineer; Sales Executive; Vice President of Marketing and Sales. **Corporate headquarters location:** This location. **Other U.S. locations:** Lynwood CA; Houston TX. **Parent company:** American Manufacturing Group. **Operations at this facility include:** Administration; Manufacturing; Research and Development; Sales; Service. **Listed on:** Privately held. **Annual sales/revenues:** $51 - $100 million. **Number of employees at this location:** 390. **Number of employees nationwide:** 550.

READCO MANUFACTURING INC.
P.O. 1552, 901 South Richland Avenue, York PA 17403-0552. 717/848-2801. **Toll-free phone:** 800/395-4959. **Fax:** 717/848-1401. **Contact:** Lois Miller, Payroll. **World Wide Web address:** http://www.readco.com. **Description:** Designs and manufactures a line of solids-processing equipment for the mixing and blending industries, ranging in size from pilot to full-scale production. **Common positions include:** Accountant; Computer Operator; Controller; Design Engineer; Sales Engineer; Sales Manager; Secretary.

SKF USA INDUSTRIES
1111 Adams Avenue, Norristown PA 19403-2403. 610/630-2800. **Fax:** 610/630-2727. **Contact:** Human Resources. **World**

Wide Web address: http://www.skfusa.com. Description: Produces tapered roller bearings.

SCHRAMM, INC.
800 East Virginia Avenue, West Chester PA 19380. 610/696-2500. Contact: Human Resources Department. World Wide Web address: http://www.schramminc.com Description: Manufactures truck- and crawler-mounted drilling rigs and self-propelled air compressors. Products are marketed to mining, water well, and general contractors.

SCHUTTE & KOERTING, INC.
2233 State Road, Bensalem PA 19020. 215/639-0900. Fax: 215/639-1533. Contact: Director of Human Resources. World Wide Web address: http://www.s-k.com. Description: Manufactures power and process vacuum equipment and turbine meter instrumentation. Founded in 1876. Common positions include: Electrical/Electronics Engineer; Sales Engineer. Corporate headquarters location: This location. Listed on: Privately held. Annual sales/revenues: $11 - $20 million. Number of employees at this location: 100.

SELAS CORPORATION OF AMERICA
2034 South Limekiln Pike, Dresher PA 19025. 215/646-6600. Fax: 215/646-3536. Contact: Robert W. Mason, Director of Human Resources and Administration. World Wide Web address: http://www.selas.com. Description: A diversified firm that engages in the design, development, engineering, and manufacturing of a wide range of specialized industrial heat processing systems and equipment for steel, glass, and other manufacturers. Corporate headquarters location: This location. Subsidiaries include: Deuer Manufacturing, Inc. manufactures spare tire holders, lifts, and related products, primarily based on cable winch designs, for use as original equipment by the pick-up truck and minivan segment of the automotive industry; Resistance Technology, Inc. designs and manufactures microminiature components and molded plastic parts primarily for the hearing instrument manufacturing industry worldwide. Operations at this facility include: Administration; Manufacturing; Research and Development; Sales; Service. Listed on: American Stock Exchange. Stock exchange symbol: SLS. Annual sales/revenues: $51 - $100 million. Number of employees at this location: 75. Number of employees nationwide: 500. Number of employees worldwide: 600.

SIEMENS ENERGY AND AUTOMATION, INC.

1201 Sumneytown Pike, MS 530, Spring House PA 19477-0900. 215/646-7400. **Fax:** 215/283-6341. **Contact:** Human Resources Department. **World Wide Web address:** http://www.smpa.siemens.com. **Description:** A manufacturer and seller of process control systems and industrial instruments. **Common positions include:** Chemical Engineer; Computer Programmer; Electrical/Electronics Engineer; Industrial Engineer; Mechanical Engineer; Petroleum Engineer; Software Engineer. **Corporate headquarters location:** This location. **Operations at this facility include:** Administration; Manufacturing; Research and Development; Sales; Service. **Listed on:** New York Stock Exchange. **Stock exchange symbol:** SI.

SMITHS INDUSTRIES

101 Lindenwood Drive, Suite 125, Malvern PA 19355. 610/578-9600. **Contact:** Vice President of Human Resources. **World Wide Web address:** http://www.smiths-group.com. **Description:** Engaged in a variety of businesses through three business groups: Smiths Industries Aerospace Group manufactures instrumentation and systems for civil and military aircraft; Smiths Industries Medical Systems Group (SIMS) manufactures surgical, dental, veterinary, and home health care supplies; Smiths Industries Industrial Group operates in four divisions. Flex-Tek produces flexible ducting and conduits. Vent-Axia produces ventilation fans. Engineering produces specialized engineering products. Hypertac Interconnect manufactures electrical connectors. **NOTE:** Entry-level positions are offered. **Common positions include:** Accountant; Budget Analyst; Computer Programmer; Electrical/Electronics Engineer; Financial Analyst; Human Resources Manager; Marketing Manager; Marketing Specialist; Sales Engineer; Sales Representative; Software Engineer; Systems Analyst; Technical Writer/Editor. **Corporate headquarters location:** London, England. **Other U.S. locations:** Irvine CA; Sunnyvale CA; Clearwater FL; Fort Myers FL; Hudson MA; Rockland MA; Grand Rapids MI; St. Paul MN; Keene NH; Florham Park NJ; Abbeville SC; Cookeville TN. **Parent company:** Smiths Industries plc. **Annual sales/revenues:** More than $100 million. **Number of employees nationwide:** 6,000. **Number of employees worldwide:** 13,000.

STOKES VACUUM

5500 Tabor Road, Philadelphia PA 19120. 215/831-5400. **Fax:** 215/831-5420. **Contact:** Personnel. **World Wide Web address:** http://www.stokesvacuum.com. **Description:** A manufacturer of vacuum metallizers, vacuum pumps, vacuum freeze dryers, and other industrial equipment.

TRW INC.
601 East Market Street, Danville PA 17821. 570/275-0170. **Contact:** Human Resources. **World Wide Web address:** http://www.trw.com. **Description:** This location produces engine valves, valve seat inserts, valve retainers, valve retainer locks, valve rotating mechanisms, and forged pistons. Overall, TRW is a diversified technology firm with operations in electronics and space systems, car and truck equipment for both original equipment manufacturers and the replacement market, and a wide variety of industrial and energy components including aircraft parts, welding systems, and electromechanical assemblies. **Corporate headquarters location:** Cleveland OH. **Listed on:** New York Stock Exchange. **Stock exchange symbol:** TRW.

TELEFLEX INC.
SERMATECH
155 South Limerick Road, Limerick PA 19468. 610/948-5100. **Contact:** Human Resources. **World Wide Web address:** http://www.tfxsermatech.com. **Description:** Operates in two industry segments: The Technical Products and Services segment includes the manufacturing of precision mechanical and electromechanical control equipment and other products for the aerospace, chemical processing, and medical industries. The Commercial Products segment is engaged in the design and manufacture of commercial controls, control systems, hydraulics, instruments, and other products with applications in the automotive, marine, and other industries. **NOTE:** Please send all resumes to Ronald Boldt, Vice President of Human Resources, Teleflex Inc., 630 West Germantown Pike, Suite 450, Plymouth Meeting PA 19462. **Corporate headquarters location:** This location.

TYCO VALVES & CONTROLS
480 Norristown Road, Blue Bell PA 19422. 610/825-2100. **Fax:** 610/832-2467. **Contact:** Human Resources Department. **World Wide Web address:** http://www.tycovalves-na.com. **Description:** Manufactures gauges, valves, steam traps, and indicators.

TYLER PIPE INDUSTRIES, INC.
101 North Church Street, Macungie PA 18062. 610/966-3491. **Contact:** Joe Maziarz, Personnel Manager. **World Wide Web address:** http://www.tylerpipe.com. **Description:** Manufactures

and distributes soil pipe and pipe fittings. Tyler Pipe Industries, Inc. is also a national producer of both plastic and iron piping for large-volume users. **Corporate headquarters location:** Tyler TX.

VICTAULIC COMPANY OF AMERICA
P.O. Box 31, Easton PA 18044-0031. 610/252-6400. **Physical address:** 4901 Kesslerville Road, Easton PA 18040-6714. **Contact:** Human Resources. **World Wide Web address:** http://www.victaulic.com. **Description:** An international marketer, manufacturer, and designer of industrial and commercial piping systems products that include pipe couplings, fittings, valves, piping accessories, specialty piping products, and pre-assembled packages. **Common positions include:** Administrator; Blue-Collar Worker Supervisor; Buyer; Computer Programmer; Credit Manager; Customer Service Representative; Department Manager; Draftsperson; General Manager; Industrial Designer; Industrial Engineer; Management Trainee; Manufacturer's/Wholesaler's Sales Rep.; Marketing Specialist; Mechanical Engineer; Metallurgical Engineer; Operations/Production Manager; Purchasing Agent/Manager; Quality Control Supervisor; Systems Analyst; Technical Writer/Editor; Transportation/Traffic Specialist. **Operations at this facility include:** Administration; Manufacturing; Research and Development; Sales; Service.

VISHAY INTERTECHNOLOGY INC.
63 Lincoln Highway, Malvern PA 19355-2120. 610/644-1300. **Fax:** 610/296-8775. **Contact:** Judy Eyerdom, Senior Manager of Human Resources Department. **World Wide Web address:** http://www.vishay.com. **Description:** Operates in three business segments: Measurement Group develops, manufactures, and markets precision stress analysis products; Resistive Systems Group (also at this location) develops, manufactures, and markets high-precision resistive products; Medical Systems Group develops, manufactures, and markets dental products. Founded in 1962. **Corporate headquarters location:** This location.

XEROX CORPORATION
100 Tournament Drive, Suite 300, Horsham PA 19044. 215/956-0200. **Toll-free phone:** 800/222-9283. **Contact:** Human Resources Department. **World Wide Web address:** http://www.xerox.com. **Description:** This location is a sales office. Overall, Xerox Corporation is a global company in the document processing market. The company's document processing activities encompass the designing, developing,

manufacturing, marketing, and servicing of a complete range of document processing products and systems that make office work more efficient. Xerox copiers, duplicators, electronic scanners, facsimile machines, networks, multifunction publishing machines, software, and supplies are marketed in more than 130 countries. **Corporate headquarters location:** Stamford CT.

YORK INTERNATIONAL CORPORATION

P.O. Box 1592, York PA 17405-1592. 717/771-7890. **Physical address:** 631 South Richland Avenue, York PA 17403. **Contact:** Amanda King, Corporate Employment Recruiter. **World Wide Web address:** http://www.york.com. **Description:** Manufactures and markets a full line of residential, commercial, and industrial air conditioning and refrigeration equipment and systems, heating systems, and food refrigeration systems. **Common positions include:** Accountant/Auditor; Electrical/Electronics Engineer; Mechanical Engineer; MIS Specialist; Software Engineer. **Special programs:** Internships. **Corporate headquarters location:** This location. **International locations:** Worldwide. **Subsidiaries include:** York Engineered Systems; York Refrigeration; York Unitary Products. **Operations at this facility include:** Administration; Manufacturing; Research and Development; Sales; Service. **Listed on:** New York Stock Exchange. **Stock exchange symbol:** YRK. **Annual sales/revenues:** More than $100 million. **Number of employees worldwide:** 25,000.

MINING/GAS/PETROLEUM/ENERGY RELATED

You can expect to find the following types of companies in this chapter:

Anthracite, Coal, and Ore Mining • Mining Machinery and Equipment• Oil and Gas Field Services • Petroleum and Natural Gas

BUCKEYE PIPE LINE COMPANY, LP
5002 Buckeye Road, Emmaus PA 18049. 484/232-4000. **Fax:** 484/232-4543. **Contact:** Administrator, Human Resources. **E-mail address:** resumes@buckeye.com. **World Wide Web address:** http://www.buckeye.com. **Description:** One of the largest independent pipeline common carriers of refined petroleum products in the United States, with over 3,000 miles of pipeline serving 10 states. **Common positions include:** Accountant; Administrative Assistant; Applications Engineer; AS400 Programmer Analyst; Attorney; Chemical Engineer; Chief Financial Officer; Civil Engineer; Computer Programmer; Computer Technician; Construction and Building Inspector; Controller; Database Administrator; Draftsperson; Electrical/Electronics Engineer; Environmental Engineer; Financial Analyst; Human Resources Manager; Management Analyst/Consultant; Marketing Manager; Mechanical Engineer; Purchasing Agent/Manager; Quality Assurance Engineer; Systems Analyst; Technical Writer/Editor. **Special programs:** Internships. **Corporate headquarters location:** This location. **Parent company:** Buckeye Partners, L.P.'s other subsidiaries include Buckeye Tank Terminals Company, L.P.; Everglades Pipe Line Company; Laurel Pipe Line Company. **Listed on:** New York Stock Exchange. **Stock exchange symbol:** BPL. **Annual sales/revenues:** More than $100 million. **Number of employees at this location:** 200. **Number of employees nationwide:** 525.

CRC INDUSTRIES, INC.
885 Louis Drive, Warminster PA 18974. 215/674-4300. **Fax:** 215/674-2196. **Contact:** Human Resources. **World Wide Web address:** http://www.crcindustries.com. **Description:** Produces a variety of cleaners, greases, lubricators, and other specialty chemicals for the automotive, marine, electrical, industrial, and aviation markets. Founded in 1958. **Corporate headquarters location:** This location.

EXXONMOBIL CORPORATION
P.O. Box 480, 600 Billingsport Road, Paulsboro NJ 08066. 856/224-0200. **Contact:** Human Resources. **Description:** This location houses a refinery. Overall, ExxonMobil is an integrated oil company engaged in petroleum and chemical products marketing, refining, manufacturing, exploration, production, transportation, and research and development worldwide. Other products include fabricated plastics, films, food bags, housewares, garbage bags, and building materials. The company also has subsidiaries involved in real estate development and mining operations. **Corporate headquarters location:** Irving TX. **Listed on:** New York Stock Exchange. **Stock exchange symbol:** XOM.

HOUGHTON INTERNATIONAL INC.
Madison and Van Buren Avenues, P.O. Box 930, Valley Forge PA 19482-0930. 610/666-4000. **Fax:** 610/666-1376. **Contact:** Human Resources Department. **World Wide Web address:** http://www.houghtonintl.com. **Description:** Engaged in the manufacture of lubricating oil and grease products for metalworking and manufacturing processes. Founded in 1865. **Corporate headquarters location:** This location.

SUNOCO, INC.
3144 West Passyunk Avenue, Philadelphia PA 19145. 215/339-2286. **Contact:** Human Resources Department. **World Wide Web address:** http://www.sunocoinc.com. **Description:** This location is a refinery. Overall, Sunoco is one of the country's largest independent petroleum refiner-marketers. With 3,500 stations operating under the Sunoco brand name, the company claims a presence in 17 states. Sunoco's lubricant and petrochemical products are marketed worldwide. **Corporate headquarters location:** Philadelphia PA. **Listed on:** New York Stock Exchange. **Stock exchange symbol:** SUN. **Number of employees worldwide:** 11,000.

SUNOCO, INC.
P.O. Box 426, Marcus Hook PA 19061. 610/859-1300. **Contact:** Human Resources Department. **World Wide Web address:** http://www.sunocoinc.com. **Description:** One of the country's largest independent petroleum refiner-marketers. With 3,500 stations operating under the Sunoco brand name, the company claims a presence in 17 states. Sunoco's lubricant and petrochemical products are marketed worldwide. **Corporate headquarters location:** Philadelphia PA. **Listed on:** New York Stock Exchange. **Stock exchange symbol:** SUN. **Number of employees worldwide:** 11,000.

SUNOCO, INC.
10 Penn Center, 1801 Market Street, Philadelphia PA 19103-1699. 215/977-3000. **Contact:** Human Resources. **World Wide Web address:** http://www.sunocoinc.com. **Description:** One of the country's largest independent petroleum refiner-marketers. With 3,500 stations operating under the Sunoco brand name, the company claims a presence in 17 states. Sunoco's lubricant and petrochemical products are marketed worldwide. **Corporate headquarters location:** This location. **Listed on:** New York Stock Exchange. **Stock exchange symbol:** SUN. **Number of employees worldwide:** 11,000.

TOTAL CONTAINMENT, INC.
P.O. Box 939, Oaks PA 19456. 610/666-7777. **Physical address:** 422 Business Center, A130 North Drive, Oaks PA 19456. **Contact:** Human Resources. **World Wide Web address:** http://www.totalcontainment.com. **Description:** Designs, engineers, and sells underground systems and products for the conveyance and containment of petroleum- and alcohol-based motor vehicle fuels including gasoline and gasohol, from underground storage tanks to above-ground fuel dispensers. Total Containment's systems and products are used in connection with the installation of new and the retrofitting of existing underground fuel containment and distribution systems worldwide. The principal end users of the company's products are major oil companies and convenience stores, as well as government bodies, utilities, and other fleet vehicle operators. **Corporate headquarters location:** This location. **Number of employees nationwide:** 85.

PAPER AND WOOD PRODUCTS

You can expect to find the following types of companies in this chapter:
Forest and Wood Products and Services • Lumber and Wood Wholesale• Millwork, Plywood, and Structural Members • Paper and Wood Mills

APPLETON PAPERS INC.
100 Paper Mill Road, Roaring Spring PA 16673. 814/224-2131. **Contact:** Brad Reist, Human Resources. **Description:** This location is a paper mill. Overall, Appleton Papers Inc. manufactures NCR brand carbonless paper, as well as other coated papers including those used in the graphic arts industry.

CONTINENTAL BOX COMPANY
1147 North Fourth Street, Philadelphia PA 19123. 215/627-4700. **Contact:** Human Resources. **Description:** Manufactures paper containers including boxes and packaging materials.

P.H. GLATFELTER COMPANY
228 South Main Street, Spring Grove PA 17362. 717/225-4711. **Contact:** Employee Services Manager. **E-mail address:** sg-hr@glatfelter.com. **World Wide Web address:** http://www.glatfelter.com. **Description:** Manufactures fine quality papers for the printing, book publishing, business forms, and technical specialties markets. **NOTE:** Entry-level positions and second and third shifts are offered. **Common positions include:** Accountant/Auditor; Buyer; Chemical Engineer; Chemist; Computer Programmer; Customer Service Representative; Draftsperson; Electrical/Electronics Engineer; Electrician; Financial Analyst; Human Resources Manager; Mechanical Engineer; Systems Analyst. **Special programs:** Internships; Apprenticeships; Training; Co-ops; Summer Jobs. **Corporate headquarters location:** York PA. **Operations at this facility include:** Administration; Divisional Headquarters; Manufacturing; Regional Headquarters; Research and Development; Sales; Service. **Listed on:** New York Stock Exchange. **Stock exchange symbol:** GLT. **Annual sales/revenues:** More than $100 million. **Number of employees at this location:** 1,100. **Number of employees nationwide:** 2,500. **Number of employees worldwide:** 3,700.

INTERSTATE CONTAINER CORPORATION
P.O. Box 317, Reading PA 19603. 610/208-9300. **Physical address:** Grace and Meade Streets, Reading PA 19611.

Contact: Personnel. **E-mail address:** hr@iripaper.com. **World Wide Web address:** http://www.interstatecontainer.com. **Description:** Manufactures corrugated shipping containers and operates a paper mill that produces corrugating medium. **Common positions include:** Customer Service Representative; Department Manager; Manufacturer's/Wholesaler's Sales Rep. **Corporate headquarters location:** Rosslyn VA. **Operations at this facility include:** Manufacturing.

KURTZ BROTHERS INC.
400 Reed Street, P.O. Box 392, Clearfield PA 16830-0392. **Toll-free phone:** 800/252-3811. **Fax:** 814/765-8690. **Contact:** Human Resources Department. **World Wide Web address:** http://www.kurtzbros.com. **Description:** A paper converter and school supply distributor.

MAIL-WELL ENVELOPE
P.O. Box 21050, Lehigh Valley PA 18009. 610/264-0535. **Physical address:** One Cascade Drive, Allentown PA 18109. **Contact:** Personnel Manager. **World Wide Web address:** http://www.mail-well.com. **Description:** Produces envelopes for the direct mail market. **Common positions include:** Accountant/Auditor; Blue-Collar Worker Supervisor; Branch Manager; Credit Manager; Customer Service Representative; Department Manager; Human Resources Manager; Manufacturer's/Wholesaler's Sales Representative; Purchasing Agent/Manager. **Corporate headquarters location:** Englewood CO. **Operations at this facility include:** Administration; Manufacturing; Sales; Service. **Listed on:** New York Stock Exchange. **Stock exchange symbol:** MWL.

MANNINGTON MILLS INC.
P.O. Box 30, Salem NJ 08079-0030. 856/935-3000. **Physical address:** 75 Mannington Mills Road, Salem NJ 08079. **Contact:** Tinique Peery, Manager of Human Resources. **World Wide Web address:** http://www.mannington.com. **Description:** Manufactures and wholesales various floor coverings including vinyl, wood, and carpet.

SMURFIT-STONE CONTAINER CORPORATION
5000 Flat Rock Road, Philadelphia PA 19127. 215/984-7000. **Fax:** 215/984-7170. **Contact:** Human Resources. **World Wide Web address:** http://www.smurfit-stone.com. **Description:** This location manufactures clay-coated boxboard made from recycled paper. Overall, Smurfit-Stone Container Corporation is the world's leading paper-based packaging company. The company's main products include corrugated containers,

folding cartons, and multiwall industrial bags. The company is also the world's largest collector and processor of recycled products that are then sold to a worldwide customer base. Smurfit-Stone Container Corporation also operates several paper tube, market pulp, and newsprint production facilities. **Common positions include:** Blue-Collar Worker Supervisor; Controller; Customer Service Representative; Electrician; General Manager; Human Resources Manager; Production Manager; Purchasing Agent/Manager; Sales Manager; Sales Representative; Secretary. **Special programs:** Training. **Corporate headquarters location:** Chicago IL. **Other U.S. locations:** Nationwide. **International locations:** Worldwide. **Listed on:** NASDAQ. **Stock exchange symbol:** SSCC. **General Manager:** Rusty Miller. **Annual sales/revenues:** More than $100 million. **Number of employees at this location:** 300. **Number of employees nationwide:** 20,000.

SMURFIT-STONE CONTAINER CORPORATION
Tulip & Decatur Streets, Philadelphia PA 19136. 877/772-2932. **Contact:** Beverly Kantner, Personnel Director. **World Wide Web address:** http://www.smurfit-stone.com. **Description:** This location manufactures corrugated boxes. Overall, Smurfit-Stone Container Corporation is one of the world's leading paper-based packaging companies. The company's main products include corrugated containers, folding cartons, and multiwall industrial bags. The company is also one of the world's largest collectors and processors of recycled products that are then sold to a worldwide customer base. Smurfit-Stone Container Corporation also operates several paper tube, market pulp, and newsprint production facilities. **Corporate headquarters location:** Chicago IL. **Other U.S. locations:** Nationwide. **Listed on:** NASDAQ. **Stock exchange symbol:** SSCC. **Annual sales/revenues:** More than $100 million.

STERLING PAPER COMPANY
2155 East Castor Avenue, Philadelphia PA 19134. 215/744-5350. **Contact:** Human Resources. **Description:** Manufactures a wide variety of paper plates, cups, and related products. **Corporate headquarters location:** This location.

PRINTING AND PUBLISHING

You can expect to find the following types of companies in this chapter:
Book, Newspaper, and Periodical Publishers • Commercial Photographers • Commercial Printing Services • Graphic Designers

AMERICAN BANK NOTE COMPANY
2520 Metropolitan Drive, Trevos PA 19053. 215/396-8707. **Fax:** 215/657-0279. **Contact:** Human Resources. **E-mail address:** recruiter@abnh.com. **World Wide Web address:** http://www.abnh.com. **Description:** A printer of counterfeit-resistant documents and one of the largest security printers in the world. American Bank Note creates secure documents of value for governments and corporations worldwide. Products include currencies; passports; stock and bond certificates; bank, corporate, government, and traveler's checks; food coupons; gift vouchers and certificates; driver's licenses; product authentication labels; and vital documents. **Corporate headquarters location:** New York NY. **Other U.S. locations:** Burbank CA; Long Beach CA; San Francisco CA; Washington DC; Atlanta GA; Bedford Park IL; Needham MA; St. Louis MO; Huntington Valley PA; Philadelphia PA; Pittsburgh PA; Dallas TX. **Parent company:** American Bank Note Corporation also operates two other subsidiaries. American Bank Note Holographics, Inc. is one of the world's largest producers of the laser-generated, three-dimensional images that appear on credit cards and products requiring proof of authenticity; and American Bank Note Company Brazil is one of Brazil's largest private security printers and a provider of personalized checks, financial transaction cards, and prepaid telephone cards.

AMERICAN BANK NOTE HOLOGRAPHICS, INC.
1448 County Line Road, Huntington Valley PA 19006. 215/357-5300. **Fax:** 215/357-5331. **Contact:** Human Resources. **E-mail address:** recruiter@abnh.com. **World Wide Web address:** http://www.abnh.com. **Description:** This location is a holographic printing facility. Overall, American Bank Note Holographics is one of the world's largest producers of the laser-generated, three-dimensional images that appear on credit cards and products requiring proof of authenticity. **Corporate headquarters location:** New York NY. **Other U.S. locations:** Burbank CA; Long Beach CA; San Francisco CA; Washington DC; Atlanta GA; Bedford Park IL; Needham MA; St. Louis MO; Horsham PA; Philadelphia PA;

Pittsburgh PA; Dallas TX. **Parent company:** American Bank Note Corporation operates two other subsidiaries. American Bank Note Company is a printer of counterfeit-resistant documents and one of the largest security printers in the world. American Bank Note Company creates secure documents of value for governments and corporations worldwide. Products include currencies; passports; stock and bond certificates; bank, corporate, government, and traveler's checks; food coupons; gift vouchers and certificates: driver's licenses; product authentication labels; and vital documents. American Bank Note Company Brazil is one of Brazil's largest private security printers and a provider of personalized checks, financial transaction cards, and prepaid telephone cards.

CADMUSMACK
1991 Northampton Street, Easton PA 18042. 610/258-9111. **Contact:** Richard Cory, Corporate Industrial Relations Manager. **World Wide Web address:** http://www.cadmus.com. **Description:** Provides a wide range of printing and publications services including publication and catalog printing, photocomposition, and binding.

CALKINS NEWSPAPERS INC.
THE INTELLIGENCER-RECORD
P.O. Box 858, Doylestown PA 18901. 215/345-3000. **Physical address:** 333 North Broad Street, Doylestown PA 18901. **Contact:** Human Resources. **World Wide Web address:** http://www.phillyburbs.com. **Description:** Publishes the *Intelligencer*, a newspaper with a daily circulation of 44,100 and a Sunday circulation of 62,000. Calkins Newspapers also publishes the *Record, Burlington County Times*, and *Bucks County Courier Times*.

COURIER-POST NEWSPAPER
P.O. Box 5300, Cherry Hill NJ 08034. 856/663-6000. **Physical address:** 300 Cuthbert Boulevard, Cherry Hill NJ 08002. **Contact:** Lori Trasmondi, Human Resources Director. **World Wide Web address:** http://www.courierpostonline.com. **Description:** A newspaper with a circulation of approximately 100,000.

COURIER-POST NEWSPAPER
P.O. Box 5300, Cherry Hill NJ 08034. 856/663-6000. **Physical address:** 300 Cuthbert Boulevard, Cherry Hill NJ 08002. **Contact:** Lori Trasmondi, Human Resources Director. **World Wide Web address:** http://www.courierpostonline.com.

Description: A newspaper with a circulation of approximately 100,000.

DAY-TIMER, INC.
One Willow Lane, East Texas PA 18046. 610/398-1151. **Toll-free phone:** 800/225-5005. **Contact:** Human Resources Department Manager. **World Wide Web address:** http://www.daytimer.com. **Description:** Designs and manufactures personal and organizational calendars, accessories, and software. **Corporate headquarters location:** This location.

ELSEVIER SCIENCE
The Curtis Center, Independence Square West, Suite 300, Philadelphia PA 19106-3399. 215/238-7800. **Contact:** Human Resources Department. **World Wide Web address:** http://www.elsevier.com. **Description:** The company publishes textbooks, clinical reference books, and periodicals for the medical, nursing, and health-related professions. Founded in 1888. **Common positions include:** Editor; Marketing Manager; Sales Representative. **Other U.S. locations:** St. Louis MO. **Parent company:** Harcourt General, Inc. (Chestnut Hill MA). **Operations at this facility include:** Publishing. **Number of employees at this location:** 400. **Number of employees nationwide:** 5,000.

THE EXPRESS TIMES
30 North Fourth Street, P.O. Box 391, Easton PA 18044-0391. 610/258-7171. **Contact:** Human Resources Department. **World Wide Web address:** http://www.express-times.com. **Description:** A newspaper publisher.

FAULKNER INFORMATION SERVICES
114 Cooper Center, 7905 Browning Road, Pennsauken NJ 08109-4319. 856/662-2070. **Toll-free phone:** 800/843-0460. **Fax:** 856/662-3380. **Contact:** Betsey Wilson, Operations/Personnel. **E-mail address:** faulkner@faulkner.com. **World Wide Web address:** http://www.faulkner.com. **Description:** An independent publishing and research company specializing in providing technical information to end users and communication and IT professionals. Faulkner Information Services publishes more than a dozen standard information services in both print and electronic formats. The company provides comprehensive intelligence on products, vendors, technological advancements, and management issues associated with a wide range of technologies from open systems and client/server to enterprise networking, workgroup

computing, and telecommunications. Faulkner also offers custom research and publication capabilities in such areas as market studies, customer satisfaction surveys, competitive analysis reports, and custom databases. **Common positions include:** Accountant/Auditor; Customer Service Representative; Human Resources Manager; Systems Analyst; Technical Writer/Editor. **Corporate headquarters location:** This location. **Operations at this facility include:** Administration; Research and Development; Sales; Service. **Number of employees at this location:** 45.

FRY COMMUNICATIONS INC.
800 West Church Road, Mechanicsburg PA 17055. 717/766-0211. **Contact:** Frank Hopkins, Director of Human Resources. **World Wide Web address:** http://www.frycomm.com. **Description:** Fry Communications is one of the top 15 printing companies in the nation. This company prints and publishes magazines, catalogs, directories, cable listings and other periodicals including *The Guide*. **NOTE:** Second and third shifts are offered. **Common positions include:** Accountant; Computer Programmer; Computer Support Technician; Customer Service Representative; Desktop Publishing Specialist; Draftsperson; Editor; Electrician; Graphic Designer; Help-Desk Technician; Production Manager; Sales Representative; Systems Analyst. **Annual sales/revenues:** More than $100 million. **Number of employees at this location:** 1,700.

IMTEK, INC.
P.O. Box 621, Bridgeport NJ 08014. 856/467-0047. **Physical address:** 110 High Hill Road, Bridgeport NJ 08014. **Contact:** Human Resources Department. **World Wide Web address:** http://www.imtek.com. **Description:** Provides complete lithography and bookbinding services. **Corporate headquarters location:** This location.

INSTITUTE FOR SCIENTIFIC INFORMATION
3501 Market Street, Philadelphia PA 19104. 215/386-0100. **Fax:** 215/387-4231. **Contact:** Brian Richards, Employment/Employee Relations Manager. **World Wide Web address:** http://www.isinet.com. **Description:** Supplies researchers and scientists with needed information in electronic formats. Institute for Scientific Information produces indexes and databases that provide information from journals, books, and other significant materials published in the sciences, social sciences, and arts and humanities. The company also offers online services and technical support.

Common positions include: Accountant/Auditor; Computer Programmer; Customer Service Representative; Database Manager; Editor; Financial Analyst; Indexer; Marketing Specialist; Operations/Production Manager; Proofreader; Quality Control Supervisor; Systems Analyst; Technical Writer/Editor; Translator. **Corporate headquarters location:** This location. **Other area locations:** Cherry Hill NJ; Mount Laurel NJ. **Parent company:** Thomson Company. **Number of employees at this location:** 450. **Number of employees nationwide:** 750.

LANCASTER NEWSPAPERS, INC.
P.O. Box 1328, Lancaster PA 17608-1328. 717/291-8681. **Physical address:** 8 West King Street, Lancaster PA 17608. **Fax:** 717/293-4311. **Contact:** Human Resources. **E-mail address:** humanresources@lnpnews.com. **World Wide Web address:** http://www.lancnews.com. **Description:** Publishes the morning *Intelligencer Journal*, the evening *Lancaster New Era*, and the *Sunday News*, with a combined daily circulation of over 100,000. Founded in 1794. **NOTE:** Entry-level positions and second and third shifts are offered. **Common positions include:** Account Representative; Accountant; Advertising Clerk; Blue-Collar Worker Supervisor; Buyer; Commercial Artist; Computer Programmer; Credit Manager; Customer Service Representative; Department Manager; Editor; Graphic Artist; Human Resources Manager; Librarian; Managing Editor; Marketing Manager; Marketing Specialist; MIS Specialist; Online Content Specialist; Purchasing Agent/Manager; Quality Control Supervisor; Reporter; Sales Executive; Sales Manager; Sales Representative; Secretary; Systems Analyst; Systems Manager; Typist/Word Processor. **Special programs:** Internships. **Internship information:** Lancaster Newspapers offers internships in journalism and marketing/advertising. Please apply by March 1 for a 13-week summer internship. **Corporate headquarters location:** This location. **Listed on:** Privately held. **Annual sales/revenues:** $51 - $100 million. **Number of employees at this location:** 1,000.

LEHIGH PRESS
7001 North Park Drive, Pennsauken NJ 08109. 856/665-5200. **Contact:** Human Resources. **World Wide Web address:** http://www.lehigh-press.com. **Description:** A commercial lithograph printer.

LIPPINCOTT WILLIAMS & WILKINS
530 Walnut Street, Philadelphia PA 19106-3621. 215/521-8300. **Fax:** 215/521-8902. **Contact:** Human Resources. **World**

Wide Web address: http://www.lww.com. **Description:** A global publisher of medical, nursing, and allied health information resources in book, journal, newsletter, loose-leaf, and electronic media formats. **NOTE:** Entry-level positions and part-time jobs are offered. **Common positions include:** Account Manager; Accountant; Administrative Assistant; Computer Programmer; Computer Support Technician; Credit Manager; Database Administrator; Database Manager; Editor; Editorial Assistant; Financial Analyst; Graphic Artist; Graphic Designer; Managing Editor; Marketing Manager; Multimedia Designer; Network/Systems Administrator; Sales Representative; Software Engineer; Systems Analyst; Systems Manager. **Special programs:** Internships; Co-ops; Summer Jobs. **Other U.S. locations:** Baltimore MD; Hagerstown MD; New York NY. **International locations:** Worldwide. **Parent company:** Wolters Kluwer. **Listed on:** Privately held. **Annual sales/revenues:** More than $100 million. **Number of employees at this location:** 400. **Number of employees nationwide:** 1,200. **Number of employees worldwide:** 6,000.

MAIL-WELL GRAPHICS
7625 Suffolk Avenue, Philadelphia PA 19153. 215/492-0200. **Toll-free phone:** 800/338-1280. **Fax:** 215/492-8241. **Contact:** Kathleen Schaefer, Personnel Director. **World Wide Web address:** http://www.mail-well.com. **Description:** A printer of catalogs, handbooks, directories, journals, and related items. **Corporate headquarters location:** Englewood CO. **Listed on:** New York Stock Exchange. **Stock exchange symbol:** MWL.

THE MAPLE-VAIL BOOK MANUFACTURING GROUP
THE MAPLE PRESS COMPANY
P.O. Box 2695, York PA 17405. 717/764-5911. **Physical address:** 480 Willow Springs Lane, York PA 17402. **Contact:** Shirley Baker, Human Resources Manager. **World Wide Web address:** http://www.maple-vail.com. **Description:** Provides bookbinding services including printing and photo composition. The Maple Press Company (also at this location) is a manufacturing facility. **Corporate headquarters location:** This location.

MONTGOMERY NEWSPAPERS COMPANY
290 Commerce Street, Fort Washington PA 19034. 215/542-0200. **Contact:** Diane Dumke, Personnel. **World Wide Web address:** http://www.montgomerynews.com. **Description:** Publishes *Today's Spirit*, a daily newspaper for the Hatboro/Warminster area and weekly newspapers in Ambler, Glenside, Huntingdon Valley, Jenkintown, King of Prussia,

Springfield, and Willow Grove. **Common positions include:** Accountant/Auditor; Mail Distributor; Sales Representative. **Corporate headquarters location:** This location. **Operations at this facility include:** Manufacturing. **Listed on:** Privately held. **Annual sales/revenues:** $5 - $10 million. **Number of employees at this location:** 200. **Number of employees nationwide:** 300.

MORNING CALL
101 North Sixth Street, P.O. Box 1260, Allentown PA 18105. 610/820-6500. **Contact:** Human Resources. **World Wide Web address:** http://www.mcall.com. **Description:** Publishes a newspaper with a daily circulation of 150,000 and a Sunday circulation of 180,000.

NATIONAL PUBLISHING COMPANY
11311 Roosevelt Boulevard, Philadelphia PA 19154. 888/333-1863. **Contact:** Human Resources. **World Wide Web address:** http://www.courier.com. **Description:** Prints and binds books, religious products, reference texts, software manuals, and technical documentation. The company also provides electronic prepress and fulfillment services. **Corporate headquarters location:** North Chelmsford MA. **Other U.S. locations:** Kendallville IN; Lowell MA; Stoughton MA; Westford MA. **Parent company:** Courier Corporation.

NEWS AMERICA PUBLICATIONS, INC.
TV GUIDE
4 Radnor Corporate Center, 100 Matsonford Road, Radnor PA 19088. 610/293-8500. **Fax:** 610/293-6204. **Contact:** Human Resources. **World Wide Web address:** http://www.tvguide.com. **Description:** Publishes *TV Guide* magazine. **Common positions include:** Accountant/Auditor; Computer Programmer; Financial Analyst; Operations/Production Manager. **Special programs:** Internships. **Corporate headquarters location:** This location. **Operations at this facility include:** Administration; Sales; Service. **Number of employees at this location:** 1,300.

NORTH AMERICAN PUBLISHING COMPANY
401 North Broad Street, Philadelphia PA 19108. 215/238-5300. **Contact:** Human Resources. **World Wide Web address:** http://www.napco.com. **Description:** A publisher of trade and business magazines. **NOTE:** Entry-level positions are offered. **Common positions include:** Advertising Clerk; Customer Service Representative; Editor; Sales Representative; Telemarketer; Writer. **Special programs:** Internships. **Office**

hours: Monday - Friday 8:30 a.m. - 5:00 p.m. **Corporate headquarters location:** This location. **President:** Ned S. Borowsky. **Sales Manager:** Pete Orsi.

PHILADELPHIA BUSINESS JOURNAL

400 Market Street, Suite 300, Philadelphia PA 19106. 215/238-1450. **Contact:** Personnel. **World Wide Web address:** http://www.bizjournals.com/philadelphia. **Description:** A weekly business journal. **Common positions include:** Accountant; Customer Service Manager; Editorial Assistant; Event Planner; Marketing Manager; Reporter; Sales Representative. **Number of employees at this location:** 40.

PHILADELPHIA INQUIRER
PHILADELPHIA DAILY NEWS

P.O. Box 8263, P.O. Box 7788, Philadelphia PA 19101. 215/854-2000. **Physical address:** 400 North Broad Street, Philadelphia PA 19130. **Contact:** Human Resources. **World Wide Web address:** http://www.phillynews.com. **Description:** *Philadelphia Inquirer* is one of America's largest daily newspapers, with a weekday circulation of more than 700,000. Sunday circulation is more than 1 million. *Philadelphia Daily News* is a daily newspaper. **Common positions include:** Accountant/Auditor; Administrator; Advertising Clerk; Blue-Collar Worker Supervisor; Buyer; Computer Programmer; Customer Service Representative; Department Manager; Editor; Financial Analyst; General Manager; Human Resources Manager; Management Trainee; Marketing Specialist; Mechanical Engineer; Operations/Production Manager; Purchasing Agent/Manager; Reporter; Systems Analyst. **Parent company:** Knight-Ridder Newspaper Group.

QUEBECOR PRINTING ATGLEN INC.

900 Business Center Drive, Horsham 19404. 215/957-9300. **Contact:** Human Resources Department. **World Wide Web address:** http://www.quebecorusa.com. **Description:** One of the world's largest commercial printers with 84 printing and related services facilities in Canada, the United States, France, the United Kingdom, Mexico, and India. The company's major product categories include inserts and circulars, magazines, books, catalogs, directories, checks, bonds and banknotes, specialty printing, and newspapers. Quebecor Printing also offers web offset, gravure, and sheet-fed printing capacity, plus related services that include advanced electronic prepress and imaging, database and list management, shipping and distribution, and CD-ROM mastering and replicating.

Corporate headquarters location: Montreal, Canada. **Parent company:** Quebecor Printing Montreal.

THE RELIZON COMPANY
P.O. Box 128, Emigsville PA 17318. 717/764-5902. **Contact:** Human Resources Department. **World Wide Web address:** http://www.relizon.com. **Description:** Provides business communications and customer relationship management solutions. **Corporate headquarters location:** Dayton OH. **Other U.S. locations:** Nationwide.

RODALE PRESS & COMPANY
33 East Minor Street, Emmaus PA 18098-0099. 610/967-5171. **Contact:** Caroline Holler, Personnel Director. **World Wide Web address:** http://www.rodalepress.com. **Description:** Publishes a wide variety of general interest trade books and magazines.

RUNNING PRESS
125 South 22nd Street, Philadelphia PA 19103-4399. 215/567-5080. **Fax:** 215/568-2919. **Contact:** Mike Bonanno, Human Resources. **E-mail address:** mbonanno@runningpress.com. **World Wide Web address:** http://www.runningpress.com. **Description:** Publishes nonfiction, children's, and art books.

ST. IVES BURRUPS
1617 JFK Boulevard, Suite 430, Philadelphia PA 19103. 215/563-9000. **Contact:** Human Resources. **World Wide Web address:** http://www.st-ives.com. **Description:** A publisher and printer of a wide range of books and magazines concerning the securities, legal, and general finance industries.

SHOPPER'S GUIDE INC.
8 Ranoldo Terrace, Cherry Hill NJ 08034. 856/616-4900. **Contact:** Human Resources Manager. **World Wide Web address:** http://www.theshoppersguide.com. **Description:** One of the Northeast's largest, free, weekly, shopper's newspapers. **Common positions include:** Administrative Assistant; Collections Agent; Sales Executive; Sales Manager; Systems Analyst. **Parent company:** Newport Media, Inc.

SIMON & SCHUSTER, INC.
100 Front Street, Riverside NJ 08075. 856/461-6500. **Fax:** 856/824-2406. **Contact:** Dee Chassey, Personnel Manager. **World Wide Web address:** http://www.simonandschuster.com. **Description:** This location is a distribution center. Overall, Simon & Schuster publishes consumer, educational, and

professional books. **Other U.S. locations:** CA; MA; NY; OH. **Subsidiaries include:** Macmillan; Prentice Hall Inc. **Parent company:** Viacom. **Number of employees nationwide:** 4,000.

SLACK INCORPORATED

6900 Grove Road, Thorofare NJ 08086-9447. 856/848-1000. **Toll-free phone:** 800/257-8290. **Fax:** 856/848-6091. **Contact:** Ms. Robin Bienias, Human Resources Manager. **E-mail address:** resume@slackinc.com. **World Wide Web address:** http://www.slackinc.com. **Description:** SLACK Incorporated is a provider of information, education, and event management services focusing mainly in the healthcare marketplace. A leader in the healthcare information industry SLACK publishes over 25 journals and medical newspapers distributed worldwide; over 125 medical and allied health books worldwide; conducts major publication-related conferences and trade shows; provides exhibit sales, management services, and advertising sales representation for association clients; produces dozens of periodical special projects each year, including supplements, monographs, satellite symposia, and industry-sponsored symposia, and customized CD-ROMs; and designs and manages customized Websites for resident training and continuing education. SLACK is certified by the Accreditation Council for Continuing Medical Education to sponsor continuing education events and periodical-based Continuing Medical Education activities. **Common positions include:** Advertising Clerk; Editor; Editorial Assistant; Graphic Artist; Managing Editor; Technical Writer/Editor; Sales Representative. **Corporate headquarters location:** This location.

TOPFLIGHT CORPORATION

P.O. Box 2847, York PA 17405. 717/227-5400. **Contact:** Human Resource Manager. **World Wide Web address:** http://www.topflight.com. **Description:** Manufactures pressure-sensitive labels. **Common positions include:** Customer Service Representative; Manufacturer's/Wholesaler's Sales Rep. **Corporate headquarters location:** This location. **Subsidiaries include:** Adhesives Research. **Listed on:** Privately held. **Number of employees at this location:** 220. **Number of employees nationwide:** 420.

UNISOURCE

One East Uwchlan Avenue, Suite 200, Exton PA 19341-0649. 610/280-5700. **Contact:** Human Resources. **World Wide Web address:** http://www.unisourcelink.com. **Description:** Markets and distributes printing and imaging papers, packaging systems, and maintenance supplies. **Corporate headquarters location:** This location. **Annual sales/revenues:** More than $100 million.

YORK TAPE AND LABEL, INC.
P.O. Box 1309, York PA 17405. 717/266-9675. **Physical address:** 405 Willow Springs Lane, York PA 17402. **Contact:** Deidra A. Foore, Human Resources Manager. **World Wide Web address:** http://www.yorklabel.com. **Description:** Prints and converts pressure-sensitive labels used for product identification. **Common positions include:** Accountant/Auditor; Blue-Collar Worker Supervisor; Buyer; Chemical Engineer; Commercial Artist; Credit Manager; Customer Service Representative; Human Resources Manager; Industrial Engineer; Manufacturer's/Wholesaler's Sales Rep.; Mechanical Engineer; Printing Press Operator. **Corporate headquarters location:** This location. **Other U.S. locations:** Columbia SC. **Parent company:** Uarco, Inc. **Listed on:** Privately held. **Number of employees at this location:** 200. **Number of employees nationwide:** 275.

REAL ESTATE

You can expect to find the following types of companies in this chapter:
*Land Subdividers and Developers • Real Estate Agents,
Managers, and Operators • Real Estate Investment Trusts*

BINSWANGER
2 Logan Square, 4th Floor, Philadelphia PA 19103. 215/448-6000. **Contact:** Ellen Diorio, Director of Personnel. **World Wide Web address:** http://www.cbbi.com. **Description:** Sells commercial and industrial real estate. **Corporate headquarters location:** This location. **Other U.S. locations:** Nationwide. **International locations:** Worldwide.

CB RICHARD ELLIS
1835 Market Street, Suite 2710, Philadelphia PA 19103-3272. 215/299-3200. **Fax:** 215/299-3292. **Contact:** Human Resources Department Manager. **World Wide Web address:** http://www.cbrichardellis.com. **Description:** A real estate services company offering property sales and leasing, property management, corporate facilities management, mortgage banking, and market research. **Corporate headquarters location:** Los Angeles CA. **Other U.S. locations:** Nationwide.

CB RICHARD ELLIS
1200 Liberty Ridge Drive, Suite 320, Wayne PA 19087. 610/251-0820. **Fax:** 610/889-9168. **Contact:** Human Resources Department Manager. **World Wide Web address:** http://www.cbrichardellis.com. **Description:** A real estate service company offering property sales and leasing, property and facility management, mortgage banking, and investment management services. **Corporate headquarters location:** Los Angeles CA. **Other U.S. locations:** Nationwide.

HIGH INDUSTRIES, INC.
P.O. Box 10008, 1853 William Penn Way, Lancaster PA 17605-0008. 717/293-4486. **Contact:** Vincent Mizeras, Director of Human Resources. **World Wide Web address:** http://www.high.net. **Description:** Operates through several areas of business including design and construction, food services, hotel management, prestress/precast concrete products, real estate development and management, and steel fabrication. **Common positions include:** Accountant/Auditor; Architect; Civil Engineer; Computer Programmer; Customer Service Representative; Draftsperson; Hotel Manager; Human

Resources Manager; Services Sales Representative; Systems Analyst. **Corporate headquarters location:** This location. **Operations at this facility include:** Administration; Manufacturing.

PENNSYLVANIA REAL ESTATE INVESTMENT TRUST

200 South Broad Street, 3rd Floor, Philadelphia PA 19102. 215/875-0700. **Contact:** Human Resources. **World Wide Web address:** http://www.preit.com. **Description:** An equity real estate investment trust engaged in the business of managing, acquiring, and holding for investment real estate and interests in real estate. The trust's principal real estate assets consist of 48 properties, 20 of which are wholly-owned and 28 of which are owned by partnerships or joint ventures.

RETAIL

You can expect to find the following types of companies in this chapter:

Catalog Retailers • Department Stores; Specialty Stores •
Retail Bakeries • Supermarkets

BJ'S WHOLESALE CLUB

1910 Deptford Center Road, Deptford NJ 08096. 856/232-8880. **Contact:** Human Resources. **World Wide Web address:** http://www.bjswholesale.com. **Description:** Sells food and general merchandise through more than 60 warehouses. **Corporate headquarters location:** Natick MA. **Parent company:** Waban Inc.

THE BON-TON

2801 East Market Street, York PA 17402. 717/757-7660. **Contact:** Sue Hulme, Manager of Executive Employment. **E-mail address:** resumes@bonton.com. **World Wide Web address:** http://www.bonton.com. **Description:** One of the largest department stores in America with over 70 locations. The Bon-Ton offers brand-name merchandise for men, women, children, and the home. **NOTE:** Entry-level positions are offered. **Common positions include:** Accountant; Administrative Assistant; Advertising Executive; Auditor; Branch Manager; Buyer; Chief Financial Officer; Computer Programmer; Computer Support Technician; Controller; Credit Manager; Customer Service Representative; Department Manager; Draftsperson; Financial Analyst; General Manager; Human Resources Manager; Industrial Engineer; Management Trainee; Network/Systems Administrator; Operations Manager; Planner; Project Manager; Purchasing Agent/Manager; Sales Manager; Secretary; Systems Analyst; Vice President; Wholesale and Retail Buyer. **Special programs:** Training; Summer Jobs. **Corporate headquarters location:** This location. **Other U.S. locations:** MD; MA; NJ; NY; WV. **Operations at this facility include:** Administration. **Listed on:** NASDAQ. **Stock exchange symbol:** BONT. **President/CEO:** Heywood Wilansky. **Number of employees at this location:** 500. **Number of employees nationwide:** 12,000.

BRIDGESTONE/FIRESTONE, INC.

180 Sheree Boulevard, Suite 2000, Exton PA 19341. 610/594-6181. **Contact:** Bob Pierce, Personnel Manager. **World Wide Web address:** http://www.bridgestone-firestone.com. **Description:** This location is a zone office responsible for

supporting and directing more than 250 retail stores throughout the Northeast. **Common positions include:** Automotive Mechanic; Retail Sales Worker. **Corporate headquarters location:** Nashville TN. **Other U.S. locations:** Nationwide. **Parent company:** Bridgestone Corporation. **Operations at this facility include:** Administration; Service.

CHARMING SHOPPES, INC.
450 Winks Lane, Bensalem PA 19020. 215/245-9100. **Recorded jobline:** 800/543-2562. **Contact:** Phil Brunone, Director of Human Resources. **E-mail address:** hr@charming.com. **World Wide Web address:** http://www.charmingshoppes.com. **Description:** A retail holding company. **Common positions include:** Accountant/Auditor; Administrative Assistant; Assistant Buyer; Blue-Collar Worker Supervisor; Buyer; Clerk; Computer Programmer; Department Manager; Financial Analyst; Planner; Systems Analyst; Transportation/Traffic Specialist. **Special programs:** Internships. **Corporate headquarters location:** This location. **Subsidiaries include:** Fashion Bug and Fashion Bug Plus specialize in the sale of junior, miss, and plus size merchandise. **Listed on:** NASDAQ. **Stock exchange symbol:** CHRS.

DAVID'S BRIDAL
1001 Washington Street, Conshohocken PA 19428. 610/943-5000. **Contact:** Fred Postelle, VP of Human Resources. **World Wide Web address:** http://www.davidsbridal.com. **Description:** Sells a full line of bridal merchandise including apparel and accessories. **Common positions include:** Assistant Manager; Consultant; General Manager; Store Manager; Supervisor. **Special programs:** Internships. **Corporate headquarters location:** This location. **Number of employees at this location:** 215.

DEB SHOPS, INC.
9401 Bluegrass Road, Philadelphia PA 19114. 215/676-6000. **Contact:** Ms. Pat Okun, Office Manager. **World Wide Web address:** http://www.debshops.com. **Description:** A chain of specialty apparel stores offering moderately priced, coordinated sportswear, dresses, coats, and accessories for juniors. The company operates 285 stores in 40 states. **Common positions include:** Buyer; District Manager; Regional Manager; Sales Executive; Store Manager. **Corporate headquarters location:** This location. **Other U.S. locations:** Nationwide. **Listed on:** NASDAQ. **Stock exchange symbol:**

DEBS. **Number of employees at this location:** 200. **Number of employees nationwide:** 2,500.

DURON PAINTS AND WALLCOVERINGS
711 First Avenue, King of Prussia PA 19406. 610/962-9907. **Fax:** 301/595-0435. **Contact:** Human Resources. **E-mail address:** employment@duron.com. **World Wide Web address:** http://www.duron.com. **Description:** A retailer and wholesaler of paints, wallcoverings, window treatments, and related items. **NOTE:** Mail employment correspondence to: Duron Human Resources, 10406 Tucker Street, Beltsville MD 20705-2297. **Common positions include:** Branch Manager; Management Trainee. **Operations at this facility include:** Administration; Regional Headquarters; Sales.

EDMUND INDUSTRIAL OPTICS
101 East Gloucester Pike, Barrington NJ 08007. 856/547-3488. **Fax:** 856/546-9340. **Contact:** Marisa Edmund, Personnel. **E-mail address:** medmund@edmundoptics.com. **World Wide Web address:** http://www.edmundoptics.com. **Description:** This location is a retail store. Overall, Edmund Scientific Company is a retail supplier of industrial optics, lasers, telescopes, and precision optical instruments through two mail-order catalogs. Founded in 1942. **NOTE:** Entry-level positions are offered. **Company slogan:** Bringing science into focus. **Common positions include:** Account Representative; Administrative Assistant; Computer Operator; Computer Programmer; Graphic Artist; Graphic Designer; Sales Representative; Statistician; Webmaster. **Special programs:** Internships. **Corporate headquarters location:** This location. **Other U.S. locations:** Tucson AZ. **International locations:** China; Japan; United Kingdom. **Listed on:** Privately held. **CEO:** Robert Edmund. **Facilities Manager:** Mike Reyes. **Annual sales/revenues:** $51 - $100 million. **Number of employees at this location:** 190.

JCPENNEY INC.
Oxford Valley Mall, 2300 East Lincoln Highway, Langhorne PA 19047. 215/752-5300. **Contact:** Corporate Human Resources. **E-mail address:** apply@jcpenney.com. **World Wide Web address:** http://www.jcpenney.net. **Description:** This location is the district office. Overall, JCPenney operates over 1,250 stores. Most stores carry extensive lines of women's, men's, and children's apparel, as well as cosmetics, jewelry, and home furnishings. Founded in 1913. **NOTE:** Mail resumes to: J.C. Penney Inc., Human Resources Department, BA/SF, P.O. Box 10001, Dallas TX 75301-8115. **Common positions**

include: Management Trainee. **Corporate headquarters location:** Dallas TX. **Other U.S. locations:** Nationwide. **International locations:** Chile; Mexico; Puerto Rico. **Listed on:** New York Stock Exchange. **Stock exchange symbol:** JCP. **Annual sales/revenues:** More than $100 million.

NEW YORK & COMPANY
9th and Market Streets, Gallery Market East, Philadelphia PA 19107. 215/627-2550. **Contact:** Manager. **World Wide Web address:** http://www.nyandcompany.com. **Description:** A store location of the national women's moderately priced specialty apparel store chain. **Common positions include:** Assistant Manager; Customer Service Representative; Department Manager; General Manager; Management Trainee; Operations/Production Manager. **Corporate headquarters location:** New York NY. **Parent company:** Limited, Inc. owns over 2,300 stores nationwide operating under such names as The Limited, Express, Victoria's Secret, Lane Bryant, and Size Unlimited, and also operates a mail order catalog business. **Operations at this facility include:** Sales; Service. **Listed on:** New York Stock Exchange. **Stock exchange symbol:** LTD.

PEP BOYS
3111 West Allegheny Avenue, Philadelphia PA 19132. 215/227-9000. **Contact:** Human Resources Department. **World Wide Web address:** http://www.pepboys.com. **Description:** Primarily engaged in the retail sale of a wide range of automotive parts and accessories, and the installation of automobile components and merchandise. Pep Boys operates over 660 stores in 37 states. **Common positions include:** Accountant/Auditor; Administrative Manager; Assistant Manager; Automotive Mechanic; Branch Manager; Buyer; Cashier; Claim Representative; Computer Operator; Computer Programmer; Construction Contractor; Credit Manager; Customer Service Representative; Department Manager; Economist; Financial Manager; Graphic Artist; Human Resources Manager; Market Research Analyst; Payroll Clerk; Printing Press Operator; Receptionist; Retail Sales Worker; Secretary; Wholesale and Retail Buyer. **Corporate headquarters location:** This location. **Operations at this facility include:** Administration. **Listed on:** New York Stock Exchange. **Stock exchange symbol:** PBY. **Number of employees at this location:** 600. **Number of employees nationwide:** 15,000.

RITE AID CORPORATION

30 Hunter Lane, Camp Hill PA 17011. 717/761-2633. **Contact:** Human Resources. **World Wide Web address:** http://www.riteaid.com. **Description:** Operates 550 retail drug stores in 12 states. Founded in 1939. **Common positions include:** Pharmacist. **Special programs:** Internships. **Corporate headquarters location:** This location. **Other U.S. locations:** Nationwide. **Subsidiaries include:** Payless Drug Stores. **Listed on:** New York Stock Exchange. **Stock exchange symbol:** RAD. **Annual sales/revenues:** More than $100 million. **Number of employees nationwide:** 83,000.

7-ELEVEN, INC.

2711 Easton Road, Willow Grove PA 19090. 215/672-5711. **Contact:** Human Resources. **World Wide Web address:** http://www.7-eleven.com. **Description:** This location houses administrative offices. Overall, 7-Eleven is one of the world's largest retailers, with approximately 7,000 7-Eleven convenience units in the United States and Canada. **Common positions include:** Field Consultant Trainee; Management Trainee; Merchandiser; Restaurant/Food Service Manager. **Corporate headquarters location:** Dallas TX. **Operations at this facility include:** Divisional Headquarters.

STRAWBRIDGE'S

801 Market Street, Philadelphia PA 19107. 215/829-0346. **Contact:** Human Resources Department. **World Wide Web address:** http://www.mayco.com. **Description:** Operates a chain of department stores in Pennsylvania, Delaware, and New Jersey. **NOTE:** Strawbridge's 150-hour buyers training program begins in September of each year. **Common positions include:** Accountant/Auditor; Department Manager; Management Trainee. **Special programs:** Internships. **Corporate headquarters location:** This location. **Parent company:** The May Department Stores Company. **Number of employees nationwide:** 12,000.

SUPERVALUE EASTERN REGION

P.O. Box 2261, Harrisburg PA 17105. 717/232-6821. **Contact:** Human Resources. **Description:** This location houses administrative offices. Overall, Supervalue is a full-service grocery wholesaler and retailer. As one of the largest grocery wholesalers in the Mid-Atlantic region, the company supplies more than 13,000 regional brand and 1,000 private label products. The grocery division also operates several Basics supermarkets in the metropolitan Baltimore and Washington DC areas. **Other U.S. locations:** DE; NJ; VA; WV.

TODAY'S MAN, INC.
835 Lancer Drive, Moorestown NJ 08057. 856/235-0725. **Contact:** Human Resources. **World Wide Web address:** http://www.todaysman.com. **Description:** A leading men's wear superstore specializing in tailored clothing, sportswear, and accessories. The company operates a chain of approximately 30 superstores. Today's Man carries a broad assortment of current-season brand name and private-label men's wear at discount prices. **Common positions include:** Accountant/Auditor; Advertising Clerk; Buyer; Computer Programmer; Human Resources Manager; Management Trainee; Systems Analyst; Wholesale and Retail Buyer. **Corporate headquarters location:** This location. **Other U.S. locations:** CT; DC; FL; IL; MD; NY; PA; VA. **Operations at this facility include:** Administration. **Number of employees at this location:** 200. **Number of employees nationwide:** 2,000.

URBAN OUTFITTERS
1627 Walnut Street, Philadelphia PA 19103. 215/569-3131. **Contact:** Human Resources. **World Wide Web address:** http://www.urbn.com. **Description:** A clothing and housewares retail chain. **Corporate headquarters location:** This location. **Listed on:** NASDAQ. **Stock exchange symbol:** URBN.

WAWA INC.
260 West Baltimore Pike, Wawa PA 19063. 610/358-8000. **Contact:** Personnel Director. **World Wide Web address:** http://www.wawa.com. **Description:** This location houses administrative offices. Overall, Wawa is a convenience store chain with operations throughout Pennsylvania. **Corporate headquarters location:** This location.

WEIS MARKETS, INC.
1000 South Second Street, Sunbury PA 17801. 570/286-4571. **Contact:** Mr. Jim Kessler, Director of Management and Development. **World Wide Web address:** http://www.weis.com. **Description:** Operates over 165 supermarkets. **Common positions include:** Accountant/Auditor; Buyer; Computer Programmer; Draftsperson; Management Trainee; Operations/Production Manager; Quality Control Supervisor; Store Manager. **Special programs:** Internships. **Corporate headquarters location:** This location. **Other U.S. locations:** MD; NJ; NY; VA; WV. **Operations at this facility include:** Administration; Manufacturing; Research and Development. **Listed on:** New York Stock Exchange. **Stock exchange symbol:** WMK. **Number of employees nationwide:** 19,000.

ZALLIE SUPERMARKETS
1230 Blackwood-Clementon Road, Clementon NJ 08021. 856/627-6501. **Contact:** Vice President of Human Resources. **Description:** This location houses administrative offices. Overall, Zallie Supermarkets operates a chain of six Shop-Rite supermarkets. **Corporate headquarters location:** This location.

ZANY BRAINY, INC.
2520 Renaissance Boulevard, King of Prussia PA 19406. 610/278-7800. **Contact:** Human Resources. **World Wide Web address:** http://www.zanybrainy.com. **Description:** A location of the retail store chain offering a broad range of educationally oriented children's toys and other products such as books, videotapes, audiotapes, computer software, and crafts. **Corporate headquarters location:** This location.

STONE, CLAY, GLASS, AND CONCRETE PRODUCTS

You can expect to find the following types of companies in this chapter:

Cement, Tile, Sand, and Gravel • Crushed and Broken Stone • Glass and Glass Products • Mineral Products

ANCHOR GLASS CONTAINER CORPORATION
83 Griffith Street, Salem NJ 08079. 856/935-4000. **Contact:** Human Resources Department. **World Wide Web address:** http://www.anchorglass.com. **Description:** Engaged in the manufacture and sale of a diversified line of household, hardware, and packaging products including glassware, commercial and institutional chinaware, decorative and convenience hardware, glass containers, and metal and plastic closures. Operations encompass over 20 divisions and subsidiaries with 40 plants and distribution centers located in the United States and abroad.

CROWN CORK & SEAL COMPANY, INC.
One Crown Way, Philadelphia PA 19154. 215/698-5100. **Fax:** 215/676-7245. **Contact:** Personnel. **World Wide Web address:** http://www.crowncork.com. **Description:** Founded in 1892. Crown Cork & Seal manufactures cans, plastic bottles, and metal and plastic closures, as well as machinery for the packaging industry and disposable medical devices and closures. **NOTE:** Entry-level positions are offered. **Common positions include:** Accountant; Administrative Assistant; Applications Engineer; Chemical Engineer; Chief Financial Officer; Clerical Supervisor; Database Manager; Graphic Artist; Graphic Designer; Human Resources Manager; Industrial Engineer; Manufacturing Engineer; Metallurgical Engineer; MIS Specialist; Secretary; Systems Analyst; Systems Manager; Typist/Word Processor. **Special programs:** Internships; Co-ops; Summer Jobs. **Corporate headquarters location:** This location. **International locations:** Worldwide. **Operations at this facility include:** Administration; Divisional Headquarters; Manufacturing. **Listed on:** New York Stock Exchange. **Stock exchange symbol:** CCK. **Annual sales/revenues:** More than $100 million. **Number of employees at this location:** 600. **Number of employees nationwide:** 22,000. **Number of employees worldwide:** 50,000.

EASTERN INDUSTRIES, INC.
4401 Camp Meeting Road, Suite 200, Center Valley PA 18034. 610/866-0932. **Fax:** 610/867-1886. **Contact:** Steve Sandbrook, Safety Manager. **World Wide Web address:** http://www.eastern-ind.com. **Description:** Engaged in the extraction of stone from quarries for the production of concrete, blacktop, and other building block supplies. **Parent company:** Stabler Companies Inc.

ESSROC MATERIALS INC.
3251 Bath Pike, Nazareth PA 18064. 610/837-6725. **Contact:** Human Resources Department. **World Wide Web address:** http://www.essroc.com. **Description:** Manufactures cement.

GLASS PRODUCTS INC.
P.O. Box 313, Carbondale PA 18407. 570/282-6711. **Fax:** 570/282-1382. **Contact:** Tom Zaccone, Branch Manager. **Description:** Manufactures laminated safety glass used in windows and doors. **Common positions include:** Blue-Collar Worker Supervisor; Branch Manager; Ceramics Engineer; Clerical Supervisor; Credit Manager; Customer Service Representative; Industrial Engineer; Industrial Production Manager; Management Trainee; Manufacturer's/Wholesaler's Sales Rep.; Materials Engineer; Mechanical Engineer; Metallurgical Engineer; Operations/Production Manager. **Corporate headquarters location:** Atlanta GA. **Other U.S. locations:** Nationwide. **Subsidiaries include:** AFGD Canada. **Parent company:** American Flat Glass Distributors (AFGD) specializes in architectural insulated units and custom tempering. The firm manufactures a complete line of insulated units for commercial and residential applications. The product line includes clear, tinted and reflective float glass; laminated, low-emissivity, tempered, acrylic, mirror, obscure, insulated, and polished wire glass; and a complete line of glass-handling, storage, and transportation equipment. **Operations at this facility include:** Manufacturing; Sales. **Listed on:** Privately held. **Number of employees at this location:** 75. **Number of employees nationwide:** 1,000.

HIGH CONCRETE STRUCTURES
125 Denver Road, Denver PA 17517. 717/336-9300. **Contact:** Human Resources Department. **World Wide Web address:** http://www.highconcrete.com. **Description:** Manufactures precast concrete for use by the construction industry. **Parent company:** High Industries, Inc.

HIGH INDUSTRIES, INC.
P.O. Box 10008, 1853 William Penn Way, Lancaster PA 17605-0008. 717/293-4486. **Contact:** Vincent Mizeras, Director of Human Resources. **World Wide Web address:** http://www.high.net. **Description:** Operates through several areas of business including design and construction, food services, hotel management, prestress/precast concrete products, real estate development and management, and steel fabrication. **Common positions include:** Accountant/Auditor; Architect; Civil Engineer; Computer Programmer; Customer Service Representative; Draftsperson; Hotel Manager; Human Resources Manager; Services Sales Representative; Systems Analyst. **Corporate headquarters location:** This location. **Operations at this facility include:** Administration; Manufacturing.

LWB REFRACTORIES
P.O. Box 1189, York PA 17405. 717/848-1501. **Contact:** Human Resources Manager. **World Wide Web address:** http://www.bakerref.com. **Description:** Produces refractory products consisting of such substances as dolomite and agricultural limestone. **Common positions include:** Accountant/Auditor; Administrator; Blue-Collar Worker Supervisor; Buyer; Ceramics Engineer; Chemist; Computer Programmer; Customer Service Representative; Department Manager; Draftsperson; Electrical/Electronics Engineer; Financial Analyst; Geologist/Geophysicist; Human Resources Manager; Manufacturer's/Wholesaler's Sales Rep.; Mechanical Engineer; Purchasing Agent/Manager; Systems Analyst. **Corporate headquarters location:** This location. **Operations at this facility include:** Administration; Manufacturing; Research and Development; Sales; Service.

LENOX COLLECTION
900 Wheeler Way, Langhorne PA 19047. 215/741-7670. **Contact:** Human Resources. **World Wide Web address:** http://www.lenox.com. **Description:** Manufactures crystal goblets, wine glasses, and dinnerware.

LEONE INDUSTRIES
P.O. Box 400, Bridgeton NJ 08302. 856/455-2000. **Physical address:** 443 Southeast Avenue, Bridgeton NJ 08302. **Contact:** Human Resources Department. **World Wide Web address:** http://www.leoneindustries.com. **Description:** Manufactures glass containers. **Common positions include:** Accountant/Auditor; Buyer; Customer Service Representative; Draftsperson; Electrical/Electronics Engineer; General Manager;

Industrial Engineer; Management Trainee; Mechanical Engineer; Operations Manager; Purchasing Agent/Manager; Quality Control Supervisor. **Corporate headquarters location:** This location. **Operations at this facility include:** Manufacturing.

PPG INDUSTRIES, INC.

400 Park Drive, Carlisle PA 17013. 717/486-3366. **Contact:** Human Resources Department. **World Wide Web address:** http://www.ppg.com. **Description:** This location manufactures flat glass. Overall, PPG Industries is a diversified global manufacturer supplying products for manufacturing, building, automotive, processing, and numerous other world industries. The company makes decorative and protective coatings, flat glass and fabricated glass products, continuous-strand fiberglass, and industrial and specialty chemicals. Founded in 1883. **Corporate headquarters location:** Pittsburgh PA. **International locations:** Worldwide. **Listed on:** New York Stock Exchange. **Stock exchange symbol:** PPG. **Annual sales/revenues:** More than $100 million.

PQ CORPORATION

P.O. Box 840, Valley Forge PA 19482-0840. 610/651-4200. **Physical address:** 1200 West Swedesford Road, Berwyn PA 19312-1077. **Fax:** 610/651-4435. **Contact:** Human Resources. **E-mail address:** hr@pqcorp.com. **World Wide Web address:** http://www.pqcorp.com. **Description:** Manufactures a wide range of glass products including reflective glass for automotive and highway safety use, decorative glass, and industrial glass products. **Corporate headquarters location:** This location.

WHEATON USA

1101 Wheaton Avenue, Millville NJ 08332. 856/825-1400. **Contact:** Human Resources Department. **World Wide Web address:** http://www.wheaton.com. **Description:** Manufactures glass and plastic tubes and containers used in the pharmaceutical and cosmetic industries. **Parent company:** Alcan Packaging.

TRANSPORTATION/TRAVEL

You can expect to find the following types of companies in this chapter:

Air, Railroad, and Water Transportation Services • Courier Services • Local and Interurban Passenger Transit • Ship Building and Repair • Transportation Equipment Travel Agencies • Trucking • Warehousing and Storage

AAA MID-ATLANTIC
2040 Market Street, Philadelphia PA 19103. 215/864-5000. **Fax:** 215/864-5438. **Contact:** Ron Gray, Manager of Human Resources Department. **World Wide Web address:** http://www.aaamidatlantic.com. **Description:** Provides insurance, travel, and a wide variety of services to motorists through a network of over 50 branch offices. **Common positions include:** Accountant/Auditor; Adjuster; Automotive Mechanic; Branch Manager; Claim Representative; Computer Programmer; Customer Service Representative; Financial Analyst; Human Resources Manager; Travel Agent; Underwriter/Assistant Underwriter. **Corporate headquarters location:** Heathrow FL. **Other U.S. locations:** Nationwide.

AAA MID-ATLANTIC
6400 Bustleton Avenue, Philadelphia PA 19149. 215/743-0775. **Contact:** Michelle Vandoran, Personnel. **World Wide Web address:** http://www.aaamidatlantic.com. **Description:** Provides insurance, travel, and a wide variety of services to motorists through a network of more than 50 branch offices. **Corporate headquarters location:** Heathrow FL. **Other U.S. locations:** Nationwide.

AMTRAK
30th Street Station, 2nd Floor South, Box 43, Philadelphia PA 19104. 215/349-1108. **Recorded jobline:** 215/349-1069. **Contact:** Human Resources Department. **E-mail address:** necjobs@amtrak.com. **World Wide Web address:** http://www.amtrak.com. **Description:** Manages and operates an interstate passenger rail service with connections throughout the United States. **NOTE:** This office is responsible for hiring in Philadelphia PA and Wilmington DE. **Common positions include:** Accountant/Auditor; Administrative Manager; Budget Analyst; Buyer; Civil Engineer; Claim Representative; Design Engineer; Designer; Draftsperson; Electrical/Electronics Engineer; Environmental Engineer; Human Resources Manager; Management Trainee; Mechanical

Engineer; Property and Real Estate Manager; Purchasing Agent/Manager; Reservationist; Structural Engineer; Telecommunications Manager. **Special programs:** Internships. **Operations at this facility include:** Administration; Divisional Headquarters; Regional Headquarters; Sales; Service.

B-FAST CORPORATION
660 Newtown-Yardley Road, Newtown PA 18940. 215/860-5600. **Contact:** James Affleck, Director of Human Resources. **Description:** Provides ground support services for general aviation aircraft including demand line services such as fueling, ground handling, and storage of aircraft.

CONSOLIDATED RAIL CORPORATION (CONRAIL)
2001 Market Street, Philadelphia PA 19101-1600. 215/209-5099. **Contact:** Human Resources. **World Wide Web address:** http://www.conrail.com. **Description:** A railroad company. **Corporate headquarters location:** This location.

CONTINENTAL AIRLINES CARGO FREIGHT FACILITY
Philadelphia International Airport, West PAC Building C-2, Philadelphia PA 19153. 215/492-4301. **Contact:** Human Resources. **World Wide Web address:** http://www.con.com. **Description:** Provides air transportation services.

GENERAL ELECTRIC COMPANY
6901 Elmwood Avenue, Philadelphia PA 19142. 215/726-2626. **Contact:** Joanne McGroarty, Human Resources. **World Wide Web address:** http://www.ge.com. **Description:** This location is the switchgear division, manufacturing components and parts. Overall, General Electric operates in the following areas: aircraft engines including jet engines, replacement parts, and repair services for commercial, military, executive, and commuter aircraft; appliances; broadcasting through NBC; industrial including lighting products, electrical distribution and control equipment, transportation systems products, electric motors and related products, a broad range of electrical and electronic industrial automation products, and a network of electrical supply houses; materials including plastics, ABS resins, silicones, superabrasives, and laminates; power systems including products for the generation, transmission, and distribution of electricity; technical products and systems including medical systems and equipment, as well as a full range of computer-based information and data interchange services for both internal use and external commercial and industrial customers; and capital services including consumer services, financing, and specialty

insurance. **Listed on:** New York Stock Exchange. **Stock exchange symbol:** GE. **Number of employees worldwide:** 230,000.

JEVIC TRANSPORTATION INC.

600-700 Creek Road, Delanco NJ 08075. 856/461-7111. **Contact:** Human Resources. **World Wide Web address:** http://www.jevic.com. **Description:** This location houses a dispatching center. Overall, Jevic Transportation is a trucking company providing freight services. **Corporate headquarters location:** This location.

LIBERTY TRAVEL

1737 Chestnut Street, Philadelphia PA 19103. 215/972-0200. **Contact:** Human Resources. **World Wide Web address:** http://www.libertytravel.com. **Description:** A travel agency. **Other U.S. locations:** Nationwide.

MARITRANS INC.
EASTERN OPERATIONS GROUP

2 International Plaza, Suite 335, Philadelphia PA 19113. 610/595-8000. **Contact:** Human Resources. **World Wide Web address:** http://www.maritrans.com. **Description:** Operates storage terminals. **Parent company:** Maritrans Inc. provides marine transportation for the petroleum distribution process, delivering about 10.6 billion gallons a year, and owns oil storage terminals. Maritrans offers a full line of distribution services including product exchanges, marine transportation, scheduling, terminal storage, and automated truck rack delivery systems. Marispond Inc. serves the growing international need for oil spill contingency planning and spill management in U.S. waters. This business capitalizes on Maritrans' spill response capabilities and is growing into the related areas of safety training and dry cargo contingency planning. **Corporate headquarters location:** Tampa FL.

PILOT AIR FREIGHT CORPORATION

701 B Ashland Avenue, Building 23, Suite 14, Folcroft PA 19032. 610/583-6200. **Contact:** Human Resources. **World Wide Web address:** http://www.pilotair.com. **Description:** A freight forwarding company. **Common positions include:** Blue-Collar Worker Supervisor; Customer Service Representative; Transportation/Traffic Specialist. **Corporate headquarters location:** Lima PA. **Other area locations:** Allentown PA. **Listed on:** Privately held.

PILOT AIR FREIGHT CORPORATION
744 Roble Road, Suite 110, Allentown PA 18109. 610/264-8777. **Contact:** Human Resources. **World Wide Web address:** http://www.pilotair.com. **Description:** A freight forwarding company. **Corporate headquarters location:** Lima PA. **Other area locations:** Folcroft PA. **Listed on:** Privately held.

PILOT AIR FREIGHT CORPORATION
314 North Middletown Road, P. O. Box 97, Lima PA 19037. 610/891-8100. **Contact:** Bill Morgan, Human Resources Director. **World Wide Web address:** http://www.pilotair.com. **Description:** A freight forwarding company. **Common positions include:** Accountant/Auditor; Adjuster; Claim Representative; Collector; Computer Programmer; Credit Manager; Customer Service Representative; Human Resources Manager; Investigator; Public Relations Specialist; Purchasing Agent/Manager; Quality Control Supervisor; Systems Analyst; Transportation/Traffic Specialist. **Corporate headquarters location:** This location. **Other area locations:** Allentown PA; Folcroft PA. **Operations at this facility include:** Administration. **Listed on:** Privately held. **Number of employees at this location:** 85.

SERVICE BY AIR INC.
850 Calcoon Hook Road, Sharon Hill PA 19079. 610/586-5050. **Toll-free phone:** 800/719-0001. **Fax:** 610/586-5511. **Contact:** Human Resources Department. **World Wide Web address:** http://www.servicebyair.com. **Description:** An air transportation company. **NOTE:** All resumes must indicate location of interest and be sent to: Service By Air Inc., Human Resources, 55 East Ames Court, Plainview NY 11803.

UTILITIES: ELECTRIC/GAS/WATER

You can expect to find the following types of companies in this chapter:
Gas, Electric, and Fuel Companies; Other Energy-Producing Companies •
Public Utility Holding Companies • Water Utilities

AMERICAN WATER WORKS SERVICE COMPANY
1025 Laurel Oak Road, Voorhees NJ 08043. 856/346-8200. **Contact:** Stanley Smith, Director of Personnel. **World Wide Web address:** http://www.amwater.com. **Description:** Acquires, manages, and services water companies across the country.

FIRSTENERGY CORPORATION
2800 Pottsville Pike, Reading PA 19605. 610/929-3601. **Contact:** Human Resources. **World Wide Web address:** http://www.firstenergycorp.com. **Description:** Engaged in the generation, transmission, distribution, and sale of electricity. The company provides service to a population of approximately 830,000. **Common positions include:** Accountant/Auditor; Administrator; Attorney; Blue-Collar Worker Supervisor; Buyer; Customer Service Representative; Electrical/Electronics Engineer; Forester/{ED: DELETE BREAK}Conservation Scientist; Human Resources Manager; Mechanical Engineer; Purchasing Agent/Manager. **Corporate headquarters location:** Akron OH.

PG ENERGY
One PEI Center, Wilkes-Barre PA 18711. 570/829-8600. **Contact:** Human Resources. **World Wide Web address:** http://www.pgenergy.com. **Description:** A gas utility company that serves over 154,000 customers in northeastern and central Pennsylvania. PG Energy maintains a distribution system of 2,300 miles of pipelines.

PPL CORPORATION
2 North Ninth Street, Allentown PA 18101. 610/774-5151. **Fax:** 610/774-4245. **Contact:** Cynthia J. Wukitsch, Human Resources and Development. **World Wide Web address:** http://www.pplweb.com. **Description:** An electric utility company serving 1.2 million customers in the Pennsylvania area. **Common positions include:** Accountant; Computer Programmer; Market Research Analyst; Marketing Specialist; Sales Manager; Sales Representative. **Corporate headquarters**

location: This location. **Listed on:** New York Stock Exchange. **Stock exchange symbol:** PPL. **Number of employees at this location:** 6,400.

PECO ENERGY

2301 Market Street, Philadelphia PA 19101. 215/841-4000. **Fax:** 215/841-5473. **Recorded jobline:** 215/841-4340. **Contact:** Human Resources. **E-mail address:** you@careers.peco.com. **World Wide Web address:** http://www.peco.com. **Description:** An operating utility that provides electric and gas service in southeastern Pennsylvania. Two subsidiaries own and a third subsidiary operates the Conowingo Hydroelectric Project, and one distribution subsidiary provides electric service in two counties in northeastern Maryland. **Common positions include:** Chemical Engineer; Computer Programmer; Electrical/Electronics Engineer; Mechanical Engineer; Nuclear Medicine Technologist; Systems Analyst. **Special programs:** Internships. **Corporate headquarters location:** This location. **Parent company:** Exelon. **Annual sales/revenues:** More than $100 million. **Number of employees at this location:** 9,300.

PHILADELPHIA SUBURBAN WATER COMPANY

762 West Lancaster Avenue, Bryn Mawr PA 19010-3489. 610/527-8000. **Contact:** Human Resources. **World Wide Web address:** http://www.suburbanwater.com. **Description:** A water utility company. **Parent company:** Philadelphia Suburban Corporation.

UGI CORPORATION
AMERIGAS

P.O. Box 858, Valley Forge PA 19482. 610/337-1000. **Contact:** Personnel Director. **World Wide Web address:** http://www.ugicorp.com. **Description:** A holding company. UGI's utilities segment is divided into two segments: the Gas Division is a medium-sized, local natural gas distributor serving 238,000 customers in 14 eastern and southeastern Pennsylvania counties; the Electric Division is a small electric utility serving 60,000 customers in the Wilkes-Barre area. UGI's propane segment is divided into two segments: AmeriGas and Petrolane, also a national propane marketer, of which UGI owns 35 percent. **Corporate headquarters location:** This location. **Subsidiaries include:** UGI Utilities, Inc. is a gas and electric utility located in eastern Pennsylvania. AmeriGas, Inc. is a national marketer of propane. **Listed on:** New York Stock Exchange; Philadelphia Exchange. **Stock exchange symbol:** UGI. **Number of employees nationwide:** 5,230.

MISCELLANEOUS WHOLESALING

You can expect to find the following types of companies in this chapter:

Exporters and Importers • General Wholesale Distribution Companies

ALMO CORPORATION
2709 Commerce Way, Philadelphia PA 19154. 215/698-4000.
Fax: 215/698-4080. **Contact:** Ms. Terry Vittorelli, Human Resources Director. **World Wide Web address:** http://www.almo.com. **Description:** A multiregional distributor of computer products, consumer electronics, major appliances, and specialty wire and cable. **NOTE:** Entry-level positions are offered. **Common positions include:** Accountant/Auditor; Blue-Collar Worker Supervisor; Buyer; Clerical Supervisor; Computer Programmer; Credit Manager; Customer Service Rep.; Internet Services Manager; Manufacturer's/Wholesaler's Sales Rep.; MIS Specialist; Systems Analyst. **Corporate headquarters location:** This location. **Other U.S. locations:** MA; MD; MO; WI. **Operations at this facility include:** Administration; Divisional Headquarters; Sales. **Number of employees at this location:** 90.

ANGELO BROTHERS COMPANY
12401 McNulty Road, Philadelphia PA 19154. 215/671-2000.
Fax: 215/767-3720. **Contact:** Gloria Mangini, Director of Human Resources Department. **World Wide Web address:** http://www.angelobrothers.com. **Description:** A wholesaler of light bulbs, lighting fixtures, replacement glassware, wall plates, lighting hardware, and other products. **Common positions include:** Accountant/Auditor; Adjuster; Administrative Manager; Advertising Clerk; Assistant Manager; Buyer; Clerical Supervisor; Commercial Artist; Computer Operator; Computer Programmer; Credit Clerk and Authorizer; Credit Manager; Customer Service Representative; Employee Benefits Administrator; Financial Analyst; Food and Beverage Service Worker; Human Resources Manager; Industrial Production Manager; Manufacturer's/Wholesaler's Sales Representative; Marketing Manager; Order Clerk; Purchasing Agent/Manager; Quality Control Supervisor; Receptionist; Secretary; Services Sales Representative; Stock Clerk; Systems Analyst; Truck Driver; Typist/Word Processor; Wholesale and Retail Buyer. **Corporate headquarters location:** This location. **Other U.S. locations:** Santa Fe Springs CA; Jacksonville FL; Chicago IL; Bensalem PA. **Operations at this facility include:**

Sales. **Listed on:** Privately held. **Number of employees at this location:** 125. **Number of employees nationwide:** 350.

APPLIED INDUSTRIAL TECHNOLOGIES
4350 H Street, Philadelphia PA 19124. 215/744-6330. **Contact:** Human Resources. **World Wide Web address:** http://www.appliedindustrial.com. **Description:** Distributes bearings and power transmission equipment. **Corporate headquarters location:** Cleveland OH. **Other area locations:** Statewide. **Other U.S. locations:** Nationwide. **Listed on:** New York Stock Exchange. **Stock exchange symbol:** AIT.

CREATIVE HOBBIES, INC.
900 Creek Road, Bellmawr NJ 08031-1687. 856/933-2540. **Contact:** Human Resources Department. **World Wide Web address:** http://www.creative-hobbies.com. **Description:** A wholesale distributor of hobby ceramics supplies including clay, kilns, pottery wheels, tools, glazes, and decorating supplies.

ENOVATION GRAPHIC SYSTEMS, INC.
301 Commerce Drive, Moorestown NJ 08057. 856/488-7200. **Contact:** Human Resources Department. **World Wide Web address:** http://www.enovationgraphics.com. **Description:** Distributes graphic arts equipment and systems.

GILES & RANSOME, INC.
2975 Galloway Road, Bensalem PA 19020. 215/639-4300. **Contact:** Richard Smith, Human Resources Manager. **E-mail address:** rsmith@ransome.com. **World Wide Web address:** http://www.ransome.com. **Description:** A regional distributor of Caterpillar heavy construction and industrial equipment including diesel engines and generators, construction vehicles, and material-handling equipment. **Common positions include:** Accountant/Auditor; Administrator; Blue-Collar Worker Supervisor; Branch Manager; Manufacturer's/Wholesaler's Sales Representative; Purchasing Agent/Manager. **Corporate headquarters location:** This location.

HYDRO SERVICE AND SUPPLIES, INC.
1426 Manning Boulevard, Levittown PA 19057. 215/547-0332. **Fax:** 215/547-5734. **Contact:** Human Resources. **E-mail address:** jobs@hydroservice.com. **World Wide Web address:** http://www.hydroservice.com. **Description:** Sells and services water ultrapurification laboratory equipment. **NOTE:** Mail employment correspondence to: Human Resources, P.O. Box

12197, Research Triangle Park NC 27709. **Corporate headquarters location:** Research Triangle Park NC.

IKON OFFICE SOLUTIONS

70 Valley Stream Parkway, Malvern PA 19355. 610/296-8000. **Contact:** Kathy Brodhag, Director of Human Resources. **World Wide Web address:** http://www.ikon.com. **Description:** Markets and distributes office equipment and paper products. IKON Office Solutions is one of the largest independent copier distribution networks in North America. **Common positions include:** Accountant/Auditor; Attorney; Computer Programmer; Paralegal; Systems Analyst. **Special programs:** Internships. **Corporate headquarters location:** This location. **Operations at this facility include:** Administration. **Number of employees at this location:** 225.

PEIRCE-PHELPS, INC.

2000 North 59th Street, Philadelphia PA 19131. 215/879-7000. **Contact:** Human Resources. **World Wide Web address:** http://www.peirce.com. **Description:** Distributes a variety of electrical appliances including washers, dryers, and air conditioners.

UNITED REFRIGERATION INC.

11401 Roosevelt Boulevard, Philadelphia PA 19154. 215/698-9100. **Contact:** Human Resources Department. **World Wide Web address:** http://www.uri.com. **Description:** A worldwide distributor of refrigerators, air conditioners, and heating equipment. Founded in 1947. **Corporate headquarters location:** Philadelphia PA. **Other U.S. locations:** Nationwide. **International locations:** Canada; France; United Kingdom.

INDEX OF PRIMARY EMPLOYERS

ACCOUNTING & MANAGEMENT CONSULTING

Arthur Andersen/50
Bowman & Company LLP/50
Ernst & Young LLP/50
Hay Group Inc./51
KPMG/51
Arthur D. Little, Inc./51
PricewaterhouseCoopers/52
Right Management Consultants/52
Synygy, Inc./52

ADVERTISING, MARKETING, AND PUBLIC RELATIONS

CC3 Communication Concepts/53
Davis Advertising Inc./53
R. H. Donnelley/53
Earle Palmer Brown/53
Harte-Hanks, Inc./54
Harte-Hanks Response
    Management/54
ICT Group, Inc./54
Inter-Media Marketing Solutions/54
Al Paul Lefton Company, Inc./54
LevLane Advertising/
    PR/Interactive/55
National Fulfillment Services/55
Tierney & Partners/55
Vertis/55

AEROSPACE

Hexcel Corporation/56
King Fifth Wheel Company/56
Lancaster Aero Refinishers/56
Narco Avionics/56
Smiths Industries/57
Smiths Industries Aerospace/57

APPAREL, FASHION, AND TEXTILES

Alfred Angelo, Inc./59
Bollman Hat Company/59
City Shirt Company/59
Congoleum Corporation/60
Craftex Mills, Inc./60
Dallco Industries Inc./60
Delta Wundies/60
Double-H Boot Company/61
Good Lad Apparel/61
Hutspah Shirts/61
Jones Apparel Group, Inc./61
Kleinert's Inc./62
Kraemer Textiles, Inc./62
Mannington Mills Inc./62
Pincus Brothers, Inc./62
Seton Company/62

Sure Fit Inc./63
Tama Manufacturing Company Inc./63
Valley Forge Flag Company, Inc./63
Woolrich, Inc./63

ARCHITECTURE/ CONSTRUCTION/ ENGINEERING (MISC.)

Acme Manufacturing Company/64
Allen-Sherman-Hoff/64
Berger Brothers/64
Buckley & Company, Inc./64
Cannon Sline/64
Carlisle SynTec Incorporated/65
Certainteed Corporation/65
Conestoga Wood Specialties, Inc./66
Exponent, Inc./66
FM Global/67
Fischbach and Moore Electric, Inc./67
Fluor Daniel, Inc./67
Francis, Cauffman, Foley, and
    Hoffman/68
Glasgow, Inc./68
Herman Goldner Company/68
Harsco Corporation/68
Henkels & McCoy, Inc./69
High Industries, Inc./69
Hill International/70
Honeywell Inc./70
Irwin & Leighton, Inc./70
Kawneer Company, Inc./70
Keating Building Corporation/71
Kling Lindquist/71
Lipinski Landscaping/72
M&T Company/72
MI Home Products Inc./72
James D. Morrissey, Inc./72
Overhead Door Corporation/73
Pace Resources Inc./73
Parsons Power Group Inc./73
STV Incorporated/73
R.M. Shoemaker Company/74
Toll Brothers, Inc./74
Washington Group International,
    Inc./75
Williard Inc./75
York International Corporation/75
Yorktowne, Inc./76

ARTS, ENTERTAINMENT, SPORTS, AND RECREATION

CMEinfo.COM/77
Comcast-Spectacor, LP/77
Elmwood Park Zoo/78
The Franklin Institute Science
    Museum/78
Longwood Gardens Inc./78
Penn National Race Course/78
Philadelphia Museum of Art/78

Southern Home Services/111
Suncom Industries Inc./111
Youth Advocate Program/111

CHEMICALS/RUBBER AND PLASTICS

Air Products and Chemicals, Inc./112
Airgas, Inc./112
ALCOA Flexible Packaging/112
Ashland Chemical Company/113
ATOFINA Chemicals, Inc./113
M.A. Bruder & Sons Inc./113
Consolidated Container Company/113
E.I. DuPont de Nemours
    & Company/113
Dynasil Corporation of
    America/114
FMC Corporation/114
Foamex International, Inc./115
GE Betz/115
GFC Foam Inc./116
Goodall Rubber Company/116
ICI Paints/116
Inolex Chemical Company/116
Lyondell Chemical/117
Occidental Chemical Corporation/117
PPG Industries, Inc./117
PolyOne Corporation/118
Quadrant/118
Quaker Chemical Corporation/118
Rhodia Inc./118
Rohm & Haas Company/119
Sun Chemical/General Printing
    Inc./120
Sunoco Chemicals/120
U.S. Filter Wallace & Tiernan/120
Wheaton USA/120

COMMUNICATIONS: TELECOMMUNICATIONS/ BROADCASTING

AM Communications/121
Agere Systems/121
CTI Data Solutions Inc./121
Capsule Communications/121
Comcast Corporation/122
Conestoga Enterprises, Inc./122
Denver & Ephrata Telephone and
    Telegraph Company (D&E)/122
Emcee Broadcast Products, Inc./123
Greater Philadelphia Radio Group/123
Motorola, Inc./Broadband
    Communications Sector/123
NBC 10-WCAU/124
PopVision Cable Company/124
QVC Network, Inc./124
Verizon Communications/125
WBEB-FM/125

COMPUTERS (MISC.)

Ajilon Services Inc./126
Altec Lansing Technologies, Inc./126
Astea International Inc./126
AverCom, Inc./127
Bentley Systems Inc./127
Brodart Automation/128
Computer Associates International,
    Inc./128
Computer Hardware Service Company
    (CHSC)/129
Computer Sciences Corporation/129
Comtrex Systems Corporation/129
Craden Peripherals
    Corporation/129
Cybertech Inc./130
Daisy Data Inc./130
Data-Core Systems Inc./130
Datacap Systems, Inc./130
Day-Timer, Inc./130
DecisionOne/130
Dendrite/131
eGames, Inc./131
ePlus, Inc./131
Executive Imaging Systems Inc./132
Formation, Inc./132
GE Energy Services/132
Global Sports, Inc./
    Global Sports Interactive/133
HMW Enterprises Inc./133
Hewlett-Packard Middleware/133
Institute for Scientific Information/134
Keane, Inc./134
Keystone Computer Associates/134
Maxwell Systems, Inc./134
McKessonHBOC/135
Neoware Systems, Inc./135
Oki Data Americas, Inc./136
PDS Inc. (Personnel Data Systems)/136
Pentamation Enterprise Inc./136
Peripheral Dynamics Inc. (PDI)/136
Prescient Systems, Inc./136
Primavera Systems Inc./137
Prophet 21 Inc./137
QAD Inc./137
RainMaker Software, Inc./138
SAP America, Inc./138
SCT Corporation/138
Safeguard Scientifics, Inc./138
Siemens Medical Solutions Health
    Services Corporation/139
Softmart, Inc./140
Storage Technology Corporation/140
SunGard Asset Management Systems,
    Inc./140
SunGard Data Systems Inc./
    SunGard Recovery Services/141
TENEX Systems Inc./141
Triversity Inc./141
Ulticom Inc./142
Unisys Corporation/142, 143

GMAC Mortgage Corporation/172
Independence Financial Group/172
Janney Montgomery Scott Inc.
    (JMS)/173
Parente Randolph, PC/173
Philadelphia Stock Exchange/174
Public Financial Management, Inc./174
Rittenhouse Financial Services/174
SEI Investments Company/174, 175
UBS PaineWebber Inc./175
The Vanguard Group, Inc./176

FOOD AND BEVERAGES/ AGRICULTURE

All Seasons Services/177
W. Atlee Burpee & Company/177
Campbell Soup Company/177
ConAgra Foods, Inc./178
Cutler Dairy Products, Inc./178
Friskies Pet Care Company/178
Hatfield Quality Meats Inc./178
J&J Snack Foods Corporation/178
Lehigh Valley Dairies, L.P./179
Nabisco Biscuit Company/179
New World Pasta/180
Oak Valley Farms/180
R.M. Palmer Company/180
Pepperidge Farm, Inc./180
Pepsi-Cola Company/181
Pepsi-Cola/National Brand
    Beverages Ltd./181
Snowball Foods, Inc./181
Tasty Baking Company/181
Taylor Packing Company Inc./182
U.S. Foodservice/182, 183
VeniceMaid Foods, Inc./183
Wampler Foods, Inc./183

GOVERNMENT

Internal Revenue Service/185
Pennsylvania State Civil Service
    Commission/185
U.S. Department of Defense/Defense
    Supply Center Philadelphia/185
U.S. Department of Health and Human
    Services/185
U.S. Department of the Air Force/913th
    SPTG/DPC/186
U.S. Environmental Protection Agency
    (EPA)/186
U.S. Federal Bureau of Investigation
    (FBI)/186
U.S. General Services
    Administration187

HEALTH CARE: SERVICES, EQUIPMENT, AND PRODUCTS (MISC.)

Albert Einstein Medical Center/188

Apria Healthcare Group Inc./188
Arrow International Inc./189
Barnes-Kasson County Hospital
    S.N.F./189
Belmont Center for Comprehensive
    Treatment/189
Benco Dental Company/190
Biochem Immunosystems/190
B. Braun Medical, Inc./190
B. Braun/McGaw, Inc./190
Bryn Mawr Hospital/191
Catholic Health East/191
Chester County Hospital/191
Cooper Health/192
Crozer-Chester Medical Center/192
DaVita, Inc./192
Dentsply International Inc./193
Doylestown Hospital/193
East Coast Technologies/193
Easton Hospital/193
Elwyn Inc./193
Flowers Mill Veterinary Hospital
    P.C./194
Fox Chase Cancer Center/194
Frankford Hospital/194
Geisinger Medical Center/194
Genesis Health Ventures, Inc./195
Graduate Hospital/195
HCR ManorCare Health Services/195-
    199
Hanover Hospital/200
Holy Redeemer Hospital/200
Holy Spirit Health System/200
Integrated Health
    Services/Broomall/201
Integrated Health
    Services/Whitemarsh/201
Jennersville Regional Hospital/201
Lankenau Hospital/201
Luzerne Optical Laboratories, Inc./202
MEDIQ/PRN/202
Memorial Hospital/202
Mercy Fitzgerald Hospital/203
Mercy Hospital of Philadelphia/203
Methodist Hospital/203
Nazareth Hospital/203
Neighborcare/204
NovaCare Rehabilitation/204
Nutri/System L.P./204
Parkview Hospital/205
Pennsylvania Hospital/205
Perfecseal/205
Philadelphia Center for Aquatic
    Rehabilitation/206
Philhaven Behavioral Health
    Services/206
Pottstown Memorial Medical
    Center/206
The Pottsville Hospital and Warne
    Clinic/207
Premier Medical Products/207
Presbyterian Medical Center/207
Regina Nursing Center/208

LEGAL SERVICES

HOTELS AND RESTAURANTS

INSURANCE

MANUFACTURING: MISCELLANEOUS CONSUMER

MANUFACTURING: MISCELLANEOUS INDUSTRIAL

MINING/GAS/PETROLEUM/ ENERGY RELATED

PAPER AND WOOD PRODUCTS

PRINTING AND PUBLISHING

Adams Cover Letter Almanac

The *Adams Cover Letter Almanac* is the most detailed cover letter resource in print, containing 600 cover letters used by real people to win real jobs. It features complete information on all types of letters, including networking, "cold," broadcast, and follow-up. In addition to advice on how to avoid fatal cover letter mistakes, the book includes strategies for people changing careers, relocating, recovering from layoff, and more. $5^1/_2$" x $8^1/_2$", 738 pages, paperback, $12.95. ISBN: 1-55850-497-4.

Adams Cover Letter Almanac & Disk

Writing cover letters has never been easier! *FastLetter*™ software includes: a choice of dynamic opening sentences, effective following paragraphs, and sure-fire closings; a complete word processing program so you can customize your letter in any way you choose; and a tutorial that shows you how to make your cover letter terrific. Windows compatible. $5^1/_2$" x $8^1/_2$", 738 pages, *FastLetter*™ software included (one $3^1/_2$" disk), trade paperback, $19.95. ISBN: 1-55850-619-5.

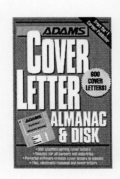

Adams Resume Almanac

This almanac features detailed information on resume development and layout, a review of the pros and cons of various formats, an exhaustive look at the strategies that will definitely get a resume noticed, and 600 sample resumes in dozens of career categories. *Adams Resume Almanac* is the most comprehensive, thoroughly researched resume guide ever published. $5^1/_2$" x $8^1/_2$", 770 pages, paperback, $12.95. ISBN: 1-55850-358-7.

Adams Resume Almanac and Disk

Create a powerful resume in minutes! *FastResume*™ software includes: a full range of resume styles and formats; ready-to-use action phrases that highlight your skills and experience; a tutorial that shows you how to make any resume terrific; and a full word processor with ready-made layout styles. Windows compatible. $5^1/_2$" x $8^1/_2$", 770 pages, *FastResume*™ software included (one $3^1/_2$" disk), trade paperback, $19.95. ISBN: 1-55850-618-7.

Visit our Web site at adamsmedia.com

THE DANCING CLOCK

And Other Childhood Memories

Helen Harris Perlman

Published in 1989 by
Academy Chicago Publishers
213 West Institute Place
Chicago, Illinois 60610

Portions of this volume have been published previously and are reprinted
here by permission of the magazines in which they first appeared:

> "Twelfth Summer" was originally published in *The New
> Yorker*, September 22, 1951. Reprinted by permis-
> sion; © 1951, 1979 The New Yorker Magazine, Inc.
> "The Persistence of Things Past" and "I Was Charlie Chap-
> lin's Wife" were first published in *Columbia*, the mag-
> azine of Columbia University, December, 1981 and
> December, 1984 respectively.
> "The sketches now called "I Was A *Good* Girl", "You Have
> Broken A Ten Commandment" and "The Patriot"
> previously appeared in somewhat different form as a
> trilogy entitled "Small Crimes and Afterthoughts" in
> *The University of Chicago Magazine*, January/February,
> 1973. Copyright 1973, *The University of Chicago Maga-
> zine*. Reprinted by permission.

The epigraph from the book, *Next-To-Last Things*, Copyright © 1985 by
Stanley Kunitz is reprinted by permission of the Atlantic Monthly Press
and courtesy of the author.

Printed and bound in the USA

Library of Congress Cataloging-in-Publication Data

Perlman, Helen Harris.
    The dancing clock and other childhood memories/by Helen Harris
Perlman.
        p. cm.
    ISBN 0-89733-343-8: $17.95
    1. Perlman, Helen Harris—Childhood and youth. 2. Social
workers—United States—Biography. I. Title.
HV40.32.P47A3 1989
361.3'2'092—dc20
    [B]   89-17803
                                                          CIP

ACKNOWLEDGEMENTS

— To each of you, my many kin and kith, who over the years or on a single day inhabited my personal world and enriched my life;

— to those cherished friends and relatives, too numerous to name, and those audiences at my occasional readings whose swift empathic responsiveness fueled my belief that I was touching well-springs within them;

— to those publishers who permitted reprintings: *The New Yorker, Columbia University Magazine, The University of Chicago Magazine;*

— to poet Stanley Kunitz, who allowed me to use his expression of my theme; to Glenn Miller, Chief Librarian of Chicago's Institute for Psychoanalysis, who not only provided me with a formidable bibliography but came up happily with this book's title; to Professor Sheldon Tobin whose work on aged peoples' memories led me to my further inquiries;

— to those dedicated librarians at the University of Chicago who kindly helped a little old lady to reach up to the top and stoop down to the bottom shelves in that thick forest called "the stacks";

— again, my heart-felt gratitude.

". . . no one can free himself from his childhood without first generously occupying himself with it," said Jung, as quoted by the poet Stanley Kunitz. To which Kunitz adds, ". . . the object is not so much to cut off from one's past as to learn how to live with the child you were."

—Stanley Kunitz, *Next-To-Last Things* (1985)

Contents

I

Program Notes

I WAS ALL but flung into what became this book when I was brought up short by an act of mine that was totally out-of-place, of time, and incongruent with my reality. After I had laughed at myself and told my story at several small dinner parties where everyone laughed with (or was it *at*?) me, I was persuaded that it might be entertaining and evocative for others. I sent the account to one of my favorite "little magazines" and its publication brought me a small stream of letters from readers who, like my dinner companions, in a combination of rue and laughter, told of some similar experiences of their own.

Spurred by these responses I have, over the past few years, given readings and commentaries on some of the sketches that appear in this book. The swift, emotionally charged, empathic responses from my hearers encouraged me to continue my explorations. Some listeners and letter-writers spoke of the memories roused in them that, while different, of course, in detail, were like mine in meaning; or they spoke of their occasional sense of déja vu—of having "seen or been here before"—or of asking themselves, after some inter-personal encounter, "Now, what made me say—or do—that?" Some spoke of their efforts but inability to capture the elusive "happening" associated with certain sensory stimuli—and so on. They stimulated me to think upon the mysteries and significance of personal memories, especially those of early childhood, and of their often still-potent powers. I took to re-examining notes of childhood experiences and emotional responses that, in fits and starts, or in sporadic detail, I had set down on paper over the years.

Since I was about eight, when I carefully pencilled my first "love poem"* and was rewarded by family praise and embraces and requests for "readings", I have loved to write.

Don't turn away yet. I know many people who hate to write. Literate and intellectually competent as they are, there is something in them that blocks the transfer of thought to paper or makes it a burden. How well I understand that! There is nothing which shakes the confidence as seeing what flamed in the mind turn dead ashen on the page. So I do not hold

---

*About Love

I have an Uncle Louis,
I love him, oh you bet!
Whenever he is lonesome
I say to him, "Don't fret—
'Cause you know I love you!"
And then you just should see—
Why we just hug each other,
My Uncle Lou and me!

"loving to write" as having any special virtue except, perhaps, that of courage.

Writing, for me, has had several purposes. It is like talking to yourself, but in a socially acceptable way; that is, you will not be put into the booby hatch for doing it. Long before the concept of the "observing ego" had been put forward, I knew that writing something up (or down) provided me with a little distance from what was sometimes a tumble of thought and feeling. I was intrigued, if mystified, by the discovery that some part of me could look at and govern another part of the same me. Later in life I came on the statement of some scholar who said he could not know what he thought until he wrote it down — and I have since been grateful to him for justifying my compulsion.

Often, for me, writing has served as a kind of catharsis; it gets things "out of my system" and provides perspective. (Thus I pray that in whatever after-life abode I am assigned to, there will be plenty of lined, yellow pads available). I started with personal explosions — as with my love for Uncle Louis or a diary entry such as "Mama was mad as a wet hen all day and scolded me *for nothing!*" But I went forward, more or less, to fantasies and fairy tales, which I soon saw as transparent plagiarisms of Anderson and the Grimms. On further to pensées, which earned me high grades in college, but that I later found, to my dismay, had been better thought and expressed by scores of thinkers over hundreds of years. Along with these were scattered jottings of occurrences and encounters in my everyday pre-adult life, set down in some effort to understand myself and my intimates, or to record my discovery that what had once seemed to be vitally important had become rather trivial, or that what once felt like a disaster seemed now to be half-comic. And to find, in retrospect, what achingly vulnerable creatures most of us are in our tender years.

Once in a while, when I could find the breathing space, I'd fashion an incident into a form that might be read by others—my family, or friends, or unknown readers. About half of the "scenes of childhood" included here have been published in one place or another.

"Are they all true?" I have been asked. Yes. They are as true as the mind of a two-year-old or six-year-old or sixteen-year-old understood them to be. However, because of my "remembering family" I have been able, over the years, to corroborate many of the unrecorded details with family members and others.

One further note on veracity: the names of a few people who have been presented in an unfavorable way have been changed. In the one instance where the name "Helen" seemed essential I have changed a few possibly identifying but non-essential details.

My selection of this particular group of rememberings was determined in large part by their resemblance to problems (though not details) common to many childhoods. These sketches have to do with rivalry, awareness of what is held to be "good" or "bad", right or wrong, of shock to the self-image, the loss of illusion, the inner conflicts about hating and loving, the life-stage-related meanings of death—and so on. It must have been a person with what my mother called a "good forgetery" who saw childhood as a time of innocence and pure pleasure, as an Eden, pre-serpent, that is. The child you yourself were, the children you may be rearing, teaching, helping with one or more of the troubles or needs that occur in childhood may find its counterpart here.

I focus on pre-adult memories because it is in our early years that we are most impressionable, most permeable. Our feelings are close to the surface; our skins and souls are most closely connected. (A four-year-old niece of mine, years ago, put it most pointedly. She was being provocatively obnoxious, and after several warnings from her mother she was given a light swat on her backside. She burst into tears. "Why are you making such a fuss about such a little spank?" asked her mother. "Because," she bawled, "You have hurt my *feelings!*")

Two sections of this book have been written during the past few years: the one on my background, "The Dancing Clock and Other Characters," may in part explain the visual and auditory retention I seem either to have inherited or to have been inoculated with. (Blessing or curse? I haven't yet decided.) The other section, "Musings", carries the burden of the ruminations and speculations I have turned over in my mind that touch on many of the yet-to-be-explored enigmas of one aspect of human mental functions. I set them before you as food for your speculations, perhaps informal, perhaps leading to some formalized research; at the least for the fun of exploring a relatively obscure but universal human phenomenon.

Perhaps what follows might call forth some echoes and resonances in you. Perhaps, along with moments of nostalgia, you may gain some fresh insights by the reunion with yourself when young. Herewith, then, a kind of book of coupons that will admit you into the small but complex world of childhood—mine and yours.

II

The Dancing Clock and Other Characters

NOW ABOUT MY daily surround—my "re-membering" family. It was to my mother's family that we were most closely attached, physically and temperamentally and in many other ways, and they were "rememberers." Somehow their yesterdays were as alive for them as were their this day's experiences. Whether in the swift shuttling of their talk together or in their quiet pauses, "remember when" or "that reminds me of—" punctuated their recountings or discussions. Validly or not, I attribute this habitual looking back in its connection with the immediate present to the fact that my mother's family had lived in the south, mostly Atlanta, Georgia, in the late nineteenth and early twentieth century, absorbing its oral tradition. All over that still-weary country in which my mother and her siblings grew up, well past the Reconstruction Period, there seemed to have lingered a kind of nostalgia for the simpler, more sensuous life of earlier days.

What was there to do on those quiet, fragrant

summer evenings other than sit together on the "verandah", as my grandfather insistently called what we
in Minnesota later named "the front porch"? Work and
school lessons done, what but to talk together about
what you had read or seen or heard or said; and then
someone would be reminded of a like past occasion or
incident to be argued or laughed over or pondered
upon. Remember? There were few other diversions in
those days—no movies, or TV or radios, no automobiles (except among the few rash rich). Kerosene
lamps and flickering gas mantles offered limited reading light for even avid readers. And so they talked
together about this day and their shared pasts, parents
and children and friends who occasionally came by,
sharing their thoughts and feelings and doings, their
amusements and their worries and their hopes, bound
together by their past and present loyalty to one
another.

Annie, my mother, was the oldest of six children
of Joseph and Hia-Kaylia. (Her younger brother, David, used to remind her that poor Uncle Willie had
been born first, but since he had died at the tender age
of three weeks he didn't count. At which my grandmother, Hia-Kaylia, in high indignation would reiter-
ate that she still missed him.) Except for the youngest
child, Marie, who entered high school when the family moved to St. Paul, the five other children were
schooled in the Boys' or the Girls' High Schools of
Atlanta. Theirs was a fairly rigorous program, with a
curriculum shaped by the expectation that it was a
preparation for college. Latin and Greek were required for boys. For girls, in the then prevalent acceptance of their natural female limitations or their antici-
pated destinies, French was substituted for Greek.

Upon her graduation, Annie was offered the chance for a scholarship at Vassar, but her father decreed that high school was enough for a girl. More relevant, probably, was the fact that he had three sons coming up who had to be sent through college. Which indeed they were. Uncle Louis became a well-known lawyer, whose extensive pro bono work probably involved him more deeply than that by which he made his living; Uncle Beb became an outstanding pediatrician; Uncle David a journalist, and humorist-columnist. Aunt Rachel undertook the gruelling training and courses, newly established, to qualify as a professionally registered nurse; and Aunt Marie, on graduation from college, became a medical social worker, one of the first who had had some advanced training.

Because their mother, Hia-Kaylia, was frequently in "poor health" (vigorously doctored for vaguely diagnosed conditions), Annie had become the "mother-person" in the family. Quick, bright, warm, witty, an avid reader, a good conversationalist and responsive listener, she was adored by her parents and siblings as the center around whom they revolved, even after her marriage that drew her to live far away, in what my grandfather dryly referred to as "the wild Indian Minnesota". One by one Annie's brothers and sisters chose to go north for their college and professional training and to be near to their Annie. When only their youngest child, Marie, was left at home, Joseph and Hia-Kaylia reluctantly pulled up their roots in Atlanta and came to live in St. Paul, reunited with us and also with their many relatives who lived within easy reach by horse and buggy or streetcar.

But I run ahead of myself. When Annie was in her early twenties, still mothering Joseph's and Hia-

Kaylia's brood, she was invited by a covey of cousins who had settled in St. Paul, Minnesota, to come for a visit. There she met Eliezer (called Lazer, for short), a handsome, debonair young man who had been persuaded several years earlier to leave New York and come to work in the rapidly growing manufacture of leather-wool-fur outdoor work-wear in which one of his cousins was becoming a highly successful entrepreneur. To no one's surprise, and to the pleasure of relatives both in St. Paul and in Atlanta (and, I daresay, to the smug satisfaction of the secretly scheming matchmakers), Annie and Lazer at once liked, and then loved one another. Within the year, they were married in Georgia, settled in St. Paul, and in the second year of their marriage they became parents—mine.

If the preceding paragraph burgeons with cousins to be "reckoned up by dozens" it is simply because that was—and is—the case. Annie and Lazer, a.k.a. Mama and Papa, were themselves first cousins who had never seen nor met each other before. Their fathers—who became my grandfathers—were brothers, two of the seven sons and one daughter of my grandparents, Abraham and Maryasha.

For the most part, within the family these complex inter-relationships became a subject of fun, teasing, jocularity. If Mama and Papa had had an argument, say, Papa would instruct me or Sonny to "Go tell your cousin, Annie, that I've gone down to the store". Sonny and I found these dual roles hilarious, especially when we figured out that he and I were only second cousins. Then, I found that I could make an indelible impression on any of my playmates by revealing to them that my mother or father was "really my cousin". There would be a look of complete incredulity, and an expostulation of "That *can't be!*" I doubt that any of them knew that marriage between first cousins was considered nothing short of incest in Minnesota. However, since Papa and Mama were married in Georgia, which clung to the British tradition of intra-familial marriage as a means to consolidate property (whether or not, as in our case, property was on the scarce side), I felt secure and only occasionally mischievous.

All eight children of Abraham and Maryasha emigrated to America at different times and under different circumstances. My grandfather Moses, (my father's father) for instance, had come to discover America when his three sons were young children. He had been so appalled by the living conditions among his acquaintances in New York's Lower East Side that he bought a return trip ticket back to Russia where he and his Blooma, owners of a feed and grain store, led a relatively comfortable life. Later, their three sons each came to America on his own, Lazer against their wishes, since he was scarcely fifteen years old. He went to work as a machine operator in a sweat shop, but, he always added, "I *lived* in the evenings", entranced by theater, music halls and the cafes where the so-called intelligensia gathered. In his early twenties he was lured from New York to St. Paul to become foreman and later a manager in his cousin's factory.

When Grandfather Moses and Blooma returned to the United States in 1905, they came as broken people, old beyond their years. In the plague of pogroms during that period, their lives had somehow been spared but their house had been looted, their store burned to the ground. Blooma, once a vivacious, dynamic woman, had suffered several strokes that left her with one dragging leg and a useless arm. Moses and Blooma were happy to make a small home for themselves in St. Paul where their Lazer and daughter-in-law/niece, Annie, welcomed them warmly and were about to present them with their longed-for first grandchild. Moreover, Moses' several brothers, nephews, nieces, cousins, etc., etc., made them welcome. (Their other two sons, Elia and Bernard, had chosen the west coast as their place of settlement.)

There was scarcely a day when Grandmother Blooma did not come flying (on foot), dragging that all but useless left leg, carrying a little brown paper bag full of chocolate marshmallow cookies and penny candies for me and Sonny. I think my first awareness of guilt was at about three or four when, hanging on our gate, awaiting Grandmother, I realized that I was more eager for the little brown bag than for her.

It was probably his brother Moses' appraisal of the miseries of life in New York that influenced Joseph (my mother's father) to make his way down the southern countryside—Pack on his back? Bony horse and rickety cart? I never had the sense to ask—to settle, finally, with his Hia-Kaylia and raise their family in Atlanta. There he became a "jobber", rescued from intellectual desperation by his own continuous study of Hebraic texts and the stimulation provided him by his bright, apt children. Once, in desperate pursuit of his dream of owning and working a farm he bought many acres of Georgia pineland at less than a song, in those depressed post-Civil War days, and it had become a sly family joke that he had sold it at an "immense profit" of about twenty cents per acre over what he had paid for it. (But maybe that was a made-up story by Uncle David whose Puckish spirit sometimes overcame his veracity.) Hia-Kaylia was not sorry—the life of a farm-wife would surely make her sick, she had threatened, and besides, how would the children get an education? So Grandfather Joseph took refuge in his heavy leather-bound tomes.

When Lazer married Annie, he was somehow embraced and drawn in as if he were a son and brother rather than an "in-law". He himself felt more connected temperamentally with the vibrant, openly expressive climate of Annie's family than with what had been his own. He was appreciated for his own attractive, if modest, talents—a grace of carriage, a resonant tenor voice—untrained but true—a nimble dancer, a lively sense of humor. He was a romantic addict of opera (it was something that he could never believe: that his Annie found opera "one of the most ridiculous kinds of theater").

He gladly joined in the dissection of political and utopian schemes that his student brothers-in-law were free to argue over. Himself quiet and reserved, he was always an intensely interested and occasionally active participant in the discussions that went on, wherever there was remembering, telling, listening and debating (amiably or hotly) over politics, poetry, philosophy, personal or public behaviors that were judged right or wrong. . . . Who was the greater statesman—Thomas Jefferson or Abraham Lincoln or, for that matter, Jefferson Davis? Which was the most workable economic system—Henry George's Single Tax or what my father vaguely outlined as that of "democratic socialism"? Who would last longest as an author—Jack London? Upton Sinclair? Dreiser?

Thus my early childhood was lived in a kind of blooming buzz of intertwined relationships. Somehow we were as if fused by our common heritage. We understood one another, often all but wordlessly, but words were always at the ready. It was a high-spirited, deeply loving, densely populated small world we inhabited, and while small may or may not be beautiful, it gave a child a sense that it was knowable, predictable, safe even in a brief storm, manageable—maybe even conquerable.

Annie and Lazer had five children. I was their first; Sonny, (as we called him until he went off to college bearing the weighty name of our great-grandfather, Abraham Jacob) intruded upon my hegemony when I was two and a half; three years later came a baby girl who died of a combination of scarlet fever and diphtheria just as we were about to celebrate her first birthday. Two little sisters were later born, Essie, when I was nine, and Judy, when I was twelve. There were, thus, two units of children—Sonny and I formed a twosome, Essie and Judy another.

Sonny and I were passionately attached to each other in all the classically conflicted ways that close sibling-ship involves: loving and hating, with and against each other, now allied against common enemies, now enemies against one another. For reasons I do not fully understand, we seem to have been made greedy not by a scarcity of love and attention, but rather by a surfeit of doting from our many nourishing "others". However, as we grew into adolescence, we both found many sources of affection and interest and pleasure outside the embracing circles of family life, and then, àt last, we became united in a goodly sustaining friendship. Our territorial imperatives were not the same any longer, and we found that we actually liked and understood one another.

As the first grandchild of four adoring grand-parents, first niece of five uncles and aunts, first-born of the cherished Annie and Lazer, I was embraced into the composite heart of the family, loved and indulged as a "little pitcher with big ears." I listened avidly to understand what was being talked about, interrupting so often to get explanations that my father began to tease me. "Whoa! Back!" he'd cry (in those horse and buggy days), "Here comes Miss Buttinsky!" He'd tease about my curiosity. "Don't ever tell Helen a joke," he'd advise. "At its end she always wants to know, 'So then what did the *other* person do?'" Every-one would laugh, but since it was clearly affectionate laughter, I didn't mind. Now I more than half-suspect that I began to relish and exploit this role of interlocu-tor in the weave of talk.

With my little sisters I had no rivalries. Rather I felt a kind of benign warmth, a once-removed pleasure in them, "once-removed" because when they inter-fered with my self-centered pursuits I could just turn them back to "where they came from".

Both were responsive, pink-and-white and gold-en-haired little ones, Essie quick to laughter and tears, Judy a compact little soul of wide-eyed observation. My memories of their babyhood are scant; they never figured as dramatis personae in what were crucial moments of my apparently increasing self-centered involvements with school and friends. When we came into adulthood we rediscovered one another, almost as if we were the same age, each involved with schooling and boyfriends, then marriages and children, with the deaths of our grandparents and the heart-aching signs of the declining vigor of our own Annie and Lazer. Then we came close together, sharing our pleasures and hurts, finding that we genuinely enjoyed as well as loved one another, that we thought and felt and understood people and happenings in astonishingly like ways.

Of their childhoods I recall only fragments, off-to-the-side moments. (I forgive myself in part because I left home at twenty, on graduation from college, when Essie was only eleven and Judy eight.) One memory I hold dear: I was due at a dress rehearsal of a play at school. A storm blew up with torrential rain; no weather to walk in, and I began to fume at fate. How would I get to the theater? Essie, seven years old, is sitting on the floor, singing to herself as she gently lays out her families of paper dolls. Then she lifts up her rosy-sunny face to me, and pipes, "Into each life *some* rain must fall!" I all but melted away.

One of Judy's first words was my name. To our amused incredulity she heard it as "Genung-genung". I corrected her over and over again — "Hel-len". Fastening her luminous green eyes on my lips she said, carefully, "Genung-genung". Decades later our guide on the island of Bali, where my husband and I were visiting, pointed to a mountain in the distance, a dead volcano. "Its name," he said, "is Genung." I was startled with disbelief. Now, Judy-luv, whatever were you doing in Bali in that previous incarnation of yours? — in which I do not believe for a moment!

Somehow now in no logical connection, there rises in my mind the memory of a languid summer evening's on-the-porch session after suppertime. On the lazy swing and a couple of wicker chairs are my parents, my uncles David and Louis, my aunt Rachel and I—about eight years old. Where Sonny is I can't recall—maybe already bedded, maybe tricycling around in the nearby empty lot.

"*Hot!*" says Aunt Rachel, waving a palm-leaf fan at herself. She is in her first year of what she calls her "slavery" in a newly established hospital program for the training of "professional nurses". Thus far she has mostly had to wash floors and carry bedpans—at least as she tells it. She has just had us "in stitches" because today when a Swedish patient had urgently asked her for a urinal she had brought him the *Minneapolis Journal;* and he had called her an idiot.

"Reminds me of when Papa pushed us all off onto that awful train to get us out of Atlanta because of the yellow fever epidemic," she goes on. "Off to Brunswick. Remember? That train must have stood on the tracks in the sun for weeks, just heating up. Open the windows and cinders and sooty smoke flew in all over us. Mama was crying, the straw seats were sticky, as if they'd been sweating, our best clothes were stuck to their varnish. I declare that was the hottest I've ever been in all my born days!"

Uncle Louis says he remembers.

"I don't," says Uncle David. "I was in my mama's stomach."

"David!" cries Aunt Rachel, rolling her eyes in my direction, and then collapsing into a giggle fit.

"What I remember about hot," says Uncle Louis, "is when Sammy Whatsisname came courtin' Annie, and she flew into the hall closet and hid with all the winter things and camphor balls, and when she finally came out, after Sammy'd gone, she almost fainted dead with suffocation."

Papa says, "Annie, you're blushing."

Mama protests, laughing. "Ridiculous! No such thing! I don't recall that *at all!*"

Silence, as my father and Uncle Louis smile at each other, knowingly. Someone then wonders what ever became of Sammy. Nobody knows.

Now Uncle David: "He was a mighty fine declaimer!" I already knew that "declaiming" was one of the major sports at the Boys' High School, and that my uncles were mighty fine declaimers too. From them I first heard of Patrick Henry, Elbert Hubbard's "A Message to Garcia" and the names of Clay and Calhoun and other southern statesmen whose orations apparently nourished and stirred the souls of the exhausted South.

"*Do* Patrick Henry, Uncle David," I coax. Pipe out of his mouth, he happily clears his throat, at which my mother interrupts to wonder aloud if we shouldn't have some cold lemonade first—that is, if there's anything left of the fifty pounds of ice the iceman lugged in yesterday. She asks me to go see, and to look-see if the water-catching basin under the icebox needs emptying. I hurry back, breathlessly, so as not to miss anything, and report everything's fine.

Aunt Rachel is glowering at Uncle David. He slowly removes his pipe again. "My good woman," he says to her, "just because you're a nurse—or trying to *be* one—doesn't mean you know everything about everything." Then he adds, "As for me, give me liberty or give me death!" We all laugh, including Aunt

Rachel, although she flaps a deprecating hand at her younger brother.

Now—why do I recall that utterly trivial, mundane scene? What was its meaning, its emotional content or import? I can only guess. Was it Uncle David crouching in his Mama's stomach? Obviously Aunt Rachel had been shocked. I cannot remember whether at eight I knew about babies' early lodgings, though I do know that it was many years later before I began to wonder how they ever got *in* there, not to speak of how they ever got *out*. But Uncle David? It was hard to imagine him—stocky, ruddy, lighting and relighting his smelly pipe—squinched into baby size and sitting inside my little grandmother.

Or was it that for the first time it dawned on me that my mother had had some sort of life before she married my father, that she had had another "beau"? Afterwards I did some thinking about Sammy Whatsisname, and wondered what would have happened if Mama had married him. What would *I* be like? Would I be *me?* Or maybe I wouldn't *be* at all! That was a discombobulating thought if ever there was one! But it was a fruitless sort of wondering, so I settled for the way things were—secure, predictable.

The "feel" I have of that carefree summertime talk is that of a comfortable togetherness, of my being let in on things that had happened, trivial as they were, before I was even born; a sense of belonging and of connection with a past, and of the pleasure of shared affectionate teasing and laughing together with "my grownups".

Is that enough to retain a memory? Or were other things said, or implied, or inferred that I pushed out of consciousness? If so, why is the feeling that permeates its recall one of security and bonding? Yet to be fathomed. . . .

    ✍   ✍   ✍

I have many far earlier memories that raise questions to intrigue me as I seek to understand the phenomena of human beings' retaining, retrieving and refashioning, consciously or unconsciously, the content and possible meanings of their memories. The two I record here raise some of the same questions as a number of others you will find in "Scenes of Childhood" to come.

My earliest memory is of the dancing clock. I was exactly two and a half years old. It became a recurring image which, until I was twelve, I had assumed to have been a dream. Until one evening when Uncle Louis was having supper with us, he suddenly commented that he'd had "a really crazy dream" the previous night. Mama and Papa murmured their awareness of how crazy dreams can be, and I chimed in to say I'd had an odd dream long ago that often popped into my mind, especially when I watched dancers or was myself either dancing or feeling happy. It was of a big-faced clock, dancing on long red-stockinged legs in front of a red velvet curtain.

Papa threw back his head and laughed. That was no dream, he said. It was real. He told then, turning to Mama for verification, of his having bought tickets for himself and her to see Victor Herbert's *Babes in Toyland.* At the last minute she decided she could not go. The theater would be sweltering (it was July, when the New York shows would "take to the road"), she was very tired, she could not think of wearing the coat she had planned to wear. Would he please take Helen instead? (Note: I was twelve years old when this story was told. Even then, nothing was said of the fact that Mama had been eight months pregnant—which is how I date my memory—nor, of course, that properly-married women were careful to conceal the evidence of their having had sex with their husbands—thus the coat on a hot July night.)

Filled with delight, I went with Papa. In an entr'acte there came out in front of the lowered red velvet curtain a big-faced clock on nimble red legs and to the orchestra's lilting music it danced, soft-shoe, joyously.

I became so excited, said Papa, that I pushed my way out into the aisle and danced with the clock. The audience around us laughed and applauded me. Of none of this do I have any image or consciousness— only of my enraptured experience of the dancing clock. I had later assumed that it had been part of a happy dream.

I've puzzled over the meaning of that memory fragment many times. Freud's speculation was that earliest memories are "screens" by which to hide unacceptable events and apperceptions. I do not find that applicable here. How, in a household where everything was talked about, except what went on between the umbilicus and the knees, would a two-and-a-half-year-old suspect that either a baby was to come or that it was a product of a forbidden activity? Moreover, the experience was for me one of sheer elation—and it rose up in my mind whenever I felt transported with pleasure.

My second earliest memory is so obvious and

commonplace as to scarcely warrant telling. It too poses some as-yet-unanswered questions.

It took place one month after the dancing clock. I had been brought by Papa to spend the night with his parents, which I had done several times before, to my pleasure. They yielded to my every wish, including stuffing me with those "boughten" chocolate marsh-mallow cookies.

In the morning Grandmother Blooma and I started to walk back home. She had given me a big orange, but after several blocks I found it too heavy, and thrust it at her. No, she said, she could not carry anything. Not on the Sabbath. Someone named God would not like it if she worked or fetched and carried on the day He decreed as "holy". I thought of this years later, after I'd started Sunday school: that I should have explained to her that God really meant that you should not be a slave, or that you were not supposed to carry big blocks of stone to build the pyramids; but I didn't realize that at two-and-a-half. Too bad!—all I under-stood was that she was being very mean to me.

We were walking on a bridge across the Missis-sippi River. Its sidewalk was made of wooden planks, and if you stooped down you could see between the cracks to the flowing river far below. At her refusal I began to stamp my feet in a dance of rage, and the planks rumbled ominously. But Grandmother only laughed, and hugged me with her one good arm and said if I broke the bridge down we'd both fall into the river. So I stopped, and continued with that hated orange, whining all the way home.

When we got there I was dumbfounded. My Mama was in bed cradling a baby in her arms. End of memory.

Some years later I was told that I had demanded that Mama "send it right home!" And that I threw the orange in the general direction of the baby. Of this I have no recall, nor of anything that happened afterwards. Why, I wonder? Was the trauma so overwhelming that it took over the whole of me? That it absorbed all the psychic energy and resources that an as-yet-underdeveloped ego could muster?

Except to be deplored, sibling rivalry, as ancient and open as Cain and Abel, Jacob and Esau, Joseph and his brethren, had scarcely been dealt with. "A big sister" (but I didn't *want* to be big!) "should *love* her baby brother," I was reminded now and then. But the fact was I had already learned that being a "good girl" was usually fondly and gratifyingly rewarded. So I suppose I tried. Of which more anon. . . .

III

Scenes of Childhood

1. The Persistence of Things Past: *Unfinished Business*

JUST WHEN YOU have sold your soul to the behaviorists for a mess of tokens, or have embraced the existentialists' conviction that Now is as potent as Then, and Here as There, you have one of those experiences that sends you crawling back to the determinists.

When I was ten years old, I wrote a story about a grain of wheat. This particular grain of wheat was planted by a Minnesota farmer, and what with sun and rain and Scandinavian husbandry, it grew to maturity, was harvested, was ground into flour by the Pillsbury Flour Mills, and was transported—in both the physical and spiritual senses—to the Purity Baking Company of St. Paul, to become part of a loaf of bread or cake.

That grain of wheat couldn't have been happier. The Purity Baking Company was St. Paul's first mega-bakery, a block-long, gleaming white-tiled factory that was soon to wipe out all the little neighborhood bakery stores. I suppose it was in the early twentieth century's belief that big is beautiful that our sixth grade class was taken on a tour of this manufacturing marvel, and all of us watched transfixed as uniform loaves of bread glided along sleek conveyor belts to be snugly bundled in cellophane and boxed by men in white uniforms for delivery to the corner grocery stores. More wonderful yet was the procession of cakes. My mother made only round cakes, frosted white or brown. But at Purity there were square and oblong cakes, iced pink or green and even baby-blue. It was astonishing.

When, not long after our visit, our teacher declared it was composition time, the wonders of the Purity Bakery leaped from my fervid mind to paper. Most of my friends hated composition time. They heaved big sighs and rolled their eyes and flopped over their desks, dropping their pencils and scrambling for them in the aisles. But not me. I was bursting to recount yet another version of the age-old miracle of transformation—from frog to prince, from a grain of wheat to a Purity cake.

I brought my composition home to show to my parents, and my Uncle Louis had a great idea. It should be sent to the baking company, he said. So his stenographer typed it and mailed it off to the president of Purity. Back came his letter. Yes, indeed, said the president, he liked this story. Maybe they would use it in their advertising some day. And here, in token of their appreciation, was a book of coupons, worth ten dollars toward the purchase of any Purity breads or cakes. I could scarcely believe my good fortune.

But Uncle Louis was angry. They could not buy my composition with a coupon book, he insisted. It deserved money. I pleaded their case, but eventually had to relinquish the visions of sugar-cakes that danced in my head because Uncle Louis was a lawyer and knew better than I, my parents said. He sent the coupons back with what he said was a polite letter. Back from the president of Purity came my composition, without any letter at all.

After a while I forgot about it. Fifty years passed. (Remember those old movies? Time's passage was told by an unseen hand that tore away big calendar pages ruthlessly, scattering them to a passing wind or crumpling them to the floor. *Sic transit.*) I am sixty years old, greying, near-sighted, dieting, worldlywise. I am a wife, a mother, a professor at a prestigious university. I am in my office preparing a lecture when the phone rings. Calling, a secretary informs me, is the vice president of a nationally-known food-processing company. I suggest, half-absently, that he must have the wrong person, since I have nothing to do with either peas or corn.

No, no, I am assured (the vice president himself is now talking to me) I am the person he wants. He is preparing to address a national meeting of dieticians, he says. A friend of his told him that I had once published an article called "Mental Health Begins in the Stomach." I wince, but admit to its authorship. Its point was that physical nurture and security are basic to a growing child's emotional balance and mental energy. It is the title I am uncomfortable with, I tell him. Oh, but, says he, that is the very thing he is after. He is asking my permission to use it. I grant that, with the generosity of disinterest, asking only that he credit the article's publication source if his address goes into print.

Now, says the vice president, he would like to do something for me in return. I assure him that this is not at all necessary, and there ensues a brief verbal *pas de deux*, in which he has the last step. I have been very gracious to him, he says, and he would like to show his appreciation.

Some weeks later an envelope arrives. In it is a book of coupons. No note, no card, just a book of coupons with which I can purchase five dollar's worth of any of the foods processed by the vice president's company.

What is my reaction? Is it incredulity? Indignation? Derisive amusement? No, none of these. With a sense of eagerness and urgency I leave my office and hurry to the grocery store. In one swift sweep I splurge the whole five dollar's worth of coupons on some eight or nine packages of frozen food. I hurry home and spread my packages elatedly before my husband. He listens to my story with a look of disbelief and bursts into laughter. Only then do I see it all. For one half-century I have waited to retrieve the reward snatched from me fifty years before. It was half of what I'd been awarded when I was ten years old. What is worse, I had felt glad to get it—at least until my husband laughed.

It gives one pause, doesn't it? I tell myself that at least *that* piece of unfinished business is wrapped up and put away. Or is it?

2. The World Is So Full:
Becoming "Big"

I KNEW I was becoming a big girl when my parents told me that I was about to go out "to see the world". Apparently I had weathered my third year without memorable incident, aided, I am sure, by my Teddy Rosevelvet who had been given me for my third birthday. He was my constant companion, a large, furry grey teddy bear, with glass eyes so big, blue and compassionate, that I was made a life-long believer (well, until inevitable disillusionment set in) that blue eyes signified true, honest, loving, faultless character. Teddy Rosevelvet—which is how I'd heard his name—was, I guess now, probably one of the first of his breed, having been given birth by an ingenious toymaker in honor of our then President Roosevelt, who, avid hunter though he was, had refused to shoot a little bear cub he had encountered.

Mama and Sonny and I were going to Atlanta to visit Mama's parents and brothers and sisters. Papa and Uncle Louis, still at his law studies, would have to stay in St. Paul, and yes, Teddy too, because Mama might need my help with bundles and such. The prospect of seeing the world made my sacrifice insignificant, so off we went.

Of the long train ride I remember almost nothing, except that Sonny was a little feverish, and he cried a lot, and Mama kept sending me down the aisle to fetch water from the tank at its end, to bring it for Sonny in our collapsible drinking cup, "and try not to spill most of it over yourself." Finally (I was later told) I complained that Mama wasn't letting me see the world at all, so she tucked me in next to the window and I saw it with wonder—endless fields of bare autumn earth and browned grass and tens and tens of telephone poles whooshing by. I remember the hubbub of laughter and tears and hugs at the station in Atlanta, and my puzzlement when I asked Mama why Grandmother Hia-Kaylia was crying, and Mama said it was because she was so happy.

Those several weeks in Atlanta, during which my fourth birthday occurred, excited me in many ways; I retain fragments, condensations, sensations of memories, perhaps because so much was new and different, perhaps because I was so eagerly on tiptoe to take it all in, or because it was one of those periods in childhood when growth and learning seem suddenly accelerated. I had set them down, those impressions and memories, when I came upon Freud's wise comment—one which, alas, he himself never followed up: "I believe we accept too indifferently the fact of infantile amnesia . . . We forget of what great intellectual accomplishments and of what complicated emotions a child of four is capable . . . we have every reason for assuming that these same forgotten childhood activities have not glided off without leaving . . . a definite influence for all future time."[1]

From among my most vivid Atlanta memories, I choose a few that seem to me to contain a consistent meaning.

Lots of people came to visit us and made a big fuss over Sonny and me, but the person to whom I made an immediate attachment was Sally, our washer-woman, who came twice a week. Big, dark, shiny-eyed, Sally would whoop with laughter the minute she caught sight of me, scoop me up in her strong arms, and all but smother me as I nuzzled into her cushiony bosom that smelled, somehow, like freshly-baked bread. We loved each other. And she taught me something that gave me great pride: how to walk "straight and tall", balancing first one, then finally three (small) books on my head, just the way she carried those great baskets of laundry. When it was time to return to St. Paul I begged her (so I was told) to come with us.

✍   ✍   ✍

Another "straight and tall" memory: I was the flower girl at somebody's wedding. (Whose it was I have no idea—nor did it matter to me at the time.) What I recall was that I walked ahead of the bride and was her herald. I scattered pink petals over a red carpet that stretched across a green lawn, and I tried very hard to walk in time to what seemed to me to be uncertain rhythms coming from two fiddlers playing under a tree.

Yet another memory of an experience that added

to my growing awareness of selfhood and sense of responsibility: During our visit my grandparents moved to a new house, and since it was only a few blocks from the old one, each of us toted some small things instead of bothering to pack them. My grandmother allowed me to carry what I thought was the most beautiful glass bowl I had ever seen. It had stood on the mantel of one of our fireplaces and I had been captured by its ineffable beauty when the sunlight coming in between the slanted shutters caught its glowing iridescence. I was sure it had once belonged to a princess and once, when I asked my grandmother if I could have my breakfast farina in it, she let me do so, while she and Sally stood and watched me, laughing together. She promised me that when I grew up it would be mine and she kept that promise.

Years later I had called in an antique dealer to look over some bric-a-brac I wanted to be rid of, and his eye lit on this bowl. It was, he informed me, a cheap piece of what early in the century had been called "carnival glass", a crude imitation of Tiffany usually given as a prize at the shooting galleries of carnivals. (One of my uncles must have won it, I suppose.) It was rare now, and the dealer offered me a decent price for it, but I told him I would no more have sold it than I would the Holy Grail. Because when I was four, carrying it before me in all its (to me) glowing beauty, I felt like a princess, approaching her waiting throne, heady, proud, responsible to my people's trust.

One day my sixteen-year-old Uncle David took me to the children's room of the Atlanta Public Library. I could not read, but I loved to turn the pages of books, mostly for pictures, I suppose, but partly because I held to some vague notion that one day the books would speak to me as they seem to do to my grownups.

My memory: I stood before an archway and over it many words were carved in stone. When I asked Uncle David what they said, he read, "The world is so full of a number of things, I'm sure we should all be as happy as kings."

"Yes," I said, "I know that. I made it up out of my own head."

Uncle David doubled over with laughter. Then he began to explain to me why I could not possibly have done so. How would the Atlanta Library know what was in a little Minnesota girl's head? And on and on. The more he talked the more insistent I became; when we got home everybody joined in trying to reason with me, but the more reasonable they, the more obdurate I.

Of course I came to realize not too long thereafter that the Robert Louis Stevenson couplet had undoubtedly been read to me more than once by my parents. Perhaps I had claimed it as my own because it expressed so exactly my then characteristic optimism about the miniature world I knew. But there remained a doubt in me. Was it plausible that such a longish verse would have been carved in stone? Perhaps the whole incident was a distortion or condensation not unusual in personal memories? Thus dubious and curious, I wrote only several weeks ago to the deputy director, Mr Casper Jordan, of the now new public library in Atlanta. His response, in part: "Your memories (sic) are very accurate!" He enclosed a photo-postcard of a large fireplace (the arch) over which, moved from the old library to this new one, was the graven-in-stone couplet. He added that he was "delighted" that their library had made "such an indelible impression" upon me, and I have just written my thanks to him. I could not resist a postscript: "Just between you and me, Mr Jordan, I *still* think (feel?) I made that up out of my own head."

Perhaps the most vivid and whole memory in those crowded weeks in Atlanta was the one which combined some fearful uncertainty and its happy resolution that underpinned my satisfaction at becoming a big girl.

Mama's best friend at high school was Bessie, and when we were in Atlanta Bessie came with her little girl, Molly, to my fourth birthday party. Molly went to a private kindergarten, and her mother suggested that I might go with her one day. I recall nothing of what happened during that morning, but when it was going-home time all the children ran off or were called for by a grown-up. Molly said "Bye" and went off with her mother's maid.

There I was, suddenly aware of being alone on the porch steps, waiting for someone to come fetch me. I tried to go back into the kindergarten room, but the door was locked and the teacher gone. Only a janitor was there, but he paid no attention to me, just swept around me to get at the dead leaves and dust.

When his broom caught up the picture I had crayoned I tried to snatch at it, but he swept it into the ashcan. It was only a scribbly picture, I told myself, and besides it was all dirty now. So I sat, searching the street for somebody to come, but no one came. I remember how lonely and deserted I felt, not yet truly frightened, but considering how I could find my way home.

I went down to the sidewalk and peered in all directions, but except for a tired-looking hound-dog not a living soul was to be seen. Then I spied a landmark I had observed before. It was a tall, round, red chimney that towered above the low buildings surrounding it, the chimney of the college where my Uncle Beb was a pre-med student. So I trotted off towards it, never taking my eyes off the smoke-stack.

It was much further away than I had thought, and I began to feel very tired, but I got there. A long flight of stone steps led to the entranceway. Sprawled all over them (it probably was the lunch recess) were lots of big-boys, laughing and horsing around. One of them caught sight of me and hollered "Look who's here!" And because he looked like a *nice* big-boy I went up to him and asked if my Uncle Beb was there. "Anybody know this li'l' gal's Uncle Beb?" he shouted, and then, to me, "You lost, honey?" I stood mute, afraid that I might cry. But there, in a few minutes, was my Uncle Beb, his always sunny face astonished, then breaking into a big grin. He swept me up in his arms and onto his shoulder, and he turned to all those big-boys and said, "This is my sweetheart—that's who *this* is!" And all the boys shouted "Hooray!"

Afterwards Mama was furious with Bessie, and Bessie was furious with Molly and the maid and the teacher. But I felt like the Winged Victory (before her head came off, of course).

So I did indeed see a new world, part outside and part inside myself. I wish that Freud had followed up on his own observations about the remarkable "intellectual accomplishments" and "complicated emotions" of which "a child of four is capable", so that I might better understand the two-and-a-half-year-old who all but merged with the dancing clock and the self-and-other-aware four-year-old who found her own way.

3. I Was a *Good* Girl: *Becoming Bad, Denial, Remorse*

SOMETIMES I WAKE up in the middle of the night and find myself crying out silently, anxiously, "Andy Ruffano! What has become of you? Where can I find you so that I can right the wrong I did you?" I am haunted, you see, by what I did to Andy in Miss Young's fourth grade.

The brand new pencil sharpener was fastened to a wall in our cloakroom. Most of us used it often, sometimes because it gave us the excuse to get up from our tight desks and take a walk, and sometimes because, as we whirred the handle and honed the stub to a fine point, there was some feeling that our brains were being sharpened too. (To this day I know writers who cannot begin a sentence until they have sharpened a fistful of pencils. All born before the computer, I daresay.)

One weekend the painters came, and on Monday morning the walls of the cloakroom gleamed with thick, freshly-laid-on schoolroom tan enamel. Miss Young was very glad, indeed, and she said we should be glad too, and careful to keep it clean. When, shortly thereafter I went to sharpen my pencils, there was the sharpener in its proper place, but surrounded now by a pure, viscous surface that somehow held an irresistible pull for me. With three impetuous strokes of a finely-honed lead pencil I carved into that still-moist, unmarred wall a large letter *A*. I can think of no reason for having chosen it except simply that it was the first letter of the alphabet. Then I went happily back to my seat.

Now about Andy Ruffano. He was an Eyetalian. Most of us had never seen an Eyetalian before Andy transferred into our class from another district. In our class, mostly Scandinavian, where the children's faces were like wintry moons, and their braids and rag curls or slick-parted hair like pale gold silk, Andy was set apart by his dark aquiline features and coarse black hair that sprouted up from his temples like small Pan-horns.

He was a wild boy, we said, because he was restive in his too-small seat, and he sometimes made funny noises, and then, when Miss Young would call his name, sharply, he would flash a dazzling grin, as if he were laughing inside himself, instead of being ashamed.

He was full of small mischiefs. Once, during silent reading time, he dropped five marbles, one by one, letting them bang and bounce and roll over the floor, and then he scrambled about for them in mock panic, like a monkey. Another time he put a long piece of chalk in his mouth and pretended to smoke it. When the school day was over, Andy went off in the opposite direction from most of the rest of us to what was called "Swede Hollow", though probably no Swede had inhabited it for more than a generation. It was at the bottom of what must have been a quarry, where recently migrated railroad workers lived with their proliferating families in lean-tos and shanties. Most of our parents had warned us not to go near there, but once a few of us dared. What we saw was the grimy, sodden poverty that lay above the tin roofs and muddy ground like a miasmic fog. On the clotheslines stretched between poles, even that day's washing looked dirty. I felt sorry for the kids, and peculiarly ashamed somehow, glad to scuttle away from it with my friends.

Nevertheless, there was between Andy and the rest of us one bond, a scarcely conscious one. It was a kind of tacit contract: he would do what the rest of us would not dare, and we would reward him with our feigned shock and furtive laughter.

Now about me. I did my lessons quickly and mostly correctly. If I found things slow and sometimes repetitive there was a two-shelf row of books lent by the public library to which you could tip-toe and find a delectable choice for "silent reading". Miss Young approved of that. I was — I guess I'm old enough to say it right out — I was her pet.

In the early afternoon someone went to the pencil sharpener — I remember now, it was Hilda Petersen, whose thick braids shone like freshly-polished brass — and with a sharp intake of breath she hurried out of the cloakroom to whisper in Miss Young's ear. She had seen the *A*. Miss Young leaped up to see it with her own eyes, and then she abruptly stopped our lesson. Who had done this dreadful thing?

It was only then, splam in the middle of our

multiplication tables and faced with the question of guilt, that I first fully took in the enormity of my act. Sickness washed over me. When it ebbed I knew for sure that I had not done it. I could not have done it. It was too heinous an act. If my parents thought I had done it they would die of shame. Miss Young would never trust me again. I could not even like myself any more, so I could not believe it of myself. I sat stiff and righteous at my desk, my hands folded, as we were supposed to do when we were "idle". I felt an urgent need to go to the basement, but I did not dare ask permission.

Miss Young was saying that everyone would stay where he was until the culprit, who had been a bad citizen, who had defaced the property of us all, had confessed. Out of the corner of my eye I saw Andy Ruffano's grin. Why was he laughing, I wondered. Did he know? Had he seen me with those black-olive eyes of his? Or was he covering over because he already knew that he was doomed to be the scapegoat?

Miss Young again: "Andy Ruffano, just why are you smiling?" He didn't know. Had he gone to the pencil sharpener that day? "Yes, Ma'am." Slowly now, she asked if he realized that he was the only person in the room whose name began with an *A?* He said honest-to-God, he didn't do it. Miss Young said he *must* have done it. I thought he must have. He was a wild boy—everybody knew that. I felt sick again, and my bowels churned perilously as we all sat still in the thundering silence. Then Andy was told to stay when the class was dismissed.

I never knew what happened between him and Miss Young. Next day, when I searched his face for some clue, he seemed quite unchanged—not shattered, not ashamed, not angry—just the same. So I put the whole thing firmly out of my mind. Except that now and again—more than a half-century later—I awake from childish dreams, and find myself wondering about Andy Ruffano.

What has become of him, I wonder? What did he make of being accused and punished for an act of which he was utterly innocent? Or of that roomful of strangers who let him take the rap? Or of a teacher who would not believe his honest denial? How did it warp and uglify your view of this world, Andy? How can I ever make it up to you?

4. "You Have Broken a Ten Commandment!"
Crime and Punishment

WHATEVER HAS BECOME, I wonder, of the Children's Page in modern day newspapers where, while your parents read and talked about the mysterious affairs of the world you never made, you could work on puzzles or connect numbers with a pencil and come out with a picture, and find jokes and riddles to tell your schoolmates; and, best of all, enter the weekly contests for poetry or story writing, which, if you won first prize, would bring you two dollars and the pleasure of seeing yourself in print.

The *St. Paul Pioneer Press and Dispatch* had such a page on Sundays when I was a child, and I had been lucky indeed. As I think of it I am sure that the hapless editor of that page must have come to it Saturday evenings three sheets to the wind, because he seemed oblivious to the fact that he had awarded me three prizes within a very short span of time, and this, as any schoolboy knows, is hardly the way to sell newspapers.

Heady with having found my metier, I had dashed off a fourth story, but when I reread it I felt it was not up to my standards. So, having pecked it out carefully on a rickety typewriter that my Uncle Louis had given me when his law practice permitted him to buy a new one, I signed my brother's name to it—not Sonny, which was what he was called, but his real name, Abraham J. Harris. Why not? I thought. It's good enough for a seven-year-old—and maybe he'll even be proud! Having disowned it, I forgot about the whole thing.

It is a peaceable Sunday morning, but outside a heavy blizzard is whirling about the house, and Papa announces that he will not drive through it to take Sonny and me to Sunday School which is some miles away. Sonny and I had chosen to attend Sunday School to our parents' astonishment, actually to my father's chagrin, since in spring and fall it interfered with his Sunday fishing. The fact was that both Sonny and I loved Sunday School. The stories we read or were told there were as good as fairy tales, and some even better, we agreed, because they were really true! Noah—and all his animals (but why did he let mean things like mosquitoes come into the Ark?)—and that darling little baby, Moses, bobbling about in his cozy cradle among the bulrushes, and then, when he became a man, leading his people to freedom by walking between scarlet whipped cream waves! And Joseph's triumph over his mean brothers, which showed that good things will happen to you if you yourself are good.

That blizzardy Sunday morning Sonny has gotten up earlier than I, so he has first rights on the Children's Page. Suddenly I hear him call out from his bedroom, "Hey! I won a prize!"

"You did?" calls Mama from the kitchen. "For what?"

"For a story here in the Children's Page."

"Sonny!" Mama cries with pride, "I didn't know you'd written a story!" She is very happy, because Sonny has been reading *Little Black Sambo* for some weeks, over and over, and my parents have begun to fear for his future.

"I didn't write it," says Sonny. "But it says here, my whole name, and seven years old, and 632 Otsego Street, and two dollars!"

Suddenly I remember, and I hitch my flannel bathrobe over my Doctor Denton sleepers and pad into the kitchen where my parents are at breakfast. "That's my story," I say, and I explain why I had signed Sonny's name.

"But you didn't ask me!" Sonny cries, rushing in. I am dumbfounded. I cannot see his point. Why should I ask him? He should be proud to have his rotten old name in the newspaper!

"I don't even like that story!" he shouts.

This is calculated to leave me speechless. "I bet you can't even read it!" I jeer.

"Anyhow," Sonny goes on, "you are supposed to ask a person's permission!" His face is bright pink with indignation.

I look to my parents for their affirmation of my rights. My father's nose is twitching, which is the sign that he is trying to control his laughter; my mother seems to be nodding her head in Sonny's favor.

"Besides," Sonny goes on, stubbornly, "it is a

sin". Measuring his words now because he knows he is coming in for the kill, he intones, "You have broken a Ten Commandment! 'Thou shalt not take my name in vain'."

I cannot believe what I am hearing. "Mama!" I am yelling now. "He's crazy! He thinks he's God or somebody!"

Sonny and I had agreed, some time ago, that the Ten Commandments were the part about Sunday School we really didn't like. Right from the first they had to be memorized and regularly chanted each Sunday, and while some of them made sense, some others seemed irrelevant. It was conveyed somehow that if you didn't know what coveting or adultery were, for instance, never mind; you'd find out some day. And now here Sonny was, invoking a Ten Commandment against me!

Now Papa rises from the table, and at the same time as I can feel he is shaking with inner laughter, he has got me by the collar of my bathrobe and is hustling me back to my room. If I don't quiet down pretty fast, he says, he'll give me something to yell about.

I fling myself onto my bed weeping and raging and beating my pillow till a flurry of feathers warns me that I'd better quit. After a while I calm down, and am curious to see what's going on in the kitchen.

The tribunal was there, each smugly reading parts of the paper, with Sonny doing the number-picture on the Children's Page, of course. Mama spoke first, gently, but I hated what she said. She said that of course I didn't know it, but they wanted me to know it now.

Sonny was not really right about the Commandment I had broken, but what I had done was wrong, just the same. First I had lied. Then I had taken what belonged to another person—his name—and a person's name is his very own, and it may not be taken and used by anyone else without his permission—and on and on. If I were an adult that would be considered a kind of crime. I listened in silence, but I did not believe her—she was making a great big mountain out of a molehill, but I kept my sense of betrayal in check. So, Mama finally finished: to repay him I ought to give Sonny half of my two dollars.

For some time thereafter, whenever Sonny and I had a falling-out I would remember that he owed me a dollar. However, after he'd given up *Little Black Sambo* in favor of attending Harvard Law School, and after President Truman had appointed him Assistant Solicitor General of the United States, and we had both found out that there were many other sources of self-fulfillment beyond Mama and Papa, our pleasure in each other flourished. I began to feel that it was *I* who owed *him*. Mind you—he had been only seven years old and he knew the law!

5. The Making of
an Arithmetic Imbecile:
Shame and Consequences

NOT LONG AFTER I entered the fifth grade my teacher slapped me across the face. In front of everybody. That is how I became and have remained an arithmetic imbecile.

Up to that stunning, blinding moment I had done reasonably well in arithmetic—as well, that is, as most girls were expected to do in those long-ago days. Addition and subtraction were plain to be seen in everyday life. Multiplication was mostly a matter of memorizing and spewing out predetermined answers on demand, usually in class-chorus "drills". It was division that began to pique my respectful curiosity. Who had been smart enough to make up all these number games? More puzzling, however, were the uses of the round, wide-eyed zeroes, which seemed (even as today) to be appearing with increasing frequency in our arithmetic exercises.

What were they, anyhow? Something? Or were they nothing?

When I asked my Uncle David, who was in college, he informed me that the zero was one of the great inventions of the Arabs. I felt friendly enough to the Arabs at that time. After all, I had read all the books in the *Our Little Cousins* series; black, yellow, red they were, and if I recall correctly, Arabs were among our "little brown cousins". Still, cousins or not, I could not see how their having made up zeroes helped them or anyone else. I'd found out that if you added a zero to a real number that ran horizontally it made that number much, much bigger. But if you added it on vertically it left the real number unchanged. How come? Uncle David said to run along and forget it—I'd understand it when I grew up. A false prophecy if ever there was one.

Now, in the fifth grade we were to learn long division. Miss B. announced this as if it were an imminent disaster. As usual she explained it in a loud scolding voice, even though nobody had done anything wrong. Long division was used, she explained, when the dividend and divisor were big numbers, but (still angry) she was going to show us her special way to make it easier.

It was hard to listen to Miss B. because you could not figure out why she was so mad. We had been forewarned by friends who had passed through the inferno of the fifth grade that Miss B. was an "old crab", an "old crank", an "old nutsy"—"old" accompanied all the fear-inspiring accounts of her. But being old wasn't Miss B.'s trouble; nor was it that her hair was the color of winter slush and seemed to be just plopped on her head, or that her wrinkled, heavy-lidded eyes never seemed to look at you. I'd decided that she was just born mean; maybe, I thought, her mother was a real witch.

Her way to make long division easier was to concentrate on the first few numbers in the dividend, and have the divisor go into them first. To concentrate we should use a "curtain". The curtain was a lightly penciled or chalked line drawn through the end numbers; this could be erased when we had dealt with the cluster of beginning ones. She surely must have explained all this further or better, but I heard none of it because that curtain bothered me—it got in my way. So I put off listening, deciding that I'd ask my mother, who was usually the best explainer I knew.

When I told Mama about the curtain she shrugged and said maybe it was some new-fangled educational idea. She'd show me how to do without a curtain just as soon as the baby quieted down. When, at last, Essie plaintively fell asleep, in the hour before Papa came home, Mama led me through the labyrinthine process of long division.

Next morning we were sent to our assigned places at the blackboards to work the problem Miss B. had given us. I could feel my heart beating as I worked, carefully, carefully—in some ominous sense not only I but my mother was on trial. The silence was broken only by chalk squeals, a muted moan here and there, and an occasional cough from the dust that puffed out from frequently-dabbed erasers. We all stole furtive, forbidden glances at what others were doing, and I saw that my friend, Edward, the smartest boy in the class, was finished first and his quotient was the same as mine. He stood smartly at attention awaiting Miss B.'s verdict.

I really liked Edward, even if he was a boy. We had become friends in the previous grade where we were often given the coveted privileges of clapping the erasers. That involved two children taking a basketful of those chalk-choked felt bars out into the schoolyard during class time, beating one against the other so that clouds of dust flew out—onto Edward's jacket and my dark pleated skirt, up our nostrils, into our eyes and hair—until they were clean again. Once, out of a blinding whirlwind of white dust, Edward revealed that he could speak Latin, and when I urged him to "say something in Latin" he said, "Requiescat in pace." My admiration for him rose in proportion to my utter ignorance of what that meant.

Miss B. began her slow circuit from pupil to pupil, starting with Edward whose answer she marked correct. Happy and proud because it was the same as mine, I stood waiting my turn while Miss B. crossly urged some dejected student to stop dilly-dallying or said, "*No!* All wrong!" and bade them start over again. At last she came to me. "Correct!" she snapped. Then, "But where is your curtain?" Bursting with barely-controlled pride, I replied that I didn't need it—my mother had shown me how to do it her way. A scorching slap across my face staggered me.

What followed I do not remember. All I recall is running, running past all my home-bound classmates at lunchtime, gasping with dry sobs, bewildered, utterly disgraced, to fling myself into Mama's arms, where her purring compassion quieted me. I was not to go back to school after lunch, she said.

By the time Papa came home, Mama was a volcano of fury at the "stupidity" and "outrage" of the total school system of St. Paul, Minnesota. In Atlanta, Georgia, where she had gone to school, such treatment was unheard of. (She said.) Papa listened somberly, and said she must go see the principal first thing in the morning. Indeed, she would not, said she. She had already written a letter to the Superintendent of Schools giving him a good piece of her mind, and would Papa please go out and drop it in the corner mailbox.

Now I began a caterwauling, pleading with them not to send it, because Miss B. would hate me more than ever. Never mind, they assured me, I would not set foot in that school until we had had a satisfactory explanation *and* an apology. Nobody talked at suppertime, and my food was ashes in my mouth.

I was saved by Essie's measles — I'd awakened the next morning to find that good old Dr Christiensen had come chugging to us in his Tin Lizzie in response to Mama's early call. "Essie has measles, all righty," he said, and neither my brother Sonny nor I should go to school until it was clear that we had not caught it.

That was how it became possible for me to sit on our front steps and face the cluster of my classmates who passed our house on their way home from school. Miss B. had been absent too, they reported. Several days later, they came with the news that Miss B. was sick. It was Edward who had the definitive diagnosis: she had had a "nervous" breakdown.

My first flash of triumph was swiftly engulfed by a dark wave of guilt. It was my fault: either I or Mama's letter had driven her crazy.

When I timorously returned to school, the substitute teacher informed me that at the term's end I was to skip over the second half of the fifth grade and go into the sixth. Who had decided that? I was afraid to ask. Maybe Miss B. to get rid of me? Or to "make up" to me? Or was the Superintendent of Schools scared by Mama's piece of her mind? I never learned why, but I was reassured by the fact that Edward was to be skipped too, and also a very quiet girl named Ingrid.

But it was a Pyrrhic victory. By that leap I missed out on being taught about fractions, and it is astonishing to me to this day how fractionated daily life seems to be. Surely some aspects of arithmetic were taught in the sixth through eighth grades, but I recall nothing of them. In high school I groped through algebra in a fugue of terror, but somehow made it, only to face geometry. That prospect paralyzed me, until early on, the sensible and sensitive teacher took me aside and (raising the curtain) revealed to me that geometry was not arithmetic at all: it was a process of drawing certain propositions to their logical conclusions. And when, in my best Palmer Method script I wrote, "Quod Erat Demonstrandum" at the end of each problem, I glowed with the thought that I, like Edward, had begun to speak Latin.

✍ ✍ ✍

Still, that slap left its mark. I find it embarrassing (though my husband finds it touching) that the only things I understand as we watch, say, the "Wall Street Week" pundits, are the puns (no pun intended). When we travel abroad I cannot seem to retain what fraction of a mile a kilometer is (or is it the other way round?) and so I am incapable of figuring out how far we have to drive to get to where we intend to spend the night. Any recipe that must be reduced or increased, depending upon the number of servings—if, for instance, I must estimate what one half of three quarters of a cup of, say, currants (oops! I almost said curtains) comes to—I toss into the wastebasket. I pray that I may be safely dead before we are strangled by the metric system. At those times when I find myself bristling at my husband's amusement, I think I would have done better to have married Edward. He would not have expected a girl to know about these things, and he'd probably have patted my bowed grey head and said something comforting, like "Amor omnia vincit".

Not long ago a savant friend informed me that the zero was not invented by the Arabs at all, but was borrowed by them from the Hindus. What for? My friend changed the subject. I have begun to suspect that I am not alone in my failure to grasp the zero. When, for instance, I've dallied with the problem of today's National Debt, I've wondered whether presidents and budget directors and their ilk have considered what I found out in the fifth grade: that adding zeroes to zeroes horizontally may lead to naught but disaster. And whether one essential condition of fitness for public office ought to be the candidate's ability to understand zeroes even *before* he/she grows up.

More seriously: she who got slapped learned many things from that experience about the subtle and complex ways in which we human beings affect one another. And about the persistence of things past. And about the dynamic nature of a trauma.

Many years later, I practiced as a psychiatric social worker in a hospital for the mentally ill. Two of my patients were in the locked ward. I had become uneasily aware that those few hours I spent once or twice a week on that ward left me feeling far more drained than was usual for me, and always with some sense of unfinished business. I reminded myself of what I had come to understand: that if one enters responsively into the anguish, the terror, the bottomless despair of psychotics, it must inevitably be exhausting and heart-wringing. But I realized, too, that I was being overly alert to patients who were not my responsibility at all—observing, scrutinizing, seeking to see behind each empty or grimacing or haunted face.

Then, one day, I thought for a fleeting moment that I recognized her, slumped in a beat-up chair against the wall—Miss B. grey-skinned, haggard, anger burning through half-closed eyelids beneath ragged wisps of hair.

I realized suddenly that I wanted to find her. I wanted to ask her carefully and compassionately if I had been the cause of her breakdown. And to tell her that now that I was no longer a child, I could understand and was truly sorry. I wanted to know if that slap was really meant for me? Or was it a final, blind lashout at a kind of life that in one fragment of a moment revealed itself to be too futile to bear?

Of course, I knew that she could not or would not have answered these now-useless questions. And my moment of false impression dissolved in the realization that Miss B. had had her breakdown more than a thousand miles away from this place and tens of years away from this time. It needed only second grade arithmetic to tell me she would by now have long been dead.

In that moment a faint recurrent echo in me went silent—and ceased. I felt almost light-hearted as I locked the ward door behind me.

6. A Birthday Party:
Shock and Forgetting

I WAS DRAWN to her on her first day in our sixth grade class. Her name, to my surprised pleasure, was Helen. I had two cousins named Sybil, and I knew three Dorothys, but I had never come upon another Helen. Even after my mother told me of its famous eponym and Uncle Louis explained its glowing Greek meaning, I still thought Helen was a very homely name. You couldn't *do* anything with it: try to turn it into a pet name and it became Hellie; turn it backwards and it was Nellie, the name of a horse I knew. But now here, reassuringly, was another Helen— Helen Lundstrum, our teacher said, who had just arrived from South Dakota a few days after school had begun.

I felt an immediate affinity for her, even as I recognized at once how different we were from each other. She was much bigger than I; her hair, a bright yellow-gold, hung thick and straight in a Dutch bob, like the little boy in the blue overalls in the advertisements for paint; her lips were pouty and very red, but when she smiled, quickly and often, she looked confident; and her teeth flashed white and even.

At recess the new Helen stood off at the side, and I went up to her and told her my name and drew her into the group that was forming for that terrifying game called "crack the whip". Afterwards I asked her where she lived and found that she could pass my house on her way home. I invited her to stop after school and play, and she smiled happily and said sure.

I could see that Mama was looking at her critically as she set out the usual after-school snack of milk and cookies. The four of us, Mama, Sonny (who gulped his milk and fled to his playmates) and the two Helens sat at the kitchen table. Helen seemed to relish her refreshments, flashing her smile, saying "Yes, thank you, ma'am" when Mama offered her seconds. But I could sense that Mama was not feeling hospitable.

"Don't you need to call your mother to tell her where you are?" she asked, and Helen replied, smiling, "She won't care." Quickly she amended this. She meant she *would* care, but they didn't have a telephone. Yet, that is. Besides, she went on, her mother worked, so she wouldn't be home. She pulled down the neck of her blouse to show us that she had her own house key, fastened by a large safety pin to her underwear.

"And your father—?" Mama persisted. She was making me feel embarrassed because she was asking so many personal questions when she herself had warned me more than once that it was not nice to do that. But Helen didn't seem to mind. She smiled or shrugged and flung back her shining bob in a manner that seemed to me both self-assured and elegant (which I would practice later in my mirror). Her father had died right after she was born. He'd been killed in a train accident. Her mother's work was dressmaking—she went to other people's houses and sewed for them. Her address (Mama asked for it) was at the very edge of our neighborhood, where, to the concern of the solid Scandinavian property owners, the area was "going to the dogs" with many of its old wooden houses abandoned, or badly in need of repairs, their yards rife with weeds. It was obvious, as I scanned Mama's face, that she had some reservations about this Helen, but she said only "It must be very hard for you and your mother". Helen said "Yes, ma'am", and we all three looked sadly into our plates.

Eager to show off my greatest treasure, I pulled Helen into my room. Three months before my eleventh birthday (he had forgotten the exact date, he said), my Uncle Bernard in Los Angeles had sent me a wonderful doll. She was one of a new breed of dolls. Her bright pink celluloid body was long and narrow, she had glittering golden hair (like Helen's!), lips which parted to show gleaming white teeth and azure eyes with lids, fringed by real lashes, which opened and shut heavily. The wonder of her, however, were her "joints"—arms, elbows, wrists, thighs, knees, ankles, and neck all movable in their sockets. You could make her sit, stand (perilously), stoop and put her arms part-way around you for a hug—altogether a marvel. Even Mama had been intrigued by her, and had helped me sew her some pretty clothes from remnants of "goods" our dressmaker had given me. I had scarcely been able to settle on what to name her and had finally given her the three most beautiful names I knew—Gwendolyn Violet Delight.

Helen sighed with pleasure at Gwendolyn's beauty, and, once she had carefully tested her various joints, she began humming tunelessly to herself, to dress her in her patent leather slippers and frilly party dress. Suddenly, she said that I might not believe it, but she too had a jointed doll. Her mother wouldn't let her play with it, though, because she was afraid it would get broken. So it was locked up in a trunk. When I asked what was the fun of having it she laughed and said that maybe sometime when I came to her house her mother would let her take it out. Then she added that I probably wouldn't believe it, but her doll's name was Gwendolyn too. I said stoutly that I sure didn't believe that. "Not Violet Delight," she added. "Just Gwendolyn." I repeated my disbelief, and she chanted, "Cross my heart, black and blue, hope to die, if I do," (tell a lie, that is). "Anyhow," said she, "if both our names are Helen why shouldn't our dolls' names be the same?" I tried but could not explain even to myself why a double coincidence would make a claim seem more suspect. I was left uneasy.

For several days I did not bring Helen home with me, but she continued to engage me with her flashing smile and the confident toss of her head. A girl I usually avoided (because she never had a handkerchief when she needed it) whispered to me that Helen was a "peroxide blonde". I didn't believe that. "In the sixth grade?!" I said.

Not long afterward Helen rushed over to me at recess and invited me to come to her birthday party the following week. She was going to be thirteen years old; she quickly explained that she had lost a grade because she and her mother had moved around a lot, with her father dead and her mother looking for work, and all. My heart went out to her, and I said she should stop at my house with me so I could get my mother's permission.

Mama seemed uncertain. Would her mother be there? Helen reassured her that she would. It was going to be just a small party, of course, because she didn't know many kids yet, and it would be right after school, from about three-thirty to five. Mama asked if she could call Helen's mother. No, they didn't have a phone yet. Reluctantly Mama said that if the party was right after school, and if I would promise to get home by exactly five o'clock, she guessed it would be all right. I promised, wondering whether the ice cream and cake would have been served by that time. Helen said, "Thank you, ma'am," happily, which made me glad. She asked to see Gwendolyn, and warmed my heart by giving her a close hug. Then Mama reminded me that I had an hour's piano practice ahead of me, so Helen went on her way.

When she'd gone Mama said, "I don't know what it is about that child . . ." But I had come to know Mama's soft spots, and reminded her of what she had taught me—that "a person can't help it if they're poor". And she, trying to hide her pleasure in me, exclaimed "You don't say!" followed by, "Just see to it that you're home at five, on the *dot!*" Next day she was nice enough to remember to buy Helen a present, a pretty handkerchief, and she wrapped it up in tissue paper and tied it with baby-blue ribbon.

On the appointed day after lunch I changed into my new plaid jumper and took the little package with me to school. Helen was in the same colorless gingham dress she had worn in the morning, but she had tied a red silk sash about her waist. Poor thing, I thought, and wished Mama had bought a more generous present.

Helen and I walked together to her house. No one else seemed to be coming along, so I asked who else would be at the party. Some kids who lived near her, she said, vaguely. My sense of unease grew, but I didn't know what to do or say, so on we went in silence. We stopped at a dilapidated duplex with an outside flight of sagging wooden steps leading to the second floor where she lived. I reminded myself firmly that she couldn't help that, and up we went. Helen tried the doorknob, and when it didn't move, she fumbled in the neck of her dress, unpinned her key and turned the lock.

From behind Helen I peered into a dimly lighted room and saw a woman standing, hastily pulling together a flowered kimono. Her heavy, pushed-up breasts showed, and her long corset gaped unlaced from her waist down. Her hair, yellow like Helen's, hung about her shoulders. "What in *hell!*" she rasped. "Dammit, girl, don't you know enough to knock before you open a door?"

Then I saw more. Behind her was a sofa and on it sprawled a man in his undershirt, his legs flung apart, his pants down about his knees. He spat out, "Jesus!" and jumped up, wrestling up his trousers and suspenders.

Helen and I stood frozen. Then, in a small voice, she said, "It's my birthday, Ma." Her mother turned her back, fiddling with her corset laces. "Ma," Helen ventured again, "this here is my best friend from school." There was no response. On the table at the sofa side I could see a tin pail and a couple of scummy glasses, and I smelled a sour dampness—of beer?

Sweat? Something stale? Not fully covered, Helen's mother wheeled about. "Just you get you and your best friend the hell out of here," she said, low, cold and mean. "But *fast*—"

The man, thrusting his bare feet into his shoes, wiping his face with a big hairy hand, lurched forward with a grin. "Hold it, Fanny!" he said. "Hold your horses! . . . Tell you what you girlies can do." He lifted the pail and held it out to Helen. "You go down to the corner, like a real good kid—to the saloon there, you know? Get this filled up. And we'll all four have a party!"

He winked at Fanny, lumbered towards us, and handed the pail to Helen. "Tell you what," he added, "here's some money for you girlies. Buy yourselfs some ice cream cones." He dug two nickels out of his pocket and tossed them at us. Helen caught one deftly in midair and stooped to pick the other up from the floor. I opened the door and ran down the rickety stairs with Helen on my heels.

Trembling, I walked beside her to the corner saloon. I was in a daze of shocked disbelief, ravaged by a sense of outrage and betrayal, by physical revulsion mixed with a gut-aching pity for Helen.

What had Helen's mother and the ugly man been doing together? Showing their "parts"? I had heard about that once in a group of furtive gigglers, but I had dismissed the idea scornfully: that would be a stupid thing to do, a game for dummies. Did grownups actually do that . . . ? And these people were drunkards too, I could see that.

Almost more shocking than all this was the fact that Helen's mother had sworn at her, at her very own child, and had kicked her out of the house. And why had Helen taken those dirty nickels from that ugly man? And agreed to go to the saloon for him? Maybe she was afraid—maybe she couldn't help it. Why didn't she run away—like to an orphan asylum? Or somewhere? Suddenly I had a sickening sense—I could not then have put it into words—that she was both accomplice and victim.

Neither of us spoke nor looked at each other. When she went through the saloon's swinging doors I stood outside, shaken and feeling dirtied somehow by the sour smell of damp sawdust and beer. When Helen came out, beer pail foaming and slopping over, I turned on her, savagely. "You told me lies," I said, "a whole bunch of big lies!"

She stood stolid, stock still. I realized I was still clutching the ribboned package. "Here!" I cried. "It's your birthday present!" And I thrust it at her so violently that more beer sloshed onto the sidewalk. Blindly I ran from her, across the street. Then I turned and looked at her again: there she stood, a big dumb peroxide blonde with pouty—probably painted—lips and a silly red sash tied around her washed-out dress. "I don't ever want to be your friend any more! Keep away from me!" And then, as if I were hurling a rock at her, I yelled, "Besides, my mother *hates* your mother!"

🕊 🕊 🕊

That was the most memorable birthday party I ever attended. Memorable, and once again puzzling as part of my quest to understand what one remembers or forgets—and why.

I have thought of Helen many times since then. I

understand why I was attracted to her quite beyond our common name. In those first few weeks of school we were both strangers in a strange land, she and I, both "new kids" in a class that had been together for some years. Uneasy that I had been promoted to a grade that I feared was beyond my capacity, newly aware that I was not only the youngest pupil in the class but also, alas, the smallest physically (when my kindly teacher put a little wooden platform under my feet so that they would not dangle, the boys had started to call me "half-pint"), I saw in Helen an ally, a kind of alter-ego—big, striking, seemingly self-assured and at the same time obviously grateful for my friendship. We were an odd couple—but for a brief time we served each other's needs.

Strangely after that street-corner anathema I seem never to have seen Helen again. How could that be? It is possible that she and her mother folded their tents like the Arabs and silently stole away during the night or the next day. Possible, but not probable. Indeed, I have an amnesia more complete than any I have known.

What happened when I returned home between me and Mama, what I told her or chose not to tell her—of this I have no recollection. I can imagine it, but I do not know it. I am reasonably sure I did not hurry home and tell Mama "all about it". I was too shaken, too confused, and I feared Mama's reaction would add to my inner turmoil. I was no stranger even then to mixed emotions and troubling contradictions between heart and mind, but this had been a stronger dose than I could digest.

So I guess that I slowed my pace and worked out a possible evasion—not a "real lie" but not the whole truth either. I might have said simply that it was a terrible party, that no other kids were there—just me. Yes, her mother was there, but she didn't seem like a very nice person—really horrible. No—I probably would not add that because I knew Mama would ask, "In what way? How do you mean?" No—her mother just seemed sort of angry and mean. Oh yes! She did give us some money to buy ice cream cones, but I didn't feel like taking it, so I just gave Helen her present and came home.

Mama would sympathize with me, and would feel sorry for Helen too, maybe. Then she would remind me that she *knew* something was odd about that girl—and it wasn't just being poor, and she had *told* me—Yes, yes, Mama, I know, I know, and I'm never going to be her friend any more. Case closed.

Closed between Mama and me, that is. But within me remains an amnesia under which simmered and sometimes boiled a number of unresolved questions. On the matter of my never seeing Helen again, I must have sedulously avoided even looking in her direction again. That was not difficult in the classroom since we were seated by size: I in the very front, with the platform under my feet, she, one of the biggest and the last pupil to enter, in the back row corner. Nor had she ever volunteered to recite or to-offer an answer to a question put to the class. Anyone who was too different could be ignored in the tumult of recess games or the pairing-off within walking-home groups.

Years later I came to understand that Helen was a classical clinical example of the child and then the person-grown who is the product of indifferent, if not totally neglecting or rejecting parenting—unwanted, unloved, tolerated at best, used when expedient, given no sense from infancy onward of being lovable, of being enjoyed, of self-worth. Many such children retreat into apathy; others become rapacious grabbers and antagonists, blindly lawless in their effort to counteract their inner sense of emptiness; still others, like Helen, canny in their observations of superficial appearances and behaviors, make their way by continuous re-invention of themselves, weaving fantasies which come to seem real to them. They have been labeled "pathological liars" or "sociopaths" because they construct false, "madeup" identities and accounts of themselves and their situations whether the external reality calls for them or not. Thus Helen—poor child-woman—did you, I wonder, become clever enough to fool most of the people most of the time? Or were you repeatedly found to be a pretender, to be empty beneath that false front, and then cast off?

Of one thing I am reasonably sure: that my innocence/ignorance, my delayed interest and lack of curiosity about sex until I was some years older ("The Pear and the Worm"), was not caused solely by my slow physical maturing nor was it the product of the unspoken but firmly established taboos within my otherwise fairly sophisticated, expressive, liberal family. I suspect, rather, that it was connected with what I saw and what I made of the scene at the birthday party.

I imagine, further, that after I got home and told my half-truths to Mama I welcomed the expectable, mundane bits of business that followed: eat your supper, help with the dishes, get to bed early so you can do your piano practice before you go to school, and (self-imposed) try not to think about it for a while.

But think about it I have, not infrequently, chiefly in my persistent curiosity about the phenomena of remembering, forgetting and the factors that govern the reactions and residuals of traumatic experiences. Of which more later. Here I will add only that one of the silly residuals of that eventful party is that the smell of beer is repugnant to me.

7. My Grandfather and God:
From Worship to Doubt, and Half-way

IT WAS NO wonder that my little brother, Sonny, and I believed that God had been created in my grandfather's image. Or, once we grew old enough and reluctantly relinquished that conviction, we agreed that grandfather Joseph was the spittin' image of the Almighty.

Tall and broad-shouldered for a man both of his generation and race, he was handsome in the Greek rather than Hebrew mold, a fully clothed Poseidon with a yarmulke on his thick, gently curling white hair, his beard carefully trimmed (corners and all, despite the prohibitions in Leviticus) revealing a sculptured chin. He had a high sense of presence, and it was no accident, I'm sure, that after he had moved his family from Georgia to Minnesota (to be close to his favorite daughter, my mother, and to Sonny and me) he maintained some of the manners and flourishes of dress that he had taken on in his long sojourn in the

South. This included even his worn but still beautiful Panama planter's hat that he wore in the summertime.

He acted like God too. To Sonny and me he was a loving, benign deity, mock-stern at times, but mostly indulgent and easily pleased by our sayings and doings. With his own grown children he was less yielding. Like God, he was something of a despot, benevolent in his rule, passionate in his love and expectations, often unreasonable, always sure of his righteousness. His sons and daughters vacillated between their devotion and pride in him and their not infrequent resentment of his dictates. (Years later, I came to understand that their powerful ties to one another arose not only out of love but also out of their shared, humor-laced conspiracies of defiance of both Papa and his alter-ego—God.)

There was no disputing his learning and studiousness. To his unending perusal of Hebrew texts and commentaries he added an orator's eloquence. So he was always at the center of scholarly and scholastic discussions and disputations in the various synagogues in which he had held temporary memberships.

"Various synagogues" and "temporary memberships" they were indeed, since he brooked no deviations from his reading and interpretation of what God had said and what He had meant. It was a *sotto voce* joke among his children that although he had never aspired to the rabbinate, he had succeeded in creating schisms and splits in congregations from Lynchburg all the way down to Charleston, Savannah, Macon, and finally Atlanta, Georgia.

Once settled in St. Paul, Minnesota, he was often sought out by bearded elders and even clean-shaven young men who wanted his opinion on what to believe and do, according to God's law. Such counsel he gave out in a benign, lordly way, angry only when he encountered "stupidity" in his hearer. He conducted these instructive sessions at home, in the small room that housed his great leather-bound tomes and the table at which he studied. I remember my grandmother hovering about the doorway to that room, glowing with a kind of reverent pride as he held forth.

Naturally, Sonny was more important to him than I was. As a man-child he was to be the carrier of tradition and learning. I took piano lessons, but Sonny took Hebrew lessons. My grandfather was dissatisfied, however, because my stubbornly non-conforming parents insisted that Sonny attend a modern school where Hebrew was taught as a living language, not in its ancient form. However, that was better than nothing in this Godless land, and my grandfather took it as— shall I say?—one of the crosses he had to bear.

To my sometime envy, he and Sonny developed some code words between them in that impossible language, and this seemed to serve as a special bond between them. Sonny's real name was Abraham and at times my grandfather would call to him in the way God did when he called upon the first Abraham to ready himself for the sacrifice of his son. "Avrahom! Avrahom!" the Lord had called, and Abraham had answered, "Henaini!—Here I am!" Thus Sonny would respond, "Henaini!" and run joyfully into my grandfather's arms to be embraced.

One Sabbath noon Sonny and I had come to our grandparents' for dinner. Grandfather had just returned from the synagogue with a coterie of disciples and this time they sat at the library table in the parlor as my grandfather held forth. Now and then, he went into his study to bring out and cite a relevant passage from one of his heavy books. Sonny and I hung around at the edges of the group, wishing they would hurry and go home, because we were hungry; yet we were held somehow, not by discussions (which we did not at all understand) but by the fact that we were related to this savant who was listened to with such respect.

At last, his lecture finished, my grandfather tendered his disciples the ritual invitation to dinner, and they, in turn, responded with ritualized thanks and regrets. Before they went, however, my grandfather called out "Avrahom! Avrahom!" and Sonny cried "Henaini!" and ran into his arms. Looking at Sonny intently, my grandfather said that there had been a Bar Mitzvah in the synagogue that morning, and somebody's grandson had read his Biblical portion and its interpretation like a truly learned man. "And what," he asked Sonny, "will *my* grandson say when he is thirteen and will be called to the Torah?" All the men waited, and Sonny showed a moment of panic. Then, slapping his hands stiffly to his sides, his eyes bright, he drew himself up and recited: " 'A birdie with a yellow bill/Hopped upon the window sill/Cocked his shining eye and said/Ain't you shamed, you sleepy head!' Robert Louis Stevenson."

I thought I would die of shame. My grandfather looked long and silently at Sonny. Then he said, gently, "You are a very stupid child." But he reached over and tousled Sonny's hair, and his eyes laughed, so everybody took the cue and laughed aloud. It was a close call, but it turned out all right.

My own close call came several years later, but it did not turn out so well. When I was twelve or thirteen, I began to have some second thoughts about

God. I had attended Sunday school regularly and eagerly for some years, but since it was "modern" we learned history, and the Bible as literature rather than as revelation. On special holidays we did dramatic versions of some of the Bible stories, and I was repeatedly being draped in white cheesecloth to play Hannah, the suffering mother of seven sons who had died in the cause of religious freedom; or Esther, who, by her beauty and feminine wiles, had saved the Persian Jews from genocide (cheesecloth dyed with purple "Rit" for that role); or Deborah, the prophetess, who recited the bloodcurdling song of victory over the hosts of the evil Sisera.

It had begun to be borne in upon me that for all that the Israelites were continuously praising and glorifying the Lord, they seemed to have been "chosen" mostly to suffer; and while God often saved them, and sometimes took vengeance on their enemies, it was by the skin-of-their-teeth that they managed to survive at all. It had come, this disillusionment with God, rather gradually, and it was tinged with malaise and fear that I might lose Him and my grandfather too, as well as my securing bonds with my long-laid roots.

One day, when I was feeling contentious about something or other, I sat myself down opposite my studying grandfather and accosted him head-on. "Where," I demanded to know, "is God?"

He looked up from his reading and said mildly, "Where? Here. Everywhere."

"But exactly where?" I insisted. "Is He here in this room? Is He outside? Is He in the garbage can?"

My grandfather gave me a cold, black look. "Now you are talking like a fool," he said. "Shame on you!"

But I went on. "Is He here *on* me? Is He *in* me? Is

He—" and I lifted up the little finger of my right hand—"Is He on this finger?"

"Yes," said my grandfather. "He is even there."

"Well, then," I said, made rash by frustration, "get *off*, God!" I took a deep breath and blew hard. "Scat!" I said, and He flew off.

My grandfather's eyes blazed with anger. After a moment he turned back to his book, completely ignoring me. I was angry with him too, because I felt he had not been honest with me, somehow. Mostly, however, I felt uneasy.

I remembered the time that had burned itself into my heart, when I had witnessed my grandfather's intimate communion with God. His daily morning and evening prayers were, for me, a matter of routine. He would bind his worn leather phylacteries upon his forehead and arms, as commanded centuries ago in *Leviticus*, face to the east, and begin his whispered obeisances and praises to his God. I knew that one must not interrupt him ever—except maybe if the house was on fire—that you must wait till he was quite finished, with his prayer shawl folded and his phylacteries put into their small purple velvet bag. But what I remembered now was a day when I was six or seven, when my grandmother had taken me to their synagogue.

It was the Day of Atonement, when all good Jews search their consciences for sins actually committed or only contemplated. Even little children could confess to sins, such as the occasional lack of respect for their parents and teachers. By resolving to do better, they could ask the Lord for forgiveness, and I liked that.

From the front row of the orthodox synagogue's balcony, to which I and all the other womenfolk were relegated, I had an unimpeded view of the altar. On it, along with the rabbi, the cantor, and a few other dignitaries of the congregation, stood my grandfather. He was cloaked from head to foot in a prayer shawl I had never seen before, one that was used for only the most solemn ceremonies. It was a startlingly dramatic covering, draped about him (I now realize) like the robes of some desert chieftain, its broad, vertical black and ivory stripes like the chiaroscuro of white-hot sunlight and black shadow of desert lands. (Many years later I was to recognize that same motif in the cathedrals of Siena, of Vezelay, and elsewhere in Europe where Saracens had influenced the ornamentation of Roman or Moorish architecture.)

So robed, standing erect, head and shoulders above the others, my grandfather filled me with awe. Then, to the continuous chanting of prayer, the holy ark was drawn open, and the spirit of the Lord shone forth, not in graven images of sculpture or painting, but in the white, samite-covered gold and silver ornamented Scrolls of the Law, beautiful, implacable, eternal. Suddenly my grandfather was the central figure. His voice rang out above all others. He sank to his knees, and then he flung himself prone before the Scrolls, before the Word, prostrate upon the altar, in complete surrender. And I was afraid.

After sunset, the twenty-four hour fasting was broken and his family gathered happily about the supper table—those who had fasted and those who secretly had "cheated"—and my grandfather said grace quietly. He still seemed somewhat remote from the rest of us. Maybe he was tired; or maybe he was still in his at-one-ment with God.

I reviewed all this after I had brushed God off.

For some days thereafter I walked a careful circle around my grandfather. I was in turmoil—partly ashamed of what I had done, partly disappointed in him because he had not saved me from myself, partly afraid that he would disown or abandon me. Within that very week in the middle of one night there was a terrible storm, with blinding lightning and ear-splitting thunder, and I cowered under the bedcovers, sure that God in His whirlwind was speaking to me. But, when morning finally came, I saw that the flowers in our garden had been beaten down and some trees had been cracked apart. Yet I, the sinner, was unharmed. (How come, God? Why did You hurt the flowers? Or are You really not there? Or have You, in your infinite understanding, forgiven me?) My blasphemy was not mentioned again by my grandfather. After not too long a time, we just naturally resumed loving each other.

Many times in my life since then, I have resurrected and even forgiven God, especially when I have felt need of Him, or when I have stood facing the mysteries of human life and have known awe and wonder and my own littleness. When God comes on, He is as He was those many years ago—handsome and proud, in his broad-brimmed Panama planter's hat, powerful, knowing, and basically loving. Just like my grandfather.

8. Twelfth Summer:
Hating, Loving, Bonding

THE SUMMER MY little brother went into business was a black one for me. Up until one hot evening in July, I was the self-respecting twelve-year-old sister of a nine-year-old boy, and then, suddenly, I was only a girl who was going to have to sit and wait while Sonny came and went as a person of affairs. We were all on the porch of our summer cottage at the lake that evening—my mother, my father, Sonny, and I. My mother was fanning herself and murmuring that if my father didn't patch some of the holes in the screens, we'd be eaten up by mosquitoes. My father said "Yes, yes" a couple of times in an absent-minded way, and kept on putting his fishhooks and flies in order. Sonny and I were playing parcheesi, and I was winning. All at once the bolt was hurled. "Son," my father said ("Son"—not "Sonny"!), "how would you like to go into business?"

"Fine," said Sonny.

"You're almost ten years old," said my father, "and I've been thinking it's time you learned something about money."

"O.K.," said Sonny, and drove me into a rage by sweeping all the men off the parcheesi board and leaning back to listen.

Sonny could have a magazine route, my father told him, and he'd make two cents on every copy he sold at five cents. My father drove back and forth to work in our town, twenty miles away, and he said Sonny could ride with him. My mother asked, For heaven's sake, what was he thinking of? What was the use of bringing children to the lake in the summer if you were going to take them right back to town again and put them to work? My father told her to hold her horses. He said Sonny would go to town only on Thursdays, his entire route would be in three big office buildings, and he'd take him to lunch every week.

"At the New Iroquois?" asked Sonny eagerly, and I knew he was already tasting the pie à la mode he always ordered at that restaurant.

"At the New Iroquois," said my father, and that cinched it. Sonny wanted to go, and none of my mother's arguments made any impression on either him or my father.

The next Thursday morning, Sonny was up early. My father thought twenty-five miles an hour was as fast as a car should be pushed, so he always gave himself plenty of time. At first, I was inclined to sulk in bed, but finally I put my bathrobe on and went and stood in the kitchen doorway. Sonny sat at the table, the shine of vaseline on his pompadour, the whiteness of his starched middy suit and his stockings, and the glory of being in business combining to make him radiant. My father sat across from him, looking pleased, and my mother buzzed about, scrambling eggs and frequently reminding Sonny that he didn't have to go if he didn't want to. Nobody even noticed me, at first. "Hello," I said eventually, and garnered some comfort from the fact that each of them said "Hello" in return.

"Looks like it's going to be a nice day," I said, and they all agreed.

"Guess I'll do some diving from the raft today," I said, pointedly, to Sonny.

"Ish ka bibble," Sonny said.

I leaned against the doorjamb disconsolately for a while, and then sat down and ate.

The fervent goodbyes my mother bestowed on Sonny, and the sight of the dust settling silently in the driveway after the car had gone, deeply saddened me, and I considered allowing myself to drown, later, when I went out to dive. The day was endless, partly because my mother kept track of the passing of each hour and wondered what Sonny was doing during it but even more because, in the course of nine years, I had grown used to having Sonny around and, reluctant though I was to admit it, I was lonesome for him. Silence lay across the lake as I swam to the raft, and though I kicked the water furiously to make some of the companionable noises of swimming, the sound died in the quiet. I dived once or twice, but the water seemed too deep and lonely, so I lay on the raft and thought, I should worry, and ish ka bibble. I kept seeing images of Sonny effulgent with success as all the men in three offices buildings swarmed to buy his magazines, and I occasionally saw heady images of myself holding a silver loving cup I had been awarded for diving, or for writing a poem, or for being an actress—it was hard to decide which. I stayed there until lunchtime, and then swam back to the cottage.

After lunch, I wound up the Victrola. Alma Gluck sang "Lo, Here the Gentle Lark," Harry Lauder sang "Roamin' in the Gloamin'," Caruso's heart and voice broke in "I Pagliacci," and an infinite sadness hung over the afternoon. I asked my mother to play cassino, but she said she never could keep her mind on cards, and to wait till Sonny got home. There was nothing to do but wait.

Sonny came at last, bearing his shield. It was a large grey canvas bag with "The Saturday Evening Post" lettered on it in black. It hung from one shoulder and flapped against his white stockings. His middy suit was rumpled and so was his pompadour, but victory shone in his face. He and my father came in together, my father's arm around Sonny's shoulders. "Well," my father said to my mother proudly, "our son is a real businessman!"

I listened to every wonderful, anguishing detail. Sonny had made a big hit. All my father's acquaintances had wanted to know where he'd got such a handsome son. They'd all been glad to become regular customers, and they'd given him the names of other men. Sonny had had to go back to the magazine distributor several times to refill his bag. Then my father said that he and Sonny had better sit right down after supper and work out a system of bookkeeping. My mother said to let the child have *some* rest, and my father thought awhile and then agreed, saying he'd like to get some fishing done before dark anyway.

Almost every evening, after supper, my father and brother and I went fishing. That hour in our boat, moving toward the lowering sun and then, as the sky grew dark, coming back toward the light on our cottage porch, had always been one of the happiest of the day for me. We spoke in soft voices, so as not to frighten the fish. Sonny and I would take turns rowing, creeping by each other carefully on the boat's damp bottom as we shifted seats. After a while, my father would slip the heavy stone that was our anchor gently into the water and would stand up in the prow, silhouetted against the sky, and begin his rhythmic casting. Sonny and I would push reluctant worms or flipping silver minnows onto our hooks, lower our bamboo poles, and wait for hungry sunfish or crappies to come by. That summer, my father had decided I was getting old enough to learn to use a rod and reel, and for several weeks, whenever the lake was calm, I had been allowed to stand and cast.

On that black Thursday, it was different. We dropped anchor and my father said, "Let Sonny try casting tonight."

I was stunned. "But he's too *young!*" I cried.

"Hush," said my father. "What's the matter with you?" Then, looking over my head toward his son, he said, "If he's old enough to be in business, he's old enough to learn casting." I decided at that moment that the next day I would drown myself for sure.

From then on, Thursday morning was a time of cheerful bustle. Sonny's hair had to be combed just right, and his breakfast had to be especially good; if it was a cool morning, there was hot cocoa for him instead of milk. Afterward, with his bag slung from his shoulder, he would be off with my father in a cloud of golden dust. Midmorning, I would walk the shady road to the post office and the grocery store. On other days, Sonny and I always went there together, and in the span of a few riddles and songs and races and arguments we were back home. Now, on Thursdays, I walked alone, and the way seemed endless. Every Thursday, the groceryman, who was called Skipper because he wore a yachting cap, though everyone knew he'd never been in anything bigger than a rowboat, would say "Where's that young brother of yours?" and I would answer "Sonny's gone to town today. He's in business on Thursdays."

Skipper would say, "That so? Fine boy, that boy. He'll be Somebody someday."

A glow of pleasure would rise in me then. After all, this future Somebody was my own little brother. But when the screen door had slammed behind me, the glow would drain away, and as I scuffed the dust and pebbles on the way home, I knew that someday, dazzling in my beauty and charm, I would sweep into Skipper's store and he would take off his yachting cap and ask "Are *you* the famous actress?" (Or "poetess," or "fancy diver.") And if he should ask "What's become of that young brother of yours?" I'd say casually "Oh, he helps me."

There was no more fishing on Thursday evenings. On the first two or three, in spite of my mother's protests, Father and Sonny went off together after supper to the library table in the living room to count Sonny's money and check his records. My father had bought him a ledger, and on its blue-and-red-lined pages Sonny wrote the names of his customers and as he made the rounds each week entered the date and the notation "Paid 5c" or "Owed 5c". He often couldn't collect for his magazines because the customers weren't in their offices when he made his delivery. The third week he had the ledger, he and my father got into an argument over it. Sonny said the lines were so close together they made the names squinchy; my father said he would just have to get them in somehow. Then my father said that "Paid 5c" and Owed 5c" was a very poor system. He said that he had already shown Sonny how to make his entries, and that there was no point keeping books unless you did it in a businesslike way. Sonny insisted that the system was good for *him*, and my father said all right, it was Sonny's business. After that, he just sat at the library table and read his paper on Thursday night while Sonny wrote and erased, and sometimes stopped to pour the shining money from his purse and build little towers of dimes and nickels.

Meanwhile, my mother and I did the dishes. Thursday night's dishes seemed the week's worst. The pots and pans apparently multiplied, and the kerosene stove would never heat water fast enough. By the time we had flapped our towels and hung them up, Sonny would have finished his checking and counting. He would put back in his purse the money my father had taught him to call "working capital" and drop his profits lovingly into his iron-courthouse bank. He would shake the bank and come to the kitchen rattling it and smiling proudly, and my mother would smile proudly back at him. I hated him.

One Thursday evening, late in August, I heard Sonny's voice rise, wailing, over the clatter of the dishes my mother and I were washing. He and my father were having another argument.

"But I have too many customers!" Sonny insisted.

"Too many customers!" said my father. "I've never heard a man in business complain of *that* before!"

My mother hastily dried her hands and went into the living room.

"This son of yours!" said my father. "The more customers he gets, the less profit he says he's made."

"Gracious!" said my mother. "How's that? Did you buy something, Sonny?"

"Buy something!" said my father, "What would he buy? *I* buy his lunch, *I* give him nickels for his afternoon root beer and cream puff!"

Sonny said, in a small voice, that he couldn't always remember who owed him from the week before, and my father replied, very quietly, that he wasn't supposed to remember—that was what the ledger was for. He added that he guessed he'd better have a good look at that ledger one of these days. He probably would have looked it over right then, but Sonny said he had a stomach-ache, and my mother said it was probably that rotten New Iroquois food and Sonny had better lie down.

Somehow, my father didn't get around to the ledger for another week. We went fishing the next evening, and visitors came for the weekend, and I suppose it just slipped his mind then, until Thursday. I remember that evening clearly. It was the night my brother went out of business.

We had lighted a fire in the livingroom grate to clear out the damp chill rising from the lake. My mother and I finished the dishes, and found my father and Sonny still at the library table. Sonny was peering at the ledger, pencilling and erasing and making much ado about slapping and blowing the shreds of eraser off the paper. My father held his newspaper in front of him, but I could see he was keeping his eyes on Sonny. I had taken an extra piece of muskmelon out of the icebox, for my second dessert, and I sat on the stool in front of the fire to eat it. I was glad Thursday was almost over, and the warmth of the fire and the luscious muskmelon juice that ran down my gullet made me feel good.

Suddenly my father said "Well?" and Sonny murmured that he'd let him see it right away.

"How can you have forty-nine customers and a forty-five-cents profit?" my father asked.

"It's a profit, just the same," Sonny said. He was sitting still, staring desperately at the ledger page.

"Profit!" my father cried. "He works all day," he said, turning to my mother and me, "I transport him, I feed him, every week he says he's got more customers, and now I find he's got less than half the profit he ought to have!"

My mother set her mouth in a straight line and bent over my brother as if she were shielding him from my father. "Sonny," she said in her gentlest, most coaxing tone, "tell us what's the trouble."

"Nothing," said Sonny.

"Nothing!" roared my father. "Don't tell me 'Nothing'!"

"Sonny," said my mother, "do you want to quit this—this monkey business?"

Sonny kept looking at his ledger, and after a minute he said, in a whisper, "Yes, I guess I do."

Then it all came out. The whole trouble, Sonny said, talking fast and breathlessly, was that he had too many customers. The more he got, the messier the names in the ledger got. He sometimes had to prop it on one knee to make his entries, and his magazine bag would pull his arm down so that often it was hard to tell whether he had written "Paid 5c" or "Owed 5c" and just who it was that had paid or owed. He said that he had figured most people would remember to pay him, and that sometimes some of them did, but not always.

At first, I thought my mother was going to laugh or cry—I couldn't tell which. Then she just put her arms around Sonny and didn't say or do anything. My father gave a little moan. "What grade are you in, son?" he asked.

My brother said he was going into the fifth grade.

My father shook his head as though he couldn't believe it. "In the fifth grade," he said. "Nine and a half years old. And he can't read his own handwriting!"

"The whole thing was nonsense," my mother said angrily, but my father didn't pay any attention. He stood up.

"Son," he said, "I'm sorry, but you'll have to learn to read what you write before I'll put you in business again."

My brother swept his purse, bank, and ledger from the table and bolted out of the room. No one said anything. My mother sat down in her rocking chair and looked at the cover of a magazine. I wanted to go to the kitchen to get rid of my melon rind, but I was afraid to stir the silence, so I sat there and looked into the fire until the heat made tears come to my eyes. After a few moments, my father sighed and walked out to the cold, dark porch. Out of the corner of my eye I could see him standing there, hands in his pockets, looking into the blackness.

I got up and tiptoed into the kitchen, and from there I crept into my brother's room. It was dark, but I knew that he was already under the blankets. I whispered "Sonny" and he didn't answer, so I went to his bed and felt for his face. He was crying, and he shook my hand off roughly. I stood there in the dark beside his bed, and suddenly I was crying, too. "You should worry, Sonny," I whispered. "You should ish ka bibble about that old business."

He didn't answer. I leaned against the cold brass bedpost and wept heavily and helplessly. I wept for Sonny, and for my father, and for myself, too, because I knew that I probably would never be a great actress after all.

That's about all there was to that summer. In another week, we were packing to go back into town, and Sonny and I were happy at the prospect of being in school again, although, as custom required, we rolled our eyes and groaned whenever we spoke of it.

Photographs

Some of the photographs that follow were taken by family members or were studio portraits, and two were by itinerant photographers. In that first decade of the century few people, if any, had personal cameras. Photographers, with tripods on their shoulders and black-hooded cameras went house to house to wheedle up business.

My Grandfather Joseph, who would look more like
God here had he not been wearing his winter
fedora and going somewhere in a hurry, totally
unaware that his picture was being taken.
Perhaps vain, or perhaps obedient to the
Commandment that no images should be made
for worship, he sedulously avoided all
photo proposals~

Papa and Mama,
early in 1905, shortly
after their December 1904
marriage ~

On our back porch on a Sunday morning, taken by
an itinerant photographer. The child in this gath-
ering has recently seen the dancing clock; her father
stands behind her (on the left), along with Cousin
Beryl who had just dropped in. Aunt Rachel is visiting us from Atlanta; Uncle Louis, a law student,
is wearing his hat for reasons of his own, whatever they were. Mama, always camera-shy, is probably in the house taking care of her new baby, Sonny!

✗ ○ ✗

Another itinerant photographer took this.
Sonny is a little more than a year old,
his sister about three-and-a-half. She
is holding her beloved bear,
        "Teddy Rosevelvet",
given her at her third birthday

About 1910: Papa and Mama,
Grandmother Blooma and Grandfather Moses,
Sonny and Helen.
This "Studio picture" was taken, I think, to
send to Grandmother Blooma's family
in Russia.

(Note: Photographers of those days never told
people to say "cheese"!)

Sonny, five years old, and
Helen at seven-and-a-half
~ around 1912 ~

1918: One of our few almost whole-family pictures, but missing Uncle Bob (who was the picture-taker), Uncle David (who was in Army camp in Texas), and Grandfather Joseph (who had gone for a walk in the woods nearby). This was on a week-end get-together at our summer cottage.

Front Row: Grandmother Hia-Kylia holding apple-cheeked Essie; Papa, giving directions and holding our baby Judy. Second Row: Helen with her arm around Mama. Back Row: Uncle Louis; Aunt Rachel, with her arm around Sonny, and Aunt Marie. ∝

The Author in 1968

9. The Patriot:
"I Pledge Allegiance . . ."

I RECALL CLEARLY the beginnings of my love of country: it was when, not quite six years old, I entered the first grade. Miss Lowry, my teacher, was a soft-spoken but firm gentlewoman with thin white hair skimmed back into a tight bun and an unrelievedly black floor-length dress; but she looked like an angel to me. She was welcoming us, she said, with two pictures drawn on the blackboard in colored chalk. And there they were, wondrous to behold, made all by herself, freehand. I see one as vividly now as I remember the Picasso I saw yesterday: a grey squirrel holding a brown acorn, sitting on the pink-and-green blooming bough of an apple tree.

The other was an American flag, with thirteen stars on it, in full flutter on an unfelt breeze. That, Miss Lowry explained, was the way the flag had looked hundreds of years ago. And then she clutched my eager heart by telling us that the red stood for courage and for the blood that had been shed by our ancestors to save our country; the white stood for peace and purity; the blue symbolized truth and honor. I thought my heart would burst at my good fortune at being born an American.

Every morning after that we stood and pledged allegiance to our flag, our hands on our hearts, our heads who knows where. At the least it was a ritual that affirmed that we were all there together, ready to begin our day's work.

Several years later, I suffered a great disillusionment. On my grandparents' library table sat a gigantic dictionary. Flipping its pages one day, I came upon a section in color labelled "Flags of All Nations". And there, to my dismay, I saw that a lot of other countries had red, white and blue flags—and they too stood for courage and purity, etc., etc. I began to wonder about the reason for the Pledge of Allegiance, especially since in the second and third grades we did not recite the pledge but wriggled about in our seats until a commanding gong resounded through the halls from the principal's office, when we folded our hands and sat at attention. (Memories again: ages later I entered a Buddhist temple in Nepal; at that moment a great gong sounded, and for one split second I froze at attention, fingers interlocked!)

However, early training drives deep and even today under certain circumstances, I all but dissolve when the American flag is raised or little children lift their heads and sing, "My Country 'Tis of Thee . . ."

And I never loved my country so passionately as during the First World War. We were so right, so true, so red, white and blue, sending our boys over there, over there, to make the world safe for democracy while we kept the home fires burning and packed up our troubles in our old kit bags and smiled. So I did everything I could to help Uncle Sam who was pointing his bony finger at me too, not just at potential soldier boys. I did "my bit" with joyous determination, going from class to class in my school as a Minute Man (today would I be called a Minute Person? Or a Minute Maid?).

I gave brief, stirring speeches about our duty to buy 25 cent Thrift Stamps which could be exchanged (when they reached five dollars, if I remember correctly) for Baby Bonds and apotheosized into fifty-dollar Liberty Bonds which would yield interest and earn a poster that could be pasted into a front window—next to, in many households, a small dark blue pennant that flaunted a star for every "near and dear" in the service—or a gold star for a loved one who had given his life.

Mama had allowed me to paste up the poster but she had demurred at hanging the pennant, even though she had two brothers in army camps. "Enough is enough," Mama said tersely. Among my other acts of patriotism I had begun to save peach pits and silver foil. I had been instructed to do this by my friend Dolly, who had two brothers in the war, one training in Texas and the other in No-Man's Land (where, as the then current song told us, "in the war's great curse, stands the Red Cross nurse—she's the Rose of No-Man's-Land"). That brother knew everything, Dolly averred. He had seen the Huns tearing dresses off ladies and kicking them in the stomach and bayoneting Belgian babies. It was true too—because I had seen all that not long afterwards in a newsreel movie, and there they were, doing just such hideous things. "German Kultur" the caption said.

About peach pits: the seed in them, Dolly said, was used to make poison gas, which was badly needed if we were to win the war. As for silver foil, it was a kind of metal, so obviously it could be used for weapons and such-like—it stood to reason. My family were slackers about peaches that summer, so after saving sixteen pits (two of which were no good because I had cracked them open to taste the poison which I found pretty bitter, but not lethal), I turned the rest over to Dolly to add to her collection.

With silver foil, I was lucky. Both my father and *his* father were heavy smokers, and every day at least two pieces of foil came off their cigarette packs. Those, added to donations from other relatives, grew into a well-packed and patted-down silver brick. When the brick got big enough, Dolly said, you could go to the junkman who would pay you by the pound. He would turn it over to our government. If it was big enough, Dolly added, you could get a lot of money for it.

It was that prospect that lured me into what may well have been an act of treason. I would sell my foil brick and the junkman would give it to our country. With the money he paid me, I would buy a Liberty Bond; thus, I would be doing two things for my country. It was a delicious idea.

But I grew impatient. Somehow that silver brick did not grow fast enough. It was as though, as with living things, it had reached a plateau where it stood still, consolidating its powers for some later spurt of growth. Each day, although I added to it, it never seemed to weigh any more. Then I had a flash of inspiration.

I began to collect hairpins to increase the brick's bulk and heft. Mama's hairpins were to be found everywhere: not only in the proper box in the top drawer of her chiffonier, but on the bathroom floor, and under chair and sofa pillows where she had been sitting; her visiting lady friends and relatives dropped some too. Added to hairpins was a handful of straight pins I found on our dressmaker's floor (she thanked me kindly for scrambling around and picking them up). I took them all up secretly to a corner of our attic; I carefully unfolded the leaves of foil, and from the brick's core on out I tucked pins into each layer. Now the brick began to show substantial growth, and I was pleased with my handiwork.

After all, I argued with the still small voice that nagged at me, pins were metal too, weren't they? So what was wrong? Why did I go into that corner in the attic where no one could see what I was doing? My vision of that Liberty Bond sustained me. "My country 'tis . . ."

I was saved from corruption, oddly enough, by what I saw as a treasonable act of my mother. Her brother, my Uncle Beb, came to visit us just before he was to go overseas. I ran to get Dolly so she could see him—my uncle, a captain of medicine, candescent in khaki. Mama invited Dolly to lunch, where we basked in Uncle Beb's glory. When Mama brought the coffee, she set the cream and sugar in front of him.

"No, thank you, Annie," he said firmly. "I don't take sugar. It's strictly rationed."

"I know it," said my mother. And to my acute embarrassment, she dumped two large spoonfuls into her cup.

"The country is short on sugar," said Uncle Beb.

"I don't believe in the war," said my mother, flatly. "Not in this one, or any one. I'm against war. That's all."

I sat numbed. It was she who had let me paste up my Liberty Bond poster, who had bought me the sheet music for "Over There" and "Pack Up Your Troubles". It was she who had dressed our three-year-old Essie in a little grey jumper and had fitted a dinner napkin into a nurse's headdress over her gold-silk hair, and had let me take Essie to my school. There, on assembly day, she was lifted onto the grand piano where she stood and gave a sweet, lilting rendition of "Keep the Home Fires Burning". Even some of the teachers wept, not just I. And here my mother sat, drinking rationed sugar and saying she was against the war to make the world safe for democracy!

And then the ugly thought swept over me: she, my own mother, was a pretending person, what was called a hypocrite. The thought sank to the bottom of my stomach. (At twelve I could not yet recognize the inconsistencies that ravage all of us at one time or another.) Suddenly I was flooded with a kind of angst. I myself was a hypocrite too, I saw, with all those pins in my foil brick.

I could hardly wait till Dolly went home. Then, telling Uncle Beb that I'd be back in a minute, I fled to the attic and feverishly broke apart my silver brick. Every pin came out. I shivered when I thought of what I had almost caused to happen. What if my country had used this brick to make bullets or cannonballs or some secret poison or whatever it had to do? And the pins had spoiled the whole effort? What if they had caused someone to lose a battle, or maybe even get killed? I realized, trembling, that I had almost been a traitor.

Not too long afterwards, the Armistice was declared. Mama wept a little, and said she was overjoyed. I said I was overjoyed too, partly because I knew I had done nothing bad to hurt my country or democracy. Bells rang and whistles tooted all over St. Paul, and I ran out into our back yard and flung my paltry silver brick into the garbage can. Because I knew there would never be another war again.

10. The Meanings of Death:
Over the Years . . .

MY EARLIEST ENCOUNTER with death, at the age of five, embroiled me in an emotional turmoil. I felt first raw pity, then hilarity, then anger and remorse. As I see it now, the pity was less for the fact that the poor little thing was dead than because he had been treated cruelly. As for the hilarity: it's not unusual to see a brief form of hysteria among adults at wakes or post-burial visits, reflecting a kind of unconscious struggle to regain equilibrium. My anger and remorse were the result of unexpected consequences, and not related to the common feeling of abandonment, amputation, helplessness at loss.

On that sweetly sunny spring morning, I came upon a dead bird under the tree in our back yard. Every child who explores playgrounds, lawns, sidewalks, finds some small wild creature dead at one time or another. A bird is something special, somehow. This one was only an untidy ball of stiff, sticky feathers. Just as I was calling Sonny to come and look at it, our neighbor Mr Shanley came ambling down the alley on his "daily constitutional".

"A jay-bird," he said. "A baby jay. Mother must of pushed it out of the nest to make it fly. Guess he didn't do so good."

"His *mother pushed* him out?"

"They all do," said Mr Shanley. "Only way you can get some baby jays to try their wings."

My heart ached for the poor thing, and I considered picking it up to pet it, but I had a sudden fear that it might burst into a frenzy of fluttering feathers in my hands. So I nudged it gently, and turned it over with the toe of my Buster Brown sandal. Now it lay on its back, its toothpick claws turned upwards as if pleading, "Help! Help me!" Poor little bird with a horrid, mean mother—maybe a wicked stepmother! There was nothing to do but bury him.

I had never seen a burial nor known anybody who had died. I suppose Mama had explained about that when, now and then, we stood at our front window and watched funerals pass on their way to the small cemetery at the edge of town. They were mysterious in a gloomily silent way. The hearse was usually drawn by two weary old horses who sometimes wore drooping black plumes on their bobbing heads; black or grey swag curtains draped the hearse windows so you could not see what was inside. Closed carriages followed, and you could catch glimpses of the people in them, stiff as boards, hatted and veiled: occasionally a gloved hand lifted a handkerchief to wipe away a tear. Plod-plod-plod they went, to stand by while the dead person was laid into the ground. Mama would look solemn, and sometimes dab at her eyes.

That was how I knew, I guess, that the little jay-bird had to be buried, and I felt a sudden elation because I knew I was going to do a good and necessary thing.

I told Sonny to go get his shovel and pail while I ran down the alley to invite my friend Dolly to the funeral. She came happily, and the three of us set about digging a wide, deep grave, into which we tenderly toed the little bird and then patted the earth into a firm mound. Now, I knew, we were supposed to cry, not just stand there smugly satisfied. In a flash of inspiration I pulled out our garden hose and instructed Dolly and Sonny to chant "Boo hoo!" as I poured water over the grave. "Boo-hoo" was what the ladies in the funnies said, in the balloons that came out of their mouths, when they cried out loud. So there we stood, graveside, boo-hooing together, drowning the little jay-bird with false tears, and laughing our heads off at our own silliness.

Mama would enjoy this, I thought, so I ran and pulled her outside to see the good thing we had done. Instead of being sad or laughing with us she screamed.

"For goodness sakes! Just look what you've *done!* Papa worked all Sunday seeding this yard—and now you've made a muddy mess of that whole corner of it! And just *look* at your new sandals! New—and soaking wet and dirty! Don't you dare come into the house with them on!" And on and on. . . .

Then I burst into real tears, tears of shock and anger. I ran around to the side of the house so I wouldn't have to see her mean-looking face, and she wouldn't see me crying. There I sat upon the ground, bawling, but no one, not even Sonny or Dolly, paid any attention. When my first paroxysm of rage had subsided I nursed my thoughts about how wicked my mother was. As mean as the jay-bird's mother. Maybe she wasn't really my own mother. I considered this uneasily; then, wiping my eyes and runny nose on my sweater sleeve, I concluded that even if she was mad at me, she really wouldn't want me to be dead. Because I knew that even if, for a moment, I had fiercely wished that *she* would be dead, it would be just for a little while. Maybe until Papa came home. Papa! Hot tears welled up again, because Papa would surely be mad at me too.

After a while, all quiet in the back yard, I decided to go in for lunch. I kicked off my sandals viciously but put them, like Goody-Two-Shoes, next to Sonny's on the porch, and I tip-toed into the kitchen where Mama had left my lunch waiting on the table. A big bowl of rice pudding it was, sprinkled over with lots of raisins and cinnamon, just the way I liked it, and a glass of milk. I supposed she really was my mother after all.

There was nothing for me to do but eat my lunch with pleasure and be very-very sorry and try to be very-very good.

✍ ✍ ✍

Almost sixty years later, my little mother lay dying, yielding to her weary heart, worn down by her eighty-seven years of vivid life. It was a warm night and her nurse had gently placed her thin arms outside the sheet that covered her crumpled-leaf body. The fingers of her hands, once strong and white, that had stroked and patted us into shape, were almost transparent. And they were curled up, as if to say "Help me!" To go? To stay a bit longer? I thought of the little jay-bird.

I learned about death—deeply—when I was not quite seven.

If it is possible to love unconditionally, unambivalently, that is how my brother Sonny and I loved our baby sister. She was as funny and darling as a little house pet. Not quite a year old, she was already toddling drunkenly between one piece of furniture and another, gasping "Oh my!" when she took a pratfall, and looking up at us quickly to learn whether this was a crying or a laughing matter.

Suddenly one day she had a bad sore throat and a high fever, and Sonny and I were packed off to stay with our grandparents who lived two blocks away. On the telephone, Mama said our baby was very sick and we could not come back into our house until she got well. But I could come after school and bring Sonny with me, and we could talk through the glass of our front door. (Front doors in those days were not the fortress doors we need today. Ours, like many others, was solid oak at the bottom and the frame; the rest was leaded and bevelled glass which caught the sun's rays and splintered them into a hundred small, winking rainbows.)

Every day when I returned from school, Sonny and I went hand-in-hand to visit Mama through the door. She stood among the rainbows, pale and tired-looking, but smiling and throwing kisses to us and we to her. We laughed together as, with gestures and exaggerated mouthing of words, she told us how beautiful she thought we were and how she wished she could hug us. Nailed on the porch wall next to the door were two signs, one red and one yellow. One said "Scarlet Fever" and the other said "Diphtheria". Those were the sicknesses our baby sister had.

On a bitter-cold morning I was shivering in front of the big-bellied, glowing stove, tugging my black stockings over my long winter underwear when the phone rang. My grandmother answered, and a terrible wail tore out from her. Our baby sister had died.

All I remember of that morning was that I was told I was not to go to school. Along with my grand-parents I wept. But I couldn't help thinking about my return to school, when I hoped I would be allowed to wear a big black taffeta bow in my hair. I had a classmate, Lizzie, who was one of a seemingly over-extended extended family, the members of which seemed strangely susceptible to death and dying. At least once a month Lizzie would be absent to go to a funeral, and she would appear the next day with a big black taffeta bow atop her orange-colored curls. In my eyes it gave her some mysterious authority and spe-cialness, and I yearned to achieve this status. Where might I find a black bow? I wondered. All the kids would cluster around me and ask "Why were you absent yesterday?" and I would bow my head with the butterfly bow and say my baby sister died, and they would fall silent respectfully and feel sorry for me. My teacher too. (For years, I realize as I set this down, I was ashamed to admit this memory to my conscious-ness; then I grew old enough to understand that the meaning of death, like the meaning of life, cannot be the same for a seven-year-old as it is for a seventeen-year-old, or, God wot, for a seventy-some-year-old.)

When all the grownups went to our little sister's funeral, Sonny and I were left in the care of our young, wet-eyed Aunt Marie. When they came back to my grandparents' house (ours had to be "fumigated" by the Health Department before we could re-enter it) they all sat down in the dark parlor, heads bowed. The heavy silence was torn only by some nose-blowing. Now and then a high whimper broke from my grandmother's lips that reminded me of a sad puppy we once had, who, Mama thought, was lonesome for his mother.

Only Mama had left the room to go into the small alcove off the dining room where she lay down on the sofa. I waited, uncertain and anxious, and then I tiptoed in to be with her. But she kept her eyes closed and turned her face to the wall. So, shivering, I went back to find Papa, but he sat with the group like a stone man, as if he could neither see nor hear.

I felt abandoned. I drew my stricken-faced Sonny with me into the hallway. There in the umbrella stand was my grandmother's umbrella that she had promised would be mine when I grew up. Its fruit-wood handle was topped by a cluster of scarlet celluloid cherries. I put my mouth around them and sucked them for a while, wondering what Sonny and I should do to make the family happy again. Then it came to me. Sonny and I had often put on the hats and coats of our elders from the hall coat rack and pranced into the parlor to "give a show". That winter we had two routines: we'd put our arms around each other and hop and jiggle in what we imagined was the current dance craze—the "turkey trot", or was it the "bunny hug"?—singing the ragtime song that went with it. Our second act was an arm-in-arm strut cakewalk taught us by our cute and flirty Cousin Jennie to a song named "Handsome Harry". We loved that one because it allowed for elaborate gestures (rolled eyes, wagged fingers and backsides) and it advised the listeners never to take out any girl except the one named Daisy. Why? " 'Cause daisies don't tell!" Tell what? one said, and the other one would answer, That you took her for a walk, silly goose. That always brought the house down. The family would die laughing and clap and say we should be on the Orpheum vaudeville circuit.

It struck me now that this was what we should do. When we burst into the parlor with the big coats dragging on the floor and the hats falling over our ears one of my uncles said "Hush!" sharply, and leaped up to shoo us out. Then, like some giant rescuing bird, Papa swooped down upon us and swept us, one in each arm, back into his chair and onto his lap. He held us tightly to him, and in a strangulated whisper he said, "Your baby sister is dead. You will never, never see her anymore."

I dug my head into his vest and felt his body shuddering with unuttered sobs. I was afraid to look up at him, but I put my hand up to pat his face and found his cheek awash with hot tears. Now, deep in the bottom of my stomach, I knew the meaning of death. It was when your mother could not look at you and when your father wept.

✍ ✍ ✍

Seventh grade. Outside our classroom's tall windows that had to be opened or closed by long, hooked window-poles, there shone October's bright blue weather, far more tempting and rare than a day in June. Seated at her heavy desk was Miss Sexton, contentedly fat, pleasantly placid, quiet but firm in manner and voice. We were going to start memorizing poetry and sayings "by heart", she said. The first was to be eight lines from a poem she had chosen called "Thanatopsis". It was written by William Cullen Bryant, one of our country's great poets, and it was about death. Thanatos was the name of the Greek god of death, she explained, and "opsis" meant something like thinking about something.

There we were, girls and boys, average age thirteen, all but bursting with the newly overflowing juices of the life-force, and there sat Miss Sexton, telling us we were to think about death. We listened silently as we were directed to copy down the lines Miss Sexton had already painstakingly written on the blackboard:

> So live that when thy summons come to join
> The innumerable caravan which moves
> To that mysterious realm, where each shall take
> His chamber in the silent halls of death
> Thou go not like the quarry slave at night
> Scourged to his dungeon, but sustained and soothed
> Like one who wraps the draperies of his couch
> About him and lies down to pleasant dreams.

Then Miss Sexton read aloud the longish first part of the poem, pointing out how Mr Bryant loved the beauty of Nature, but that he understood that all living things must die, by Nature's laws. But she said that "So live . . ." were the important words to think about. By the week's end we were to have learned those lines. Any questions? There were none. Most of us, I guess, were either stupified or just plain mystified, but who would admit it?

Uncertain as I was about why we had to learn this, I found myself captured by the piece as I studied it. Perhaps it was the delicate imagery that it set afloat in my mind: that endless caravan of high-headed camels and silent, white-robed walkers, silhouetted against a pale violet desert sky. I liked the idea of a chamber of my own (though I hoped it would have a window) since what was once my very own room I now had to share with two little sisters. I recalled pictures I'd seen of draped Greek statues and effigies of kings and queens, all serene and elegant in their sculptured death-sleeps.

Or perhaps I was impressed with Miss Sexton's earnestness as she explained the poem; maybe, I thought, *she* was going to die in not too long a time. I still wonder today what made her choose "Thanatopsis" as our introduction to the memorization of poems or literary passages, a practice that would continue throughout high school English classes. Whatever criterion of utility or beauty or virtue had determined her choice for seventh-graders? Especially since poems about love, springtime, the buoyant joys of life, and the beauty of the world about us would have been closer to our hearts and were as abundantly strewn about for the picking as dandelions in April meadows.

And why, I ask myself, do those eight lines persist in my mind-and-heart memory, arising now and again to actively influence my reflections and behaviors? Of which more later.

When the time came, I was called on to stand in front of the class and recite the stanza, to be followed by a chorus recitation by all of us together. I remember the fixed, glassy-eyed stare of my classmates as they listened to my solo recitation, and my sense of being somehow a representative of William Cullen Bryant: I must not let him down. Then, when Miss Sexton praised me, I felt that in some way "Thanotopsis" had become my poem: I possessed, or was possessed by, it.

After school I hurried home, eager to try it out in action. The setting was rather discouraging. We had no couch; our maroon plush sofa would have to do; such draperies as we had hung listlessly at the windows. Then I thought of a new Hudson's Bay blanket I'd been given recently in preparation for the coming winter—cuddly, creamy-white it was, with bold stripes of red, green, yellow and black across it. I fetched it out and wrapped it clumsily and heavily about me (it *would* not drape!). Thus, sustained and soothed, I lay me down upon the sofa—and there came Mama.

"What's the matter, honey?" she asked anxiously, her hand swift to my forehead. "Are you sick?"

No, I was not. Somewhat resentful at having been thwarted in my rehearsal for death, I explained sheepishly that I was trying out a recitation for which I had been praised by Miss Sexton.

"How nice!" Mama said. "Recite it for me!"

Up I got, gladly, unwrapping myself, to stand "straight as an arrow" as we'd been taught to do for recitations. Mama sat rapt, her hands folded, her dark-amber eyes glowing with pleasure, drinking in every word. Then, quietly, she joined me. "—sustained and soothed, as one who—"

I was astonished. "Do you know it too, Mama?"

Indeed she did! The whole thing—well, maybe she'd lost a line or two—but it had been one of the required "memorizations by heart" in her senior class in the Girls' High School of Atlanta, Georgia, 1898.

She reached out and hugged me tightly, and I hugged her. A swelling sense of a new kind of bond between us arose in me. Bound as we already were by love and the continuous linkages of daily family life, we were drawn together more tightly by a long-dead poet who had opened for us both a fresh perspective by which to view life and death. I felt elated that Mama and I had begun to inhabit the same world.

11. The Spoiler: *"Shades of the Prison House Begin to Close . . ."*

MISS BRIDGES WAS the frosting on the cake. Even the Board of Education must have realized that, because she had been saved for last, for the eighth grade. Even the dummies looked forward to her class, not only because it marked the end of their incarceration in school but because stories about Miss Bridges regularly trickled down the school grapevine, to the anticipatory delight of all of us.

She was *fun*, the kids said, tough but fun. For one thing, she swore all the time. Not nasty words, but she'd bust out loud with things like "Great Scot!" or "Jumping Jehosephat!" as in "Jumping Jehosephat, George, get your head off your desk and get to work!" or "Tarnation" as in "Tarnation! I don't have a decent piece of chalk in this whole darn room!" For another thing, she laughed a lot, and, if you passed her open door on your way through the hall, you would often hear her and her kids laughing their heads off.

She had burning-orange hair, ratted in front to form a pompadour, but her side- and back-locks kept falling down, in spite of the variety of bone and wire hairpins she'd twist into her fiery mop, muttering under her breath as she did so. She stood out among the other teachers like a macaw among sparrows. Most of them dressed somberly, but Miss Bridges wore scarlet or pink-and-green plaid shirtwaists with khaki-colored skirts that some malicious rumor-monger said were made out of the old uniforms her fellow must have worn during the war. She gave the impression of being a vibrant, cheery, slap-dash but no-nonsense lady, whether she was sitting at attention in school assemblies, taking her turn in the hallway or clapping her hands to set the rhythms of our marching to and from the school's doors.

As I look back, it is clear that Miss Bridges was an original, a natural-born teacher. She understood children and had an engaging way of involving them in striving to learn; it is very doubtful that all this was instilled in her by the teacher-training schools of her day (called "normal schools", for some mysterious reason). Imaginative herself, she was swiftly responsive to imagination in her pupils, and she gave pleased attention and breathing space to such small evidences of creativity as they evinced. She cherished both the children she taught and the subject matters they were to learn. (If only she could have been multiplied by the thousands unto the present generation!)

It was in my first weeks in Miss Bridges' class, that I decided that one of the things I wanted when I grew up was to be a teacher. In part I was fired by the sense of warm devotion that flowed between this teacher and her pupils but also, I confess, by the heady prospect of being in charge of an eager, orderly but free populace in an encompassable kingdom. I became acutely aware, too, that while up to this point I had looked forward to finishing grade school, I now felt some hesitancy, some reluctance to leave this nurturant and stimulating eighth grade Eden and the lovingly guiding and demanding human being who governed it.

Ironically, it was while in this demi-paradise that I first glimpsed the ugly face of human evil.

The day had started happily. It was one of those tender golden days of Minnesota's Indian summer. Down the street the yellow water-wagon waddled behind the heavy-rumped horses that pulled it. From the rear end two crystal wings of water arched out, gently tamping down the golden dust of the street. The scent of leaf-smoke stirred some sweet-sad awareness that it was the beginning of the end—of what? Summertime? Grade school? Childhood? In the empty schoolyard, not yet dotted with children because it was early, the mellow limestone schoolhouse sat like a fat tabby cat, warming itself in the sun. It seemed to me infinitely more beautiful and desirable than the newly built, too big and overpowering high school I was soon to enter.

I had taken to coming early to Miss Bridges' class. It gave me a few private minutes in her presence, and she would let me help her by watering the geraniums that sometimes bloomed but mostly wilted on the window sills, or by washing the blackboards with a big mushy Greek sponge. That morning, as I finished the last board, Miss Bridges gave me a quick thank-you hug, and began to write a series of sentences on the dried board in bright green chalk. When the class came in, she told them that we were going to have composition time first today, so "Out with your pencils and pads". She then explained that what she had written down were "sayings". We were to choose one of them and write either a story or a composition that would explain what that saying meant to us. The list (as nearly as I can recall) consisted of these (or like) statements:

> Honesty is the best policy.
> Haste makes waste.
> Hope springs eternal in the human breast.
> Beauty is only skin deep.
> Satan finds mischief for idle hands to do.

I knew at once what I would write about: "Hope springs eternal". "Hope," I wrote, "is a feeling that you want to go onward. It is like a dream, not one that is past but one that is always ahead of you." I raced on to tell my hope that I might become a teacher like Miss Bridges — but then I swiftly erased those last three words because it sounded like a toady. I wanted to be a teacher who loved children and wanted to help them learn. Or, maybe I would be a writer who might make other people feel hopeful. Hope has some sadness in it too, I thought, because you may be disappointed after all. But somehow it would lift up its head again, like a small bird waking up in the morning. (I had not yet read or heard the lines that Emily Dickinson had penned many years before: "Hope is the thing with feathers/That perches in the soul." Nor, of course, did I know that the saying I was struggling to elucidate was that of yet another poet, Alexander Pope.) I rushed ahead, feverishly searching to express the experience I was having that morning of looking back with longing on the familiar things I wanted to stay with forever, and looking forward with anticipation to the new and unknown. That was a little scary, but I hoped. . . .

Several of us were not yet done when Miss Bridges called time, but she said she'd settle for as far as we'd gone. Then she called on that week's captain to lead us in our body exercises. Each week she appointed a different pupil to take us through our daily required ten minutes of stretching, breathing deeply (windows wide open, whatever the weather) and walking on the balls of our feet, which Mr Hall, the physical education supervisor, had decreed was the proper way to walk. So we stretched, breathed, and wobbled up and down the aisles between the fixed desks while that week's leader called the shots—"Stretch! Breathe! Up on your balls!" While we did all that, Miss Bridges flipped through our papers to select which should be read aloud for class discussion.

Suddenly she called me to her desk. "This," she said quietly, holding out my paper, "is a beautiful composition." She would like me to show it to someone she was sure would enjoy it. Miss Bridges' eyes looked sort of teary, so my eyes watered too. She wanted me to take it to Miss Tibault.

Miss Tibault was the principal. Her office was not unfamiliar to me. I had often been a message-bearer from a teacher to this office, and sometimes a guide to school visitors. In the outer room, all shiny and sunny-looking in polished oak, sat shriveled Miss Nolan, the principal's assistant and secretary. Miss Nolan always said, "Yes?" as if it were a question, and as though this question meant the same as "Hello" or "What is it you want?" She took your proffered slip of paper, or handed one to you, or motioned the visitor to sit down on one of the hard, slippery benches that faced each other at the office entrance—all this without ever really looking at you. The door to Miss Tibault's office was always closed; it was opened only by the unseeing Miss Nolan, to let someone in or take something out, or by Miss Tibault herself when, occasionally, she came sweeping out, like a dark wind.

She was a tall, iron-grey-colored woman who showed herself only rarely. She walked imperiously, so swiftly that her long, full, black skirt trailed a little wind behind it. When important visitors came to observe classes she would accompany them, placing herself in the background and watching—was it mockingly?—the performances of the gracious visitor, the flustered teacher and the all-but-petrified class. If you passed her in the hall and said, "Good morning, Miss Tibault," she would return your greeting with a little sidewise smile, and move on. When the whole school gathered for special assemblies, she would stand before us, regal in her high-collared shirtwaist, fastening her large grey smoldering eyes upon us until the very silence shuddered. Then, in a voice at once quiet and resonant, she would welcome us as if we were guests. She would tell us the reason for our being there—a speech from the superintendent of schools, a graduation exercise, a celebration of a national holiday like Thanksgiving (and oh! how great my pride when once I was chosen to be "the spirit of corn" in a pageant!). Often she would end with a few lines of poetry, a quotation from the Bible or Shakespeare or a patriotic slogan, and your spine would prickle at something in her voice or message. As she passed down the aisle to take her accustomed seat in the back row, you sensed in her some charged, pent-up power that could have no possible outlet in this small homely place.

The door to Miss Tibault's office was closed, as usual, and Miss Nolan said "Yes?" as usual, and, in response to my explanation of why I was there, she waved me to one of the benches to wait.

Seated on the opposite bench was a woman, still as stone, her face so yellow as to seem to be part of the bench. Her eyelids were lowered, and the only sign of life in her motionless body was a jumping twitch of a vein in the hand that clutched her frayed shawl tightly around her. Somebody's mother or grandmother, I thought, watching her, feeling sorry for her because she looked poor, wondering why she seemed to be cold on this warm day.

Then it struck me that this must be one of the "toughies' " mothers. The toughies had only recently come into our school; they were dark-skinned, with straight black hair that needed cutting. Their fathers had come up from another country — Mexico? — to work in St. Paul's expanding railroad yards. The children, mostly boys, were ragged and dirty-looking in our spotless, light-skinned, predominantly Scandinavian school population. You sometimes felt sorry for them but then they would act mean and rough, and most of us felt safer keeping clear of them; we were uncomfortable with their halting, sometimes unintelligible speech, and wary of the hostility which seemed to lie under both their crude, teasing behavior or their dark, stand-off silence. They had been put into a special class, big and little ones together, to help them "catch up", it was said. At recess on the playground, they clustered together. Sometimes a bold one would try to intrude on a game, or a timid one would stand outside the group, watching—were they sad or mad?—but usually they would be called back by one of their own group. When school was out they ran, cat-calling, swatting and teasing one another, in the opposite direction from the rest of us, to some long-abandoned shacks near the railroad yards.

Behind the shut door of Miss Tibault's office, there was a sudden rise of voices. Then I heard a heavy sound—thud-thud-thud—and a raucous, tortured shriek tore the air: it ripped through the walls and rocketed about the outer office. I froze. I looked to the woman across from me for some sign of meaning, but she only moved to tighten her grip on her shawl. I looked to Miss Nolan, but her white head was bent over papers, unheeding. Now again—thud-thud-thud-thud—and the screams came fast upon one another, as if, torn from the guts of an animal. The room rocked with the counterpoint of thud and shriek. Then, silence. I trembled uncontrollably, but I sat still, my eyes fixed on Miss Tibault's door.

It opened, and a big boy shuffled out, bent over, his black head bobbing and jerking, half-hidden in the crook of his arm. His stomach heaved against the torn rope belt that held up his pants, and as he passed between the two benches I saw that his shirt was sweated through, plastered against his back in dark streaks. Still bent over, his face still hidden, he stopped before his mother. She rose stiffly, and suddenly, her eyes dilated with anger, she made a fist and struck the boy a swift, violent blow between his shoulder blades. He lurched forward, cried out hoarsely, and then he rubbed his dirty sleeve across his face to mop up his running eyes and nose, and wet, slobbering mouth.

When they had gone down the hall, I turned and saw Miss Tibault standing in her doorway, erect and cool in her crisp, starched shirtwaist, smiling her half-smile.

"I understand Miss Bridges sent you to see me," she said. I stood up, blind and mute, and held out my pages at arm's length.

"Come in," said Miss Tibault, in her deep quiet voice. "Sit down."

I went through her door and onto the chair next to her desk.

"So!" she said, looking at me closely, and then she read aloud my name and grade from the top of the paper. "Do you like school?"

"Yes, ma'am," I whispered. "I do."

"I'm glad to hear that," said she. "I'm glad to know that there still are children who like school."

"Yes, ma'am." I was unable to look at her. But she put a finger under my chin, tilted my head up and searched my face.

"Are you afraid of me?" she asked, and I said no, ma'am, I was not.

"No good child needs to be afraid of me," she said. "No good citizen ever needs to be afraid." She seemed to be waiting for a response, so I whispered that I knew that.

But I was afraid, with a fear that I have never known before. I could not have put it into words.

I was not afraid that Miss Tibault would do something to me. It was rather an ominous presentiment that in my golden world, unseen but hideous forces of evil lurked, leashed but ready to spring.

Miss Tibault turned to read my composition, and I watched her, still trembling, trying to hold my stomach still by clasping my hands tightly across it. Her finely sculpted nostrils quivered slightly as she read, as if she were smelling something delicious.

I dared now to look about her office, which I had never seen in all my years in school. It was a quietly elegant room. Several intricately patterned fringed rugs lay on the dark, polished floor; fresh lace curtains hung at the windows; and preening itself in the sunlight was a great burst of green fern in a shining brass jardiniere. Next to the desk was a bookcase, full of books. Against the opposite wall stood a gleaming dark-wood table, big as a bed, and empty, except for a glass vase of bright purple asters pushed into one corner. And next to that lay a cut-off piece of a rubber garden hose.

I could hear the loud sound of my heart in my chest, and I was afraid that Miss Tibault might hear it too. But she was just finishing the last sentence of my paper and smiling.

"I see you didn't quite finish this," she said. "I would like to see it again when it's done." She rose and again put a finger under my chin. "This is a beautiful composition," she said, "and you are a lovely child. Take this back to Miss Bridges and tell her I'm grateful—" But I scarcely heard her for the thudding of my heart and the palsy of my body. I kept wanting to look again to see if the rubber hose was still there on the table.

She held out my composition, and I faltered to my feet. I shook my head mutely. "I don't really want it," I said.

"Oh, but you must, my child," Miss Tibault said coaxingly. "You must finish it. It is a lovely piece."

"I don't want it anymore," I heard myself saying,

and I was frightened at the raised pitch of my own voice in this quiet place. Sweat poured over me, and I reached for the doorknob. But Miss Tibault was upon me. "Whatever is the matter, child?" she asked, and she cradled my shoulder with her arm.

"I don't want to finish it!" I cried. "It's spoiled! It's all spoiled!" I broke from her arm and fled from the office. Then I suddenly remembered the rule about no running in the halls, so I checked my flight abruptly, and tip-toed back to Miss Bridges' room.

What happened thereafter I do not remember. Surely I must have seen Miss Tibault again, certainly at graduation time, and she and Miss Bridges must have had some talk about this high-strung, over-wrought child. And did I not tell Mama about the whole thing? I cannot recall.

One thing I know. This century has presented a glut of events that have roused my memory of that quarter hour in Miss Tibault's office. Sometimes I have thought that, unwittingly, she prepared me better than any teaching I had had to face the existence of human evil, to ponder on its many facets and guises, to wonder why, for instance, evil is more hideous and violating when it manifests itself in cold blood rather than in passion, when it is the product of "reason" rather than of madness.

12. I Was Charlie Chaplin's Wife: *Transition from Childhood*

IT WAS IN the spring not long after my thirteenth birthday that we suddenly became poor. Because of that I got mad at my parents. Because of that I read my first movie magazine. Because of that I entered and won a contest—no, it had nothing to do with beauty or talent, as you will see. And because of that I became Charlie Chaplin's wife.

Always before, at the end of school, we had packed up and gone off to the lake for the summer. (Minnesota has ten thousand lakes, but we Minnesotans simply said "to the lake" no matter which it was.) Sonny and I both loved the lake. So we were shocked when, on a sickly grey day in March, Mama announced that we would not be able to go there the coming summer. By the way she snapped it out and set her mouth tight, and by the way Papa stayed behind his newspaper, we knew better than to argue. Mama went on to say that Papa had bought us this nice new house we were living in and it was all we could do to make ends meet. Whatever that meant.

A funny thing was happening to me on my way to adolescence. I had always felt at one with Mama and Papa. If they had worried about something, I had worried about it too. But now I found myself indignant with them. Something was pretty wrong, I thought, if parents didn't know how to make ends meet. Not long before, when I had suggested that since I was thirteen my weekly allowance ought to be raised above fifty cents, they talked to me about my extravagances. Now I felt like talking to *them* — but my courage failed me. So instead I confided in my best friend, Ada.

Ada thought it was a darn shame about my parents' dereliction. With her unfailing generosity she offered to lend me her latest copy of a movie magazine — in fact, I could borrow the whole stack she kept under her bed. Ada got these — and twenty-five cents an hour — as payment for babysitting for some children whose mother went out to play mah-jongg. Ada had proffered them to me before, but as I was reasonably sure that Mama would not approve of such trash, I had put that temptation behind me. Now I grabbed at it, determined to do as I pleased. Parents aren't perfect, I grumbled to myself, part-proud to have discovered that, and part-scared at my heady sense of independence.

It was a new world that I found as I riffled the pages of those magazines.

First thing I saw there was that Theda Bara was the daughter of a fabled Oriental potentate and that she had trunk-loads of fabulous jewels and that her mother had weaned her on serpents' blood. Now I understood why she had both fascinated and repelled me when I'd once seen her in a movie. Another article cheered me, however. It said that Mary Pickford was — I remember the exact words — "as cute and coy and kittenish" in real life as she was on the silver screen. Maybe, I thought, maybe someday I might be. . . .

Then opportunity knocked. On a back page a contest was announced. It offered ten dollars and publication if you would write about a moviemaker's mistake you'd caught. Out came my trusty fountain pen. That very week I had seen and recounted to Mama a movie in which Wally Reid had leapt out of his snappy roadster bare-headed, had gone into a friend's house briefly, and had come out with a jaunty automobile cap on his head! (No, Mama, he was *not* picking up the cap he'd left there the day before. That wasn't why he went in there!) Off went my letter. Within a few weeks, back came a check for ten dollars, and not long thereafter my letter was in print.

At that time Charlie Chaplin was married to a film star named Mildred Harris. I had seen her in several pictures — a blond, thin-arch-browed, Cupid's-bow-lipped young woman whose intense, agitated acting made me somewhat nervous but whose beauty was undeniable. I was pleased that my last name was Harris, too — and now it was clearly printed in a movie magazine along with my address on Ashland Avenue, St. Paul, Minnesota. (I had left off adding U.S.A., Western Hemisphere, The Word, The Universe, when I graduated from grade school.)

To my incredulous delight, letters began to drift in from people all over the country who wrote me either as Mildred, their "favorite movie star", or as Charlie Chaplin's wife. One batch was fan letters from people who asked how to become a movie star. I showed the first few to Mama, but she said (meanly, I thought) that the world was full of morons, so I quit showing her everything. After chewing the end of my pen a lot, I did ask Mama what you'd have to do to become a movie star. She laughed and shrugged and said you'd have to be very pretty and talented and ready to take a lot of hard knocks. If she had ever heard of the casting couch—which there is reason to believe existed even then—she did not speak of it to me. But really, she said, it was kind of a silly question, wasn't it?

Not to me. I answered all queries conscientiously. They gave me purpose and occupation, and as I wrote I found rising in me a new sense of authority and power. I told of all the hardships that had to be conquered to climb the ladder of fame. I signed my real name, and I never heard from any of those fans again. Either they were saddened by the prospects I'd set before them, or maybe they got smart.

But the letters that addressed me as Charlie Chaplin's wife were more exciting and problematic. One or two said they loved me *and* Charlie. One asked how such a beautiful woman as I could stand living with that baggy-pantsed clown. The most intriguing letter grew into a correspondence across the seas and across the summer. It was from an American soldier in the Philippines.

His name was George and he was a fan of mine. He went to every movie I was in, not that there were many where he was. He begged my pardon, but it was just one big h—l hole where he was, "hotter than blazes, pesky inseks, people who can't even speak English, and lonely as h—l". Would I write to him? Pretty please, even if I was married to Charlie Chaplin? He would be highly honored if I would be his pen pal.

Two things bothered me. The first was that George wrote on stationery of a passionate magenta, deckle-edged in gold. When I showed the letter to Ada she said it looked like paper from a "*wh*ore-house". (We both pronounced that with the full "*wh*" sound.) I was somewhat taken aback, since I had already encountered the word and its derogatory meaning somewhere in my readings (Shakespeare?), and Ada and I had laughed our heads off not long before when she had come upon the title of John Ford's play, " 'Tis Pity She's a Whore", and toyed briefly with identifying someone of our acquaintance to whom this could be applied. However, I had assumed that this term had gone out with the seventeenth century, along with buskins, ods blood, lanthorns and the like. I decided that Ada was probably jealous of me, and that took care of the pink and gold paper problem.

Far more difficult was the problem of my name. If I signed "Helen" I might never hear from George again, as had happened with my earlier fans. Yet, as I had bitterly learned when I had taken my brother's name in vain, it was a kind of crime to use the name of another, and I did not dare risk becoming a juvenile delinquent.

The solution came in one of those creative leaps. I had no given middle name. Once, when I complained about this to Mama, she said I was lucky because I could choose one myself. I recalled that when my Catholic friend, Gertrude, was confirmed she had taken the name Margaret so that she could be called Meg, as in *Little Women*, instead of Gertie. Now, at last, I knew I would choose Mildred as my true middle name.

I ran into the kitchen, where Mama was busy cooking and Sonny was hanging around, and announced my decision. Mama cried, "Mildred! I declare! But *why?*" But she did not wait for an answer. She was very self-centered that spring, it seemed to me—maybe because we were poor, or maybe because she was really a selfish woman, which I had never noticed before. Anyhow, I wasn't going to tell her as many things as I used to. Of course, Sonny had to put his two cents in. "Mildred!" he sniffed. "That's a pewky name!" It was not easy to mind your own business and have other people mind theirs in our household. Even the mailman, when he delivered the next letter from George, inquired mildly, "Who's Mildred around here?" "*Me!*" I said, snatching at the pink envelope. "That's really my name."

I had written to George expressing compassion for how hot he was, how miserable insects can make a person feel, how sad it was to be far away from home and all alone. I sure felt sorry for him, I said. I did not mention my husband. I said I had looked up the Philippines in an old geography book, and they seemed very wild and interesting. He should try to be cheerful. Sincerely—Mildred.

Back came George's answer as fast as ship and train could carry it. Same stationery, same complaints. But my letter had made him feel "real good". He had read it three times. He wanted to "ax a big favor". Would I send him a picture of myself? Autographed? That he could show to his buddies? He hoped it would be all right with Charlie. George would be watching and waiting.

The picture request was a stopper, but not for long. I wrote that I had been far too busy with my career to take time out for portraits (which was true, I told my murmuring conscience). And, as the seed of deceit sprouted, I was pretty sure that Charlie wouldn't really care if we wrote to each other, (which was also true). Besides, Charlie and I were very proud of our boys who were helping Uncle Sam to save democracy all over the world. (I *hoped* that was true.)

That "Charlie and I" began to grow on me—the Mildred, wife, movie-star persona. I thought a lot about it, swinging idly on our front porch in the afternoon, looking up at our sky-blue ceiling. She was very beautiful, I knew, and so she must be good and kind, too. Mama had always said that goodness shone out of people's faces. I resolved to work on being more kind and good, even to Sonny. I supposed that Mildred's goodness must have been the reason for her marrying Charlie, because I had to admit that he was ugly as sin, and jerky, and never even cracked a smile. She must have felt sorry for him.

"Charlie," I said on the swing, "where shall we go out to dinner tonight? Where shall we drive to in our limousine, with the silken curtains pulled down and the perfect tea rose you gave me nodding in the backseat vahz?" But Charlie would only shrug, and tip his derby, and swing his cane. Worst of all, his pants looked as if they were about to fall down. "Charlie, dear heart," I coaxed, "could you put on a different suit for going out in?" But he'd only look at me with those eyes that were like black holes in a white paper face and waddle away. It was not easy to be Charlie's wife.

In the mirror of my dresser I practiced moues and arched brows. I could not know what Mildred's voice was like, but I was reasonably sure it was gentler and more refined than mine, so I practiced lowering my pitch and pacing my words. At dinner, I announced that henceforth I was going to call Mama and Papa "Mother" and "Father". Papa said that was fine with them, but did I have to make such silly faces with it? Mama laughed and said he should "leave the child alone" *(child!)*, that I was having growing pains. Life with them was impossible.

But when I went out to the porch swing, Charlie wasn't much help. "Charlie, sweetheart," I said, "let's have a big party with butlers and maids and fountains and lights and invite our best friends, like Wally Reid and Mary Pickford and Douglas Fairbanks—but not Theda Bara—and I will wear the diamond bracelet you gave me—" But he only waddled away. I began to wonder how long I could stay married to him.

George's next letter began "Dear pen-pal, sweetheart." He would be looking for my picture. He would cover it with kisses. He hoped "ha-ha" that I would not show this letter to Charlie. But maybe Charlie had a good sense of "umor". Seemed like. Anyways—when he got back to the good old USA he would try to get together with me. To tell the honest truth, he wanted to press his lips to mine, not just to my picture. Boy oh boy! A series of Xs followed.

I panicked. I did not want to meet, much less press lips with, a hot, sweaty, flea-bitten, dirty soldier who wrote on *wh*orehouse stationery. Worse, he probably didn't want to meet me—a shortie with babyish bobbling plain brown curls and eyeglasses.

I took the coward's way out. I did not reply. I resolutely pulled the stack of movie magazines out from under my bed and gave them back to Ada, and I took George's letters up to my old toy trunk in the attic and laid them on top of Gwendolyn, my dead jointed doll. (That was where I found and avidly reread them when Mama sold our house some years after Papa's death.)

School was already in full session when George's last letter arrived. He had been looking for a letter from me, but no luck. He hoped he hadn't insulted me, or maybe made Charlie mad. He could hardly wait to get out of that h—l hole. What saddened me was his valediction: "yrs. respeckfully", without a single X.

I felt awful. I wished I'd never entered that rotten old contest. Especially since my ten dollars had been frittered away on all those writing tablets and postage stamps and those other movie mags I bought, and—oh, yes—treating both Ada and Sonny to a double chocolate marshmallow banana split, Ada in gratitude, and Sonny in a flush of compassion for his unrelieved poverty.

Funny thing: after school was in full swing my parents became much less obnoxious. And when Ada came to me breathlessly one day to announce that Charlie and Mildred were getting divorced, I told her loftily that it was no surprise to me at all.

13. The Pear and the Worm:
Sex Education in the Dark Ages

I AM IN the unsteadying life stage of recurring astonishment. I push a small button on the TV and am confronted in vivid color with the writhing bodies of two people tumbling about under sheets that only partly conceal their nakedness. And they're really nice people too, it turns out!

I pay my entry fee and buy my tub of popcorn and feel my way to a cushy seat in the movie house — and find larger than life people on the screen assaulting one another with three- or four-letter words that, when I was a girl, were never said aloud, or were bleeped out, or spelled with only the first letter, a dash, and the last. And I recall with affection that stern, upright black janitor I knew at the New York public school where I was the school social worker. Once a week Mr Jason took a small brush and can of paint into the boys' and girls' "washrooms" to transform two words that were repeatedly inked onto the walls and booth doors from what they were into BOOK and SHIRTS.

At home, I settle down in the pleasant anticipation of reading a highly acclaimed new book by a highly acclaimed author and find his characters engaging in licit, illicit, explicit sexual orgies or fantasies that even she who runs, flipping pages as she goes, may read.

My astonishment, let me make clear, is not that these leisure-time activities take place. After all there was the forbidden Tree of Knowledge in the Garden of Eden and Lot's daughters and all that, way back before I was born. My amazement, rather, is that within only a few decades there has been such radical change in the attitudes and values of masses of people about matters that for centuries were hidden from sight, repressed, suppressed, spoken of, if at all, in whispers or euphemisms, considered to be shameful, bad, ugly, disgraceful, dangerous. How does it happen, I wonder? How can the accrual of the standards of generations, of reiterated must-nots and ought-nots and what-is-right and what-is-wrong collapse in a few short years, to be replaced by what-you-will? I am astonished, you see, by the apparent flexibility — or is it the fragility? — of mores and values that impel or impede human behavior.

So much for the preface to my recollections of my own sex education. If you are under forty you may find them incredible, but I daresay it was probably not too different from that of many others of my superannuated generation.

My awareness of the major difference between the male and female anatomy came early, when my little brother was born. He had a dingle-dangle which (I am embarrassed to confess, Dr. Freud) seemed rather unfinished to me, like some raggle-taggle piece of fabric that should have been tucked in.

As I grew older, however, I recognized its usefulness in performing elimination functions on the long, hot automobile rides we often took on Sundays to visit cousins or to the concert at the bandstand in Como Park. (This, of course, was long before "rest areas" and gas stations offered their amenities to the small bladders of children who'd had too much lemonade or watermelon.) Sonny could get out anywhere on the road and relieve himself at the car-side; he didn't have to find a bush and stoop down behind it and be careful not to splash his patent leather Mary Janes. That was my benighted basis for what I later learned was called "penis envy".

I suppose even at this late date I should be further ashamed to admit that when I first encountered Freud, some sixty years ago (in that courageous but turgid translation by Brill) I was amazed to learn that a girl was destined to be envious of the penis. Sonny and I had slept in the same bed together until I was six-ish and he three, and the only part of his anatomy that really held interest for me were his feet, and even that interest was a seasonal condition. Sonny always had warm feet, even in wintertime, while mine were always cold. So in those icy, crystalline Minnesota nights I would coax or bribe Sonny to let me warm my feet on his. Sometimes he would be generous, but at other times he would complain, and so loudly as to bring Mama running to scold him or me or both of us, and tell us to just go to sleep. As if we didn't know what we were supposed to do.

Many years later I came to recognize and accept the non-literal, non-genital meaning of "penis envy". It had high applicability to the dominant position of men in what was clearly a male-controlled society.

Once, when I was in my twenties and an avid student in an advanced seminar taught by one of the country's leading psychoanalysts, I timidly ventured a question. Was it possible, I asked, that some men might experience "breast or womb envy" because of the manifest nurture and caring and life-giving functions these organs offered? In the silence that followed no pin dropped. My would-be teacher and my classmates stared at me in dismay and disbelief. Then, with a wide smile of crocodile compassion he uttered a one-syllable word. "No." (But nobody can keep me from wondering.)

As I have said, my family talked and discussed everything. Except sex. I do recall a small tiff between my mother and Cousin Daisy, in which Mama defended Emma Goldman's advocacy of "free love". "But she's an anarchist!" Cousin Daisy protested. Mama said she didn't care what her politics were—if she wanted free love that was her business. Wasn't all love free, I wondered? But I did not pursue this because I knew that Mama thought Cousin Daisy was not very bright, and anything that Daisy proposed Mama disposed of, whether she herself believed what Daisy said or not.

My first conscious curiosity about adult sex was when I was about eight. My mother took me with her to a matinee at the Blue Mouse Theater where Clara Kimball Young was starring in a movie that Mama wanted to see. At the beginning of the movie I was mostly involved in cracking, peeling and munching the peanuts Mama had bought me on the way to the theater—a big ten-cent bagful—so I have little recollection of the story as it unfolded on the screen. Then, suddenly Mama found that the new face-veil she had worn and had removed so as not to have to see the movie through black chenille dots, had slipped off her lap and was somewhere on the floor. I scrambled about in the dark under the seats to try to find it, bumping my head, spilling a lot of my peanuts, which I then tried to retrieve. When I couldn't find the veil, Mama told me to for heavens sake get up and sit down and be quiet.

When I settled back into my seat, there was Clara Kimball Young casting large sad eyes at a velvet case being shown her by a tall, white-faced, dark-lipped man. He opened the case, and in it lay a string of pearls. He lifted them out, and tenderly fastened them about her neck. At this she turned, and with a mournful intensity she said (that is, the printed words on the screen said she said) "I will be your wife. But in name only." I quick-whispered to Mama, asking what that meant, but she said to hush, she would tell me later.

Soon as we got out I asked again. Mama said she was *sick* that she had lost her veil, and it was a rotten movie anyhow. Responding to my insistence, she said it meant that Clara Kimball Young would marry this man but she wouldn't love him. This mystified me. I had assumed that you only married a person you loved, and vice versa. I myself was the author of a long, two-and-a-half-page story in which a princess had chosen to marry a shepherd boy simply because she loved him most of all her suitors, and, as my title proclaimed, "Love is Better than Grandeur". So I remained as much in the dark as I had been in the Blue Mouse, under the seats.

At suppertime, as she ladled out our soup, Mama told Papa about our afternoon, and I snatched at the chance to ask again why the lady would marry someone she didn't love. I was aware of an amused glance that arched over my head between Mama and Papa. Mama replied that it was beyond her, and that was why the movie was so silly. So there I was, and there was sex education, muffled in the bosom of a warm, middle-class, expressive, fairly sophisticated family in the second decade of the twentieth century.

Nor was I actually prepared for the onset of menses. From my somewhat older friends I knew what "the curse" involved, though its purpose I remained unclear to me. I did not go to Mama, my "best explainer", for reasons that I now understand better than I did then. She had become somehow less close to me—or was it the other way round? By the time I was twelve two more babies had been born, my little sisters, Essie and Judy, and my mother was now divided among four children and her husband and her beginning-to-fail parents and parents-in-law, all devotedly dependent in many ways on their Annie. Added to this, we were having some financial tensions, I think, because I had caught fragments of talk between Mama and Papa about strikes and lock-outs at the factory where my father was a manager (torn always between his identification with the "workers" as against the "bosses"). I was no longer an avid listener; I had other fish to fry.

Moreover, I was retarded in my physical maturing. I did not begin to "shoot up" or show signs of physical changes until I was sixteen. When, in the spring of that year I filled out my application for entrance to college in the fall there was a question that embarrassed me. "Have you ever matriculated before?" "Before what?" I wondered, and then, with barefaced courage I wrote, "No. Not yet." (How did they ever let me in? But, glory be, just before school opened I achieved womanhood, a height of five feet two, and equality with my fellow women!)

It was from my best friend at high school, Ada, that I learned the so-called facts of life. Ada was a year older than I, but her greater sophistication was due more to her superior intellect than to her age. She was reading George Bernard Shaw's *Prefaces* while I was engrossed in Porter's *Scottish Chiefs*, concerned with how the heroine, named Helen, could have travelled for weeks with a whole clan of warrior-men and manage going to the tawlet. Ada also had the dubious advantage of being the only girl in a hassle of three brothers, and thus she had learned about and took in her stride what her street-wise brothers talked about or let drop. It was she who enlightened me about how babies got into a mother's stomach, and how they made their exit.

The former explanation seemed absolutely ludicrous to me; the latter seemed implausible, both because it was not very nice and because it seemed structurally impossible. I shrieked with disbelieving laughter at what Ada hinted at or sketchily described, and we would stagger down the sidewalk on our long walks home from school, laughing to beat the band. "But how does he *ask* her?" I wanted to know. "What does he *say*?" And Ada, doubled up with the comedy of it all, said she had no idea. So we made up what we

found to be convulsively funny imaginary sexual conversations, and laughed all the way home. Thus I
became "street-wise". But somehow it all seemed
unreal to me.

Early in my freshman year in college I heard
about the sex lecture that was given as part of our
"physical education" course. Two rumors circulated
the locker rooms. One was that unless you could swim
twenty-five (or was it fifty?) yards you could never
graduate. Easy as pie. The other was that we would be
told about sex, and that some girls fainted with shock
at what they learned. I could hardly wait. I was
determined that no matter what our instructor told us
I would *not* go under, and I was glad that now, at last, I
would know.

Blackboard ready and chalk in hand, our teacher
began by carefully drawing a picture of a large pear,
standing upside down. Below it, apparently making
its uncertain way towards it, was what looked like one
of the slimy angle-worms or big-headed minnows we
used to maneuver onto fish hooks as bait for sunfish
and crappies. The pear, the instructor said, was a
womb. The worm was a sperm. Now, as she drew, the
pear sprouted stems and round leaves in which eggs
would be produced, and if one of those worms got to
one of those nested eggs the result would be pregnancy. There was some tittering in the class, but to my
chagrin nobody fainted. I sat fixed, staring at the still-
life on the blackboard. It had taken on the appearance
of a Rube Goldberg cartoon. Something, I felt, was
being held back, but I was afraid to show my ignorance by asking my questions. Obviously something
was being held back, because no one was fainting, and
really what was there to faint about?

Not long afterwards I had a tennis date with a kind of cute boy in my rhetoric class. He arrived to pick me up in a new yellow Stutz Bearcat roadster, with shining silver coiled pipes coming out of either side of the elongated tonneau. He was a swell, obviously, but to make matters worse Papa acted like a kid. He'd been on the front porch when Harry drove up, and he was absolutely agog over that car. He ran down to it and stroked its flanks. "That's some machine!" he said, and then asked us to wait while he went in for his Kodak. Out again, he posed us up against the car. I was annoyed, and no less so when the picture was developed. The focus was on the Bearcat; Harry's white ducks stood out clearer than his face; and there was I, in a longish pleated skirt, my racquet over one shoulder, looking both sloppy and sullen. Honestly! Of all the childish things for a person's father to do!

We played three sets in a merciless, broiling sun. My game, never really good, both because of nearsightedness and short-leggedness, was unmitigatedly miserable—my score: love, love, love. Harry was steadily charitable and indulgent, which only added to my irritation. He was patronizing me, that's what! We drove back in silence.

I knew I should invite him to come in, for a cold glass of something or other, but I was tired and sweaty and cranky. Besides, I was afraid that Papa might get too fired up again. (Maybe he was hoping I'd *marry* Harry, just because he was *rich!*) So, I simply said "Nice game, Harry—but I'm really *dead!* Ta-ta!" And I stepped stylishly over the car's low-cut door, waved another "ta-ta" and ran up the steps to the house. His engine roared angrily.

Nobody was home—probably all off to Como

Park for the afternoon, and I was glad of it. I remembered that early that morning Ada had brought me a book that she said was "really swell", and that I must read it at once. I knew a bath should be my first priority, but thirst and hunger drove me first to the icebox. I poured me a tall glass of milk from the quart bottle, sliced me a wide wedge of fudge-frosted cake, and sat me down at the kitchen table with its flowered oilcloth covering. With Ada's book.

It was called "The Sheik". The milk gushed down my gullet, I mouthed the luscious cake, I smelled the not too unpleasant sweat of my body, and I flipped the book open. It parted of its own accord, as if its spine had been pressed down hard at these particular pages.

There was this Arab sheik. He had just galloped in on his fiery Arabian steed, carrying the kidnapped blond English beauty into his silken tent that was richly carpeted with precious rugs of the Orient. He placed her on his colorfully cushioned divan, and discreetly left her in her state of shock, indignation, and bewilderment. When he returned, there she sat still, still shocked, indignant, bewildered. Then he came in close to her, and put his hot lips to her shell-like ear. "Must I be your valet as well as your lover?" he murmured.

I got it! All at once I got it—the cold milk, sweet cake, musky sweat, richly flowered oilcloth, and yes, that yellow Stutz Bearcat, and yes again, the no longer static pear and worm—all, all surged together in one leaping lick and sunburst of flame. I understood it all, with a joy that was part panic, part ecstasy. What I had known in my head I now knew in the whole of me.

So—how to convey this?—how "teach" about sex?

I recall with mixed amusement and unease an incident between myself, a supposedly "enlightened" mother, and my four-year-old-son. My husband and I had taken him with us to an art exhibit simply because we wanted very much to see it and were unable to find a sitter that day. On view was a rare collection of Italian renaissance paintings. The crowds of adults at the Art Institute moved in orderly, even reverent, lines past the ropes that marked the distance between viewers and the treasures to be seen, and our Jonathan was a model of quiet and attention. One room was dominated by Botticelli's "The Birth of Venus" and there was utter silence as worshipers stopped in veneration of the painting's exquisite efflorescence.

Suddenly our child's voice rang out. "Look at her *hair!*" he cried. "It's all the way down to her *penis!*" I hustled him out of the room, aware that while some viewers were laughing, a few others looked censorious ("Why *will* people bring a child here!") and annoyed, that my husband just stood there, chuckling. The moment for enlightenment was not here and now, I decided, so I whispered to Jon only that people were not supposed to talk out loud in art museums.

Once home, I sought Jon out to reintroduce the subject. He was in his room, busy putting together a jigsaw puzzle of the Three Little Pigs. "Jonnie," I began, "about that picture—I just wanted to tell you that girls and ladies don't . . ." But he was deaf and irritated. "Mom," he complained, "somebody has gone and lost some of the pieces of this puzzle!" So I crawled about on the floor looking with him, thinking that another time might be more propitious. I don't recall if or how I ever got around to it—but he must have found out about it somehow, someplace.

Seriously, though, it's no laughing matter. The age-old business of the pear and the worm, of sex "education" has become one of the most troublesome and complicated problems of today's society. The differences and connections between the offering of an anatomy lesson, to be taken in by the mind, and dealing with the facts and implications of potent glandular and emotional arousal, the freedoms from parental and personal inhibitions that are everywhere to be found—these and other factors raise innumerable questions about the what, when, where, how, by whom sex education can best be made meaningful to the impatient, over-stimulated young.

But I continue to wonder: which are the dark ages? Those long ago? Or these, right now?

IV

Some Musings
on Memories

IF YOU HAVE come along with me thus far, perhaps you will come a bit further? In your reading among these childhood memories, perhaps you have experienced echoes and evocations of your own re-memberings?

For many reasons you may have discovered, your own early memories will prove to have far more meaning than their superficial content reveals. Indeed, it is when experiences are charged with emotional meaning that they remain alive in us. Play with your remembrances of yourself when young, and of your vital "others"; lift these memories up to the light of your present greater knowledge and insights, so that you can experience once again what they meant to you, and think over now how and why they made an impress upon the heart and soul that in our childhood pulses so close to our tender, permeable surfaces. Learn, perhaps to your surprise and gratification, how differently you may view and interpret them now, underpinned by your different perspectives.

It is a puzzling fact that in the vast Alexandrian library of philosophies and explorations of the human psyche, so little attention has been given to early childhood memories. "Childhood amnesia" has indeed been identified, but not pursued. It was almost one hundred years ago that Freud first noted that common forgetting and blotting-out of most early childhood experiences, those within the first five-to-six years of life, and commented that childhood memories are both "important" and "interesting". But, with other human phenomena having more immediacy for him, he left that subject for others to probe. His basic hypothesis was that childhood memories were "screen" or "concealing" fabrications, defending the young child from awareness of a frightening, forbidden or "un-understandable" perception. He later raised some questions about this—questions that have not had the attention they cry out for: ". . .we accept too indifferently the fact of infantile amnesia . . . we may have reason for assuming that those forgotten childhood activities have not glided off without leaving . . . a definite influence for all future time." Further, "We forget of what great intellectual accomplishments and of what complicated emotions a child of four is capable . . ."[1] I say a fervent "Amen!" reinforced in my quest to understand further the inner life of pre-adults and young children, in periods when they are still plastic, vulnerable, unfolding.

Quickly I interject here that most dynamic psychotherapies have long encouraged the retrieval and re-view of such early experiences as seem to bear upon the problem-in-work. Several critiques of this usage suggest themselves, but I will touch here on only one which is implied in the qualification "as seem to bear upon the problem-in-work". Certain selected sorts of memories tend to be groped for, or (as Freud later himself suspected) fantasized, in the desire to meet the therapist's suggestion. At least one recent study reveals that the patient's own conception of what material is "wanted" or has possible relevance to his problem results in the production of certain kinds of content, often stereotyped or skewed by the preordained purpose it is assumed to serve. The wish to please the therapist and/or to aid one's own recovery may play a potent part in the patients' rememberings.

Within the past few decades there has been an attempt to retrieve, reactivate, and thence to re-assess the autobiographical memories of the aged. Fueled by such prescient psychologists as Erik Erikson and Robert Butler, the "life review" has become subject both for research and for supportive therapy, whether in individual or in group sessions.

Who among us, young or old, does not relish talking about ourselves? Being found interesting? Finding that as we talk and are responded to there are points or segments of our lives, long neglected, that now seem to have taken some new significance—perhaps because of the fresh pair of eyes and ears and the different perspectives that the listener or questioner may bring? And who longs more for such attention and such help than the shelved and often socially isolated old?

Of the therapeutic values in such shared and empathically received rememberings, there is much to be said. However, based upon my own occasional interviewing of aged men and women and supported by a number of current research reports, it is my impression that there is not high reliability in the early memories produced by the aged. Loss of mental acuity and time orientation may be one factor; another is that the old-old of this century are largely a group born and reared before interiorized meanings in behavior or reactions were common subjects for introspection, so both insights and interpretations may be limited. Further, few if any means remain of corroborating or correcting their accounts.

Most important, perhaps, is the phenomenon we all know: that at any age, our present affects our view of the past in what and how we remember. Feeling miserable and utterly useless, one person may view his whole life as having been beset with hurts and disappointments; another, still fighting to maintain self-respect and self-direction despite deterioration, may build up his sense of integrity by embellishments of his accomplishments, his place and import in the lives of others—and memory fragments will be fashioned (again only part consciously) to support this sense of selfhood. Thus the limitations.

I have wondered why so much more attention has been given to our dreams than to our early memories. Since Biblical times (remember Joseph, raised to high esteem in the Egyptian court because of his power to explain the meaning of dreams?) dreams have been probed, combed over, held to be prophetic, then to be wish fulfillments, then the expression of suppressed anxieties, then to be efforts at problem-solving. Perhaps they are all of those. Yet the fact is that dreams are as thready, elusive, as forgettable and inscrutable as our early memories. Certain it is that the latter, as Freud postulated, had far more potency in shaping, motoring and directing our persons and behaviors.

More important: our memories are subject to revisions, to changes in our attitudes and understandings by re-views and not infrequently re-interpretations of their meaning. The ancient philosopher, Zeno, is quoted as having said that he could fathom a man's nature "by his dreams". Would that he had added "and by his early memories"! A seventeenth-century essayist, Owen Feltham, had suggested, "The best we can make of dreams is observation, and by that our own correction or encouragement." How immediately applicable that seems to me to be to the observation and work-over of early memories!

("Eureka!" I cry, all but leaping from my bath. I see it now! My association with Zeno, the Stoic, that is. I have just learned that the Stoics were so-named simply because their "school" was held on a *stoa*, the ancient Greek word for a "painted porch". Remember the verandah in Atlanta, and the big porch in St. Paul, that made an "academy" of a family's recounting of memories?)

Now stoutly stoical, I go on to explore a few of the many questions that confront anyone who ponders the mysteries of human mental-emotional experience, and to suggest some of the possible everyday usefulness in our communing now and then with that mother of the Muses, the goddess of memory, Mnemosyne. It was from her loins—remember?—that all of the arts, including that of living a full-hearted, spirited human life, came forth.

☞   ☞   ☞

Memories, as Prospero said of his fleet and canny sprite, Ariel, are "tricksy" things. Fascinating to muse upon for what they may tell us about ourselves, for their possible meanings and import, for their frequent elusiveness and inscrutability, they connect in obvious or arcane ways with our this-day's living. Some are ready to be called up at will, to be taken out and fingered wonderingly, as one might do with material artifacts, speculated upon, re-lived yet once again. Others skulk about in the dark recesses of the mind, presenting themselves, unbidden, as if to assert their relevance for what is presently being experienced. Some are seemingly trivial, cloudy shreds that float up into only partial awareness, roused by some puzzling association with the present. Like dreams, which on our awakening we try to capture, they may dissolve into will-o'-the-wisp fireflies, lighting up but eluding our heavy-footed efforts to give chase.

Even more elusive fragments engage and mystify us at times. All of us know sensory stirrings (perhaps first roused in our pre-verbal or subconscious state?) that seem suddenly activated by a chance aroma, a musical phrase, the flash of a face or place, a taste— Proust's "little madeleine" with its "impalpable drop of essence" that brought alive a pageant of places and people. (There may even be as Proust postulated, "an instinctive memory in the limbs".)

Our remembered pasts may often be not fully congruent with the actuality. "What really happened" is not necessarily the same as one's memory of it. Because of a young child's limited understanding, he may quite misread the meaning of a happening. We may have found the event or situation psychologically indigestible, and thus, as Freud proposed, "screened it out" of consciousness. Further in our continuous quest to "make sense" of what seems irrational, we may have

quite unconsciously refashioned the actuality. However, as that insightful social psychologist, W.I. Thomas, said many years ago, "If men define situations as
real, *they are real in their consequences.*" (Emphasis mine.)
That is, certain emotional convictions, behaviors and
bents of attitudes and action will ensue. Which is why
I continue to pursue those childhood mental-emotional experiences whose powers shaped our being,
but which may still be susceptible to changed interpretations and views of their meanings.

From among the many diverse and intriguing
questions that remain to be explored I have chosen
only a few to begin our heuristic considerations and (of
course) arguments. These have repeatedly arisen in
my mind, not only because of my own crowded collection of early memories, but also of those drawn from
some of my clients, and those recently proffered by
about fifty friends and acquaintances who, with grace
and unfailing interest, responded to my queries.

Among the yet-to-be-answered questions:

Why are traumatic and painful events recalled
far more vividly and frequently than joyous or fulfill-
ing happenings? Are misery, pain, fear, actually far
more common in early—or all—human life than comfort, pleasure, joy? Do human expectations somehow
by far exceed what usual life experience has to offer?
Thence the ensuing bitterness, fear, protestations of
"unfair"? Or is it that, conditioned by supermarket
versions—sometimes sophisticated ones too—of psy-
chodynamic theory, we search to find cause in "something that happened" to me, something that was done
to me?

What came popping out first in my "light-touch"
inquiries about "earliest memories" were those of

traumatic events. Most frequent were tonsillectomies at between three and five years of age—of which there were apparently a plague some years ago! What was recalled was not pain, but rather a sense of having been misled or betrayed by parents who had inadequately prepared the child; a fear of having been abandoned when the parents had deposited the child in the care of a doctor or nurse; of having been "fooled" by parental promises of ice cream and "good stuff" afterwards that did not materialize. Second in frequency was the shock or resentment at the birth of a younger sibling, of having been promised a "playmate" that turned out to be a squally, red absorber of attention. Physical fears were frequent—such as being sat upon a too-high pedestal in a photographer's studio, and the black hood worn by the cameraman; of having to walk across an iron grate in a sidewalk in terror that one could fall through the cracks. Few "screen memories" appear among these.

Most commonplace was the forgetting of "What happened then?" "What did you or they do?" Why was post-trauma forgotten? Was everything made "all right" again? Or was the barely emerging ego working too hard at regaining stability? The defense system—the varied ways by which coping may occur—is in an elementary form early in childhood; its range and skills are dependent upon the further development of many faculties of brain and body, plus the accumulation of many kinds of knowledge. So the young child's openness to hurt and fear and confusion is readily understandable.

A trauma, as we all know, is an unexpected blow to the total personality system—physical, mental, emotional. It rocks or shatters the customary balance

or stability in motion that is adequate for the antici-
pated course of events. When trauma occurs early in
life, the defenses and strategies for coping are in a
nascent state; thus, the sense of helplessness may be
overwhelming. Perhaps hurt, fear, pain, do indeed
drive deeper and with greater intensity into the core of
the person at no matter what age, and thus dwell
longer in us than do pleasure, gratification, joy.

Come to think of it, there are very few autobiographical or imaginative narratives of being "possessed" by pleasure or joy, except very briefly. Freud,
for instance, knew himself to be his mother's "golden
child". One sees, in his development, a central core of
confidence, a readiness to take risks, a courage in
breaking the molds of conventional thought—qualities
which seem in large part to be product of the confidence instilled by a mother whose child is her treasure. Is it not interesting that he scarcely touches upon
the pleasures he absorbed from that happy status?

Tolstoy was probably right when, characteristic-
ally wracked by guilts and doubts and rage, he wrote
that all happy families are "alike"; that only unhappiness holds interest for those who would understand
the human condition. Indeed, our world's great literature deals, for the most part, with the tragedies in
human life, and even in folk tales the central characters have to cope with innumerable obstacles to happiness until, at last, having overcome them by arduous
labors or sheer luck, they are hustled into "living
happily ever after". (Even as a child I began to protest
the fact that no one told me what "happily after"
consisted of. No one answered my "So what did they
do *then?*" They only laughed. Except Mama, who once
suggested that I myself should write that part of the

story, a prospect that I found rather less than compelling.)

Back to the nature of traumatic memories. I have puzzled over the (unconscious) selectivity of memory, illustrated both in my personal recollections and in those of most of my interviewees. Details preceding the shock are more frequently recalled than the trauma itself or its aftermath. This is in some way different from Freud's passing comments that there is a "tendency to forget the disagreeable" and that "painful memories merge into motivated forgetting with special ease."[1] Would that not suggest that the shock itself would be blotted out or at least considerably transformed? Or is it that the trauma "knocks us cold — knocks us out", as we say, and that the usual mental processes of adaptation and maintenance of balance are thrown into chaotic disarray?

I turn back to the four personal earthquakes I experienced between the ages of two-and-a-half and twelve: the unprepared-for entry into my happy life of Sonny; Miss B.'s making me an arithmetic imbecile; the Birthday Party; and Miss Tibault as the spoiler. In each I vividly recall both the overwhelming shock and also what had preceded it. In only one can I coax up any fragment of the aftermath.

The meanings of the physical assault upon me by my fifth grade teacher were so utterly confusing, so inconsistent, as to remain partially undigested until well into my adulthood. My confusion was confounded by the fact that what I had done was "right"; but something had been "wrong" and I could not understand what it was. Combined with my self-pity and confusion, there lay some guilty sense that I had been the cause of my teacher's illness. Yet it was inexplicable that I got a reward by being "skipped" to a higher grade instead of being "put back". No wonder a whole block of brain cells went awry in that struggle to make sense of irreconcilable events!

But now I had a different post-traumatic reaction. It occurs to me for the first time, as I set this down, that this trauma was followed by many gratifications. Everybody was "on my side", was *with* me, even the Superintendent of Schools! I was supported by everyone who mattered to me. I later gleaned from my clinical experience the knowledge of how healing it can be to have empathic acceptance and backing from meaningful others at times of stress or confusions. True, now and then there arose that sense of "fault" in my teacher's breakdown but it was mild and, in my adulthood, it dissolved in my increased knowledge of my field and, what we call "common sense".

After the "Birthday Party," amnesia. Yet, it seems odd to me now that I so clearly recall our walk together to her house and my growing uneasiness about what I had gotten myself into. . . . How so?

What I told Mama, or indeed *if* I told her I do not remember. I would have had to tell her something because surely she would have asked. I was "finished" with Helen but not with the confusions and disgusts that eddied inside me, so bewildering that I did not even know how to sort them out or to speak of them. So the work-over had to be done by me, alone, with mental-emotional reorganization and rationalizations and avoidances that probably consumed all my psychic resources. Thus amnesia, I suppose, or thus, perhaps, the affirmation of Freud's guess that there is a "tendency to forget the disagreeable"?[1] Thus my grateful resumption of all the safe trivia of habitual behavior and my conscious self-determined resolution to "forget about it" in order to mitigate my inner disorder and early sorrow. With which my defense system fully cooperated. (Can one *will* amnesia?)

In my fourth childhood trauma, I again recall the pre-shock details, the experience itself, and, again, a loss of what happened afterwards. This situation was of a rather different sort: I was more witness than participant. But I was flooded by new insights into human behavior that all but sickened me. Perhaps I was particularly vulnerable—in a period of buoyancy, high hopes, open and eager to take delight in the day, with my protective defenses totally somnolent and unready.

From what I saw and heard and then vicariously experienced, I had a realization that rocketed like lightning between my mind and the pit of my stomach: that under a surface of cultivation and cool courtesy there could surge terrible evil. And that cruelty could be calculated, sleekly masked, even made to seem rational and necessary. That, I think, was mostly what shattered me. My anguish at what I felt was happening behind the principal's closed door was doubled when I saw a mother savagely turn against her own child (once again!). Everything, everything was "spoiled", and I felt sickened by the torturer's touch and honeyed words to me.

Some years later I discussed the incident with my mother (some Nazi atrocities and their subsequent rationales had brought it to mind) but she had no recollection of my ever having told her about it. Surely Miss Bridges must have asked me what Miss Tibault had thought of my piece? Surely I had encountered Miss Tibault again, if only at our graduation exercises where I was featured as "class poet"? Nothing of that do I recall. But everything do I remember of the anguishing insights I experienced on that hope-filled, golden Indian Summer day.

Again—is it naive of me at this late date?—I stand in mystified awe at the powers of the human unconscious to erase or to hide in its crevices and crannies such memories as might interfere with or undermine essential human development. Or is it the mystery of the hope that springs eternal, the resilience of the human spirit that most deserves our awe and admiration? Or is each the servant to the other?

You will understand, I think, why I did not include the death of my baby sister as a "trauma". We were not unprepared for what happened. The regular early morning ring of the telephone, when Mama called us at our grandparents', went through each of us like a drill-saw. The night had not been a good one . . . and yet . . . the doctor was doing all he could . . . and yet . . . and yet that "thing with feathers that perches in the soul—". When death came we knew what we had known.

The loss I felt most achingly and longest was less for our dead baby (what six-year-old understands "never-never"?) and more for the emotional separation, temporary but seemingly endless, from my taken-for-granted immediate at-one-ness with my mother and father, a security now somewhat thinned out by their own time of deadness as they mourned. That period of turned-inwardness among all "my grown-ups" was the first time I had ever felt what being essentially "all alone" could mean. Sonny and I clung together, but that was not enough. I felt, somehow, that I ought to "be bigger", that I was somehow responsible for making things happy again. Different from a trauma, it was rather an experience of settling in as quietly as I could for what seemed like an endless wintertime of sorrow.

Ordinary daily living resumed, on the surface. We moved into another house, nearby. I returned to school (at once, Mama insisted, never mind what Lizzie did or didn't do!) One day after school I came home and found Mama preparing supper, her eyes brimming with tears. When I asked her (in a sudden panic) why she was crying, she said, "Don't you see— I'm cutting onion?" But I knew in my clutched throat that wasn't why.

Almost four decades after Freud presented his speculations about the nature of childhood amnesia and added his encouragement for further exploration, Alfred Adler published a markedly different view (expectably) of the dynamics of early memories. Quite aside from their basic theoretical conflicts on the dynamics of personality development and the nature of mental-emotional disturbances, one must recognize in the time span between Freud's hypotheses and those of Adler, there had occurred revolutionary changes in the western world's socio-psychological cultures, as well as in the views of human psycho-social development.

In his 1937 article on early memories, Adler suggests that recollections within the first five years of life seem to be in consonance with the person's [later revealed] "lifestyle or temperament"; that they give clues to the person's characteristic attitudes; that they "are proto-typical", which is to say that they are exemplifications of the individual's characteristic perspectives, moods, life-views [as seen in succeeding life stages]. There will be traumatic events, of course, but these often reveal "signs of the person's activity" and such qualities as "social feeling" and "courage".[2] Adler's major observations seem to fit with aspects of my own early memories, persuading me of the applicability and validity of his views which, at the very least, deserve further exploration.

So I turn once again to examine my own early memories in the light of Adler's illuminating speculations. My first, this of the dancing clock and its frequent recurrence, did indeed exemplify a characteristic reaction I had as a child—and yes, even now. I have never quite lost the sense of wonder and awe combined with a kind of joy when I have come upon what seems to me to be in some way "wonderful", whether in the myriad faces of nature, or in the arts and other human achievements, in acts of love and compassion; in short, when it has seemed to me that some leap beyond the expectable has occurred, that the usual limitations of body or spirit or mind have been transcended. At such times, in almost a heart-bursting way, I have felt lifted up out of the narrow confines of my small self into an experience of fusion with the beauty, imagination, wonder of some transcendent experience.

We come into the world, trailing clouds not of

"glory" but of predispositions of temperament and reactivity of one sort or another. Those predispositions will be subject to changes, constructive or otherwise, by our relationships and circumstances in early childhood.

But why is my first remembered experience of sheer joy followed by amnesia? I am sure Papa must have told anyone who would listen about my having danced in the aisle with the clock and of the laughter and applause from our surrounding audience. The answer, I think, is made evident by recent findings in child-development research: that the sense of selfhood, of "I" as a separate entity from one or more others to whom attachment is felt, is usually not fully achieved until well into the third year. I must have felt completely "at one" with the dancer, all but merged with him. Such identification with another actually occurs throughout the lifetime of empathic people. We weep, laugh, anguish, revel in the joys or ache with the sorrows even of fictional characters in books and plays. The difference, as we mature, is that such merging is temporary. We grow into being able to resume full awareness of our separateness, become able to step back into our own shoes, so to speak. That ability to know ourselves as *like* but *separate* from others is achieved over time, as part of our mental-emotional maturing.

Something of that same phenomenon of early childhood fusion must explain what occurred when at four I was totally convinced that I was the author of Robert Louis Stevenson's couplet ("The World Is So Full"). Read to me probably more than once, it so aptly affirmed my own then-inchoate feeling about the world as I knew it, that it became "mine".

Thus, perhaps, amnesia for early childhood events has several different explanations. Surely it must serve as a defense against what at the time feels intolerable or unmanageable. But it may serve the necessary economy of mental functioning when experiences that are not perceived fully, not "taken in" as personally meaningful, leave no mark upon the memory apparatus.

A further contribution to our efforts to understand early childhood is offered in Adler's perception that even in traumatic events one may see evidences of "social feeling", "courage", and efforts to cope. And I look for such evidence in my fourth year with Freud's reminding me of how little appreciation we have given to the tremendous capacities that may develop by that time.[1]

Taking "social" in its superficial and elementary sense: for my fourth birthday we had a family party in Atlanta to which mostly grown-up good friends came. Aunt Rachel had made me a big jelly roll as my birthday cake. I hated jelly roll (still do, although age has tempered hatred into mere dislike). But I carefully watched the grownups who said it was "delicious" so I said it was delicious too, and ate my (too generous!) piece all up, ruminating on the realization that being "big" meant being nice even if you didn't feel like it.

Further thoughts on "social": I recall briefly feeling sad and resentful that I was not allowed to take Teddy Rosevelvet with me to Atlanta (after all, Mama took her Sonny!) but at the same time I recognized the need for me to help Mama—that was expected of me. And on the train to Atlanta (Mama rolled with laughter as she told about it long afterwards, making fun of herself at having expected so much of a not-yet-four-year-old) I had made at least five staggering trips up and down the aisle of the train to get water for Sonny before I protested at my demanding "social" obligations. Apparently the rewards were worth it—chiefly, I guess, my feeling that I was such a good girl.

As for "courage": perhaps the most telling evidence of that came in the face of what might otherwise have become a crisis—the fact that no one had come to fetch me at the kindergarten and I had been left all alone. I wonder now how it was that I did not panic, what gave me the courage to try to find my own way home? Perhaps it was a sense of trust that nothing really "bad" would happen to me? At any rate, my taste of triumph and the subsequent praise from my family slid happily into my developing sense of "I did it! I can! I am able!"

Least explored have been happy childhood memories, those of pleasure, exciting or serene, heart-lifting or quietly gratifying. Why so? Is it that, as I suggested, we somehow take good fortune as our due, and are roused to strong feelings chiefly by disappointment and distress? (I have rarely heard a person who has had sudden good fortune cry out, "Why *me?*") Or is it that pleasures, contentment, gratifications are ego-syntonic, easily merged with the self, readily digested, in contrast to a trauma which is a turmoil, a setback, that requires repair work towards achieving re-equilibrium?

Whatever the child's inborn temperament, his giftedness or deficits, he will be heavily influenced by his everyday surround, by what we call "environment" which, in its most potent forms, consists of the people with whom we are in significant interaction. Of course childhood contains single events that are recalled as happy or joyous: a special treat or celebration or spectacle; a small triumph at home or school, particularly if it is recognized by valued others; receiving a longed-for or intriguing gift. Mostly, however, my inquiries of young and old adults about what they found "happy" in their childhood have elicited rather vague accounts of repeated pleasurable activities, such as, "We always used to" go on picnics, swim, play house, go down to watch the circus parade when it came to town, and so on. From some there were accounts of points of high pleasure found in personal relationships—a beloved teacher, a mother or father reading aloud at bedtime; gratification in some difficulty worked out "all by myself", or at the dissolution of a feared situation that did not materialize. The accounts (and I must add that they were top-of-the-head rather than thoughtful memories) were largely commonplace occurrences, undramatic fragments of feeling "good", of playing together with good friends, of discovering how something "works", of excursions with parents, of being "chosen" in class or on the playground, of being told, spontaneously, out-of-the-blue, "I love you!"

I have become reasonably sure that in a "happy" childhood there is a consistent, predictable, equable, temperate climate and tenor of everyday life. For this I like to use the word "dailiness" coined by Virginia Woolf in a different context.

"Dailiness" holds few dramatic peaks or black holes. Rather its characteristic quality is that it settles us into habits and expectations that keep us in relative balance-in-motion. Thus we are free to observe, explore, learn, consider, watch others, take in or cast off the innumerable stimuli that enter or pass across our consciousness. The many childhood problems in "becoming", in socialization, are only rarely encountered or resolved in one single great thunder-clap and blazing white light of perception. Rather we are aware of them in small incidents, problems-to-be-coped-with in the evolving transactions between ourselves and our vital others as we engage in the enjoyable or distasteful tasks of working, playing, loving.

The probability is that early childhood dailiness is only vaguely recalled by most of us because of its business-as-usual aspects. Yet that so frequently forgotten "business-as-usual" subtly shapes the young child in his typical sense of security (or anxiety), of being enjoyed by his others (or simply taken for granted), of being respected (or continually put-down), of being worth hearing-out and being responded to (or ignored, sometimes dismissed by a too-swift application of a psychological band-aid). All these daily interchanges significantly affect the young child's prevailing mood and view of himself and of his world. Thus the development of his capacity to cope with hurt or shock, his ability to recognize, savor, and enjoy and remember what was "good" depends not only upon his basic temperament and inborn capacities but also upon the nourishment he is given regularly by his daily family or caretakers. [3]

What *ought* childhood's dailiness be like? How would we shape it if we could? Must it be all wine and roses (or, more appropriately, milk and cookies)? Again I draw on my own memories of what I judge (feel) to have been a happy childhood. As you have seen, there were many moments and periods of high anger and burning antagonism between me and my most important others. I hated, I resented, I scorned, for hours or sometimes days. But underlying these ugly, mean feelings for these ugly, mean people lay a solid base of trust and security, a deeply entrenched feeling that I was loved, wanted (even if at times found wanting), treasured (even when needing correction). I myself had averred in the title of a story I had pencilled at eight or nine that "Love is Better than Grandeur". I had reason to believe that, and now and then my parents would slyly remind me of it. True, I had never experienced grandeur, but I had known love that was unshakable. Maybe that is what frees a child to dare to break out from parental despotism even though that despotism may be "benevolent"? Certainly it is what spurs a child into wanting to meet most expectations of him.

I mull over my own memories of dailiness in the search to understand what constitutes "happiness", uncertainly, critically, aware that ifs, ands, and buts will hum about me like pesky insects:

I think back to that summer evening on the porch with my grownups; commonplace, everyday trivial talk, none of it directed to me. Yet I had that sense of contentment that I "belonged". And I am reminded of the stirring sense of at-one-ness with Mama when she and I both knew and shared the lines of a poem about death. What were we sharing? An unspoken, even unrealized gladness at being alive together? I see again that grey squirrel with the brown acorn that on my first day at school made me feel happy. That was because Miss Lowry told us she had drawn it herself to welcome us, so I felt glad because it showed she *wanted* us to be there.

A more complicated example from the third grade: I loved Miss McGuire, though I can't remember why. One day, for want of something to occupy myself with during what was called "quiet study time" I inked a face on each of my fingernails, and I trustfully trotted up to Miss McGuire's desk to show her what I'd found out: that fingers are like families—they can work or play together, "help each other, hug, and things like that." She gave me a completely blank look; then she said, "Helen Harris, you go right down to the basement and wash all that foolishness off!" I felt hurt and ashamed, and really mad at her.

Suppertime was telling time. When I told Mama and Papa they laughed about it and said they thought it was a "very cute" idea—I must tell it to Uncle Louis. Then Mama said maybe Miss McGuire was having a bad day—all of us sometimes do. Maybe she had a stomach-ache. Maybe she had lost her best beau—so she felt cranky about everything? I caught on! Teachers weren't teachers all the time. Just like everybody else. They were "human beans" too! So I forgave Miss McGuire. Which left me "happy" with a sense of both understanding and magnanimity. What I see now was that I was able to accept and forgive Miss McGuire because I had first been accepted and understood and supported appreciatively in what had been, for me, an unhappy situation. I was restored, thus able to resume my former "happy" relationship with my teacher.

Trivia—and Tolstoy confirmed! What is there to say about little daily occurrences that leave one contented and steadied without sounding fatuous or simple-minded?

Now about love—the keystone. Everybody knows about love as the basic nutrient for the growth and enrichment of the human being. Here, forsaking all temptation, I shall limit myself to only one aspect of love that, it seems to me, is central to a (reasonably) happy childhood.

I suggest that love, as it is experienced in early childhood, is a reliable supply and demonstration of affectionate *attention* combined with demonstrated and/or explicated *intention* to understand the other— what he feels, what he means, how he perceives and interprets what happens to him and what he makes to happen.

Affectionate attention does not mean a continuous hovering over the child, anticipating his every need, smoothing over all rough spots, offering too ready assurance. It means, rather, taking or making the time now and then for eye-to-eye communication during interaction; cocking the ear, often the "third ear", to take in the meaning (sometimes not apparent) of what is being said or done; putting in a question or comment here and there to make sure that one understands, and to give evidence that one is listening.

The intention, explicit or implied, is that "I want to be *with* you, either to help you cope, or to help myself understand better, or to share your pleasure or hurt. (Mark Twain once said that to share an unhappiness is to "halve it"; to share a pleasure is to double it.) Actually, as one thinks of it, those are two manifestations of love that are held precious and essential in a love relationship at any time of life.

"Precious and essential", but not always easy to manage in today's hectic life, whether within parent-child relationships or those of marriage, love and friendship—or combinations of these on any given day. So lapses must be allowed for. What a general tenor of attention and intention conveys to the recipient, I propose, is a sense of "mattering" to loved or needed or admired others who can be depended upon to accept and rejoice in what one tries to do on his own, and to cushion, rather than brush off, failures.

A person who "matters" is one who is held to be of consequence, of importance, by valued others. To develop and sustain a sense of confidence in one's self and trust in others we must be given open evidence that what we do or feel *matters* to those who matter to us. To "matter" is basic to self-esteem; self-esteem is basic to the drive for mastery; the motivation to master one's age-appropriate tasks and to incorporate the aspirations and expectations (realistic ones) of those with whom we feel at-one is strengthened by the encouragement and, when necessary, correction, that listening, questioning and responding with interest and empathy contribute to the growing child's daily life. Perhaps this sense of "mattering" is the undramatic but solid foundation of a childhood recalled as "happy"?

Back now to you and me and all of us still-growing "grownups". What is the point, the use, of our exploration of childhood memories when we are all but breathlessly involved in our dailiness, in making a living or making a life, in giving and getting, in seeking and offering the warmth and interest and supports that enhance our work and play and loving relationships? How, if at all, does it contribute to our "encouragement and correction"?

The "uses" are modest ones. Recall may offer review; perhaps from that, some re-vision of ourselves and our others. It offers a kind of re-acquaintance with yourself. There is no need, as today's saying goes, to make a Thing of it. Take it on now and then, not as a do-it-yourself psychotherapy but as a kind of heuristic exploration—as a free-floating form of inquiry into aspects of your now multi-faceted self. Be buttressed by Socrates, who in the hour of his death, averred that "the unexamined life is not worth living". No magical transformations will occur; no rah-ta-ta-ta of trumpets will announce your enlightenment. But you may find that the person you are today sees and feels the child you were with some considerable difference. That is because you are far more informed, more understanding, more equipped to be "master of your soul" than any child can be.

Others, more sensitively attuned than most of us, have affirmed the potential uses of carding the fleece of childhood memories. An insightful poet, Stanley Kunitz, quotes Carl Jung as having said that one cannot free one's self from childhood without first "generously occupying" one's self with it. Kunitz adds, ". . . the object is not so much to cut one's self off from one's past as to learn how to live with the child you were . . ."[4] And I presume to add: "and from that to know and to act on your expanded, enlightened conscious awareness of your still unfolding, maturing self".

Three potential intertwined outcomes may emerge from your recalls and reviews: surely some greater self-knowledge; from this comes some expanded capacity for empathy with other "only human" and/or "remarkably human" beings; and some greater sense of self-possession, which is the essential condition for inner freedom and consciously determined self-management.

Where to start? I'd suggest it be with those memories that are readily accessible to you as you rummage about, or those that are called up, somehow, by some present stimulus. Give them breathing space, invite them in. Some of them may still be deeply unsettling, still charged with discomfort, still puzzling in their import—("now, why do I think of *that?*" or "whatever made me say, feel, act as I did today?"). Many rememberings seem almost spontaneously to have changed their meaning, and are to be found suddenly understandable, illuminated by our more sophisticated perspectives, made trivial as we recognize the difference between past and present reality. Some, once considered disgraceful, now strike us as funny and we feel pleased that we seem to have developed some sense of the universality of the human comedy; some rouse our compassionate understanding of both ourselves and those others who were involved in a given situation, and we resonate to the pathos that weaves through the whole fabric of the human condition. Such changed perspectives tend, in varying degree, to mitigate or even to defuse the power that certain past experiences had to overdetermine our present actions and reactions. (Perhaps it should be said at once that when we are deeply torn by conflict or hag-ridden by distress, we may need to seek the help of a professionally qualified, supportive guide to free us to face and understand what we had long ago consigned to oblivion.) Here and now we limit ourselves to those memories that are accessible and acceptable to our particular psychological digestive system.

Simply remembering and recounting may provide entertainment and camaraderie, or it may serve as a temporary catharsis. Prolonged exploration may be too much, tempting though it may be to retreat from your current reality to find your past self such a fascinating subject. You were and you are. In truth, we *all* are, once the top layers are peeled back a bit. But you must not lose sight of your target: an informed, mature perspective on aspects of the child in you plus an appraisal of what is still to be treasured or reviewed and changed.

Remembering is only the beginning. If we are to "generously occupy ourselves" in order to "learn how to live" with the child we harbor, there must follow the search to understand what meaning was attributed to the experience at the time of its occurrence. Why did it imprint itself upon your vulnerable heart and mind? How do you see it now? How is it different? Or how not? Surely you are now far more knowledgeable, far more able to see the complexities that tangled the web of person-to-person, person-to-circumstance transactions.

As you pursue these interchanges, you will come to know yourself as having incorporated many parts of other selves, and you begin to recognize yourself as your own special person, and as bonded with many other human beings. Perhaps, with Terence, the slave who became one of ancient Rome's great playwrights, you may say, "Nothing human is alien to me." You may begin to discover some attitudinal and behavioral changes that are moving in you even now, subtle as they may be. They are the product of your now–examined experience, enlightened by the remarkable revelations that this century's explorations of man's inner space have revealed to all of us. Sometimes they serve to affirm and support the long-ago-you, sometimes to correct the misapprehensions and misinterpretations that were only natural in childhood but which, when accessible, are now subject to your reassessment.

You may, for instance, come on that startling, if obvious, awareness that those persons who shaped you had *also* had childhoods that shaped what they said and did. They, too, were products of a past, often quite ignorant of what was good or bad in child-rearing, often themselves beset and bewildered by concerns that blinded them to the needs of the child you were. Should they have "known better"? Desirably. But usually such knowledge as you now carry was scarcely available to them. Did they have the means, the education, the inner freedoms to see and know what we in this day see and know? Often not. So we begin to understand that those who reared us, or those who, in a single encounter, drove deep into our inner being, were also "caused", by both people and circumstances in their unfolding years.

Further, you may discover that what *you* said and did affected the behavior and feelings of your seemingly more powerful and responsible caretakers. Wittingly or not, you were often a "cause" of much that they did and felt. The cranky baby creates the tensional mother; the child who does poorly in school rouses parental embarrassment, anger, defensiveness; the secretive adolescent stirs up fears and resentments. Even love does not always conquer all, because even love is subject to lapses and feeds on responsiveness. (Once, interviewing a loving, self-punitive and frantic mother of a pre-psychotic child, I quietly asked, "And what does *he* do to *you?*" From her outpouring I learned yet again what I had long known: how "innocent" children may undermine the very roots of parental security and self-esteem. With the inevitable turn-about of cause-effect.)

Before one is ready to know and understand others it is necessary to "know thyself". (How canny were those ancients who carved that adjuration into stone at the entry to the Delphic oracle!) The re-acquaintance with one's self and one's others in the light of our expanded and deepened understanding of the human condition makes it possible to examine one's being-into-becoming with some greater inner comfortableness and acceptance that takes the place of denial or inhibiting defenses.

"Self-acceptance" does not imply smug self-satis-faction (no little Jack Horners we!) or a sense of defeat. It means, rather, coming to some reconciliation with what may now be understood by you as "natural" or "only human" in the light of many impinging circum-stances. "Acceptance" obviously is not synonymous with approval. It means, rather, making some peace with a past that cannot be undone, but—and this is an important "but"—its archaic, more elementary mean-ing can be recognized and submitted to re-view, re-assessment, re-vision. Thence encouragement and cor-rection.

You will find yourself still puzzled and even troubled in some instances. You may, however, clearly see that many acts and circumstances were often not "willed" by their perpetrators but were rather the result of ignorance or mental-emotional disturbances, chronic or momentary, or of external circumstances in which those who seemed powerful were in fact helpless. Acceptance extends to you, yourself, too—the bad things you did, all your small sins against your vital others, and while you may rue them, neither rue nor rage will undo them. Some self- as well as other-forgiveness is involved in "acceptance", chiefly because most of what you are forgiving is not unusual among our many human frailties.

Now turn "only human" over. Try to recall in what ways people were good to you. Who loved you, and for what? What experiences gave you recognition or an inner sense of competence, worth, even being admirable? What warmed the cockles of your heart? What did you see or hear or do that lifted your spirits and hopes? Give yourself over now to tasting these joys again, feeling them again; appreciate yourself, as if you were your own child. Had you—could you have—had any notion that what you did or did not do was in all probability part of that common, human cause-effect chain reactions?

When we are able to be more accepting both of our human selves and of those who sculpted us, we have become more fully aware of the inevitable tragi-comic complexities in all human living. I guess we are truly matured when we arrive at that mixture of ruefulness and risibility which is at the very heart of compassion for ourselves and our kind.

"Know thyself." That is the basic condition for compassionate insight into another. One can never truly understand or accept in another person what has not been known, in some form, acknowledged, accepted, and understood, in greater or lesser degree, in one's self. Therein lies another reason for an unafraid exploration of the self, as it was, as it has become, and as it is becoming.

The ability to feel with, or into another person's emotional state or reaction we call "empathy". In any vital caring relationship, temporary or on-going, whether part of a professional relationship or between parents and children, marital partners, friends and lovers, grown children and needful parents, empathy is the basic condition for bonding. Empathy is the ability to feel *in* to another, to create a sense of at-one-ness so as to take in and fully relate to what the other is feeling. (The German term, "ein-fuhling"—literally "in-feeling"—expresses it far better than does our rather pallid English equivalent.) Feeling "in to" another is not the same as feeling "just like" that other. It is lending of one's self to "knowing" what the other person feels. The basis for "knowing" may be some combination of intuition, acutely sensitive observation, reactions drawn from the feeling person by questions or suggestions. The empathic response, verbalized, expressed in body language or sub-verbal sounds, lets the needful person know that you are *with* him and *for* him. (Note: empathy, happily, also enters into our capacity to share another person's joy and pleasure and triumph. It is not limited to misery, a fact we ungrateful humans tend to forget!)

There is a subtle but powerful difference between feeling *in* to another person and feeling "just like" him. Empathy involves the ability to get back into your own shoes (to put it inelegantly). It is this ability the hurt person must also count upon. In any needful situation, it is your difference which is sought for—that of strength, resourcefulness, expertise, and the objectivity that the would-be helper is expected to have.

Empathy is probably the most potent, moving factor in any form of psychotherapy. I daresay it explains how it is that the many widely divergent, heatedly argued forms of therapy may claim "successes". How does empathic capacity come about? Recent observations of neonates suggest that its predisposition, like many other sensitivities, may be inborn. Like our other inborn capacities, it may be nourished and enhanced or starved out and diminished by early infancy or childhood interactions.[3]

Here I return to my basic theme: that the reviewing and re-experiencing of our own early memories, their raw emotional meanings and dynamic powers, in the light of broader perspectives and greater knowledge is one possible way not only to "know thyself" but to be more free to enter into understanding the inner selves of others.

As you come to some comfortable relationship with that child in you (still alive, though you may have long neglected him or kept him darkly closeted), as you accept him as your own, your early self, do not overlook his past and present contributions to your pleasures and gratifications. There are many aspects of that child in us that are to be cherished. The openness to surprise, the eagerness for new experiences, the readiness for wonder, the spontaneity and playfulness — all these, when they have not been quashed, are blessings, often the founts of our creativity. Savor them. The better you know and appreciate that child, the greater the chances that you will be his possessor, rather than being possessed by him. In brief, I am proposing that knowing the child in us with acceptance and empathy is an essential condition for becoming a self-possessed adult.

Quickly I add that by "self-possessed" I do not mean narcissistically smug, impregnable, ignoring all others. Rather, I mean, being aware of what stirs in us, and of what today's external reality seems to call for by way of appropriate attitudes and actions. Self-possession is, I suggest, rather different from self-control. The latter often involves a cool detachment, a rigid determination not to give way, a stiffening of the defenses between one's self and others as well as within the self. The self-possessed person has faced with acceptance and empathy that many feelings and interpretations were pushed under and disregarded in childhood, that many others remain unmodified. Still accessible, they may be subject to revision and reappraised. So the self-possessed adult pays attention to the child in him, correcting it when necessary, so as to behave in appropriate ways to this time and place and purpose.

A big order, self-possession! Perhaps I counsel more than can be sustained consistently. One thing is certain: one cannot manage what one does not have a firm hold on.

✍ ✍ ✍

At its very least: the business of "occupying one's self generously" now and then with aspects of one's childhood, whether recalling its high spots or low, or the general undulating tenor of its dailiness, offers some change of scene—almost like travel to another place and time. You may find that you have had a far more interesting and varied life than you'd assumed, that you'd touched and been touched by more people than you'd given mind-room to for many years; that your life had had more scope and interest than you'd credited it with, that you are and have been not "only human" but, at times, "remarkably" so. Like armchair travel, remembering is a relatively comfortable, undemanding undertaking.

For your own reasons, you may wish to take this journey into the interior alone. Or you may decide you need a professional guide. But the occasional calling-up of childhood memories may also be shared with others in a congenial group: you may find yourselves forming bonds of at-one-ness in the realization of how comically touching and how poignantly resonating those recollections of one's "age of innocence" can be. The interest lies not just in the telling but in your explorations of meanings and reasons, whether of those that have remained fixed or those that have undergone transformations.

Will you join in this? On some summer evening, say, on the front porch, or verandah, or stoa? Over a sweet-sour lemonade (no fear of ice shortage now!) or a glass of milk and boughten cookies, or a martini-on-the-rocks, carefully measured, so that the child in you will not run amok?

V

End Note

(From an Octogenarian's Journal)

ONE FURTHER MEMORY nudges me, asking to be included as I come to closure. It carries a moral, which I should have learned long ago from the red-legged dancing clock.

When I was not quite five, my mother and I were invited to the first birthday party of a boy cousin. In our adulthood I have come to both admire and love this cousin, but when he was one year old he was of minimal interest to me. He probably was crawling about or sitting soberly in his go-cart or highchair, as self-involved as I, and I have no image or memory of him at his first party.

What I do remember is a wide green lawn where this August afternoon party was held. At its center was a round, freshly planted flowerbed. Millie, my baby cousin's mother, had brought their phonograph out to the porch, wound it up and suggested that we children could dance to the music. I loved that.

I also vividly remember the party dress I wore. It had been made for me by a "modiste" (no mere dressmaker, mind you, but a "modiste") who just happened to be a cousin and I was enchanted with it, both because everybody admired its fine tucks and embroideries, and because its little French skirt, banded by Valenciennes lace, floated out prettily when I walked or twirled.

I began happily to dance. Round and round the flowerbed I went, hopping, skipping, waving my arms, hazarding a kick now and then, entranced by my flaring skirt and the pulse of the music that seemed to flow through me. After a bit I became the solo dancer, the other children having gone off to more enticing pursuits. Then Cousin Millie came over to me and asked if I didn't think I had danced long enough? I was told, much later, by my mother (who rolled with laughter as she related it) that I stopped dead and replied firmly, "No. I want to keep on dancing."

So I did. I recall that I began to feel a bit unsteady. I wavered, essayed an uncertain kick, and fell, splam-flat into the fresh-laid earth. I cried bitterly, not because I'd hurt myself, but with embarrassment. After saying that I should have minded Cousin Millie, Mama petted me down, and assured me that the mud would wash out. Which it did.

The moral: There comes a time, as the dancing clock showed me when I was two years old, when you must dance into the wings. The red velvet curtain goes up on other people, other scenes, other acts. You cannot keep on dancing.

Notes

Since I wish this to be a "readable" book — which, by my capricious definition, is one that may be read in an easy chair rather than sitting up straight at a desk, marker at the ready — I have eschewed footnotes except in the cases of Freud and Adler. In addition to notes to my quotations from them, I include here some references which can be pursued if you are inclined to explore further recent theories and research relevant to the development of the personal and social self in early childhood.

[1] Sigmund Freud, "Childhood and Concealing Memories" from *The Psychopathology of Everyday Life*, originally published in German in 1899 and reprinted in *The Basic Writings of Sigmund Freud*, translated and edited by Dr A.A. Brill (New York: Random House, Modern Library, 1938), 62–68. Indexed under "Memories — Childhood", 128.

[2] Alfred Adler, "Significance of Early Recollections" in *International Journal of Individual Psychology* (Oct., 1937), 283–287.

[3] In the last few decades two fertile minds have offered fresh perspectives on the emotions and mentality of infancy and early childhood: Dr Heinz Kohut on "self-psychology", on the conditions and course of development of selfhood and social responsivity, and Dr David Stern who has engaged with colleagues in empirical research on the responsivities and learning of infants and young children. In a tightly condensed but illuminating article, Miriam Elson had elucidated and connected the thoughts of both men: "Kohut and Stern: Two Views of Infancy and Early Childhood" in *Smith College Studies in Social Work* LIX, #2 (March, 1989). See also *The Kohut Seminars*, Miriam Elson, ed. (New York: W.W. Norton, 1987).

[4] The quotation from Stanley Kunitz appears in his *Next-to-Last Things*, (New York: Atlantic Monthly Press, 1985), 29–30.